LOGICAL WRITINGS

JACQUES HERBRAND (in the center)
On the expedition during which he fell to his death

(Photo Courtesy of Suzanne Lautman)

JACQUES HERBRAND

LOGICAL WRITINGS

Edited by

WARREN D. GOLDFARB
Harvard University

A Translation of the 'Écrits logiques', edited by

JEAN VAN HEIJENOORT

HARVARD UNIVERSITY PRESS
CAMBRIDGE, MASSACHUSETTS
1971

JACQUES HERBRAND: ÉCRITS LOGIQUES

First published by Presses Universitaires de France, 1968

First published in the U.S.A. and Canada 1971

HARVARD UNIVERSITY PRESS, CAMBRIDGE MASS.

Library of Congress Catalog Card Number 74–146963

SBN 674 53835 8

PREFACE

In 1968 Jean van Heijenoort published an edition of Herbrand's collected logic papers (*Herbrand 1968*). The core of the present volume comprises translations of these papers and of the biographical notes also appearing in that edition. With two exceptions, this is their first appearance in English; the exceptions are Chap. 5 of Herbrand's thesis and *Herbrand 1931c*, both of which appeared in *van Heijenoort 1967*, the former translated by Burton Dreben and van Heijenoort, and the latter by van Heijenoort. These two translations have been reprinted here, thanks to the permission of the Harvard University Press, with only minor changes. The remainder of the present translations are my own; I am grateful to van Heijenoort for providing an English draft of *1931*, which forms the basis of the translation appearing here.

In these translations, the bibliographical references have been standardized (see p. 299 below) and the notation has been changed so that it is fairly uniform throughout (any differences from Herbrand's original notation are mentioned in footnotes). Herbrand's technical terminology is not always translated literally; the principal instances of this are 'réduite', translated 'expansion' (except in *1930*, Chap. 3, § 3, where it is translated 'relativization'), 'champ', translated 'domain', and 'symbole de variable apparente', translated 'quantifier'. In other cases of this sort, the French terms appear in double brackets immediately following the English renderings. In addition, Herbrand's texts contain numerous oversights and typographical errors; these are corrected without note when Herbrand changed them himself in published Errata, and are noted otherwise. Herbrand also tended to express himself rather hastily, resulting in many obscurities; in these translations an attempt has been made to balance the demands of literalness and clarity. In Chap. 5 of *1930*, since the subject matter is more difficult, the translators have departed somewhat more from the original than is the case in the rest of this volume.

Moreover, the present volume contains many footnotes and more extended notes which clarify or correct the text and compare Herbrand's investigations with other work in logic. Each Note is connected with a particular passage of the text, and would, were it not for its length, appear there as a footnote. These Notes follow the appropriate paper, except in *1930* where they follow the appropriate chapter; the passage with which a Note deals is indicated by a footnote and this footnote is mentioned below the title of the Note. There are also cross-references between Notes and footnotes. Notes E–I are Dreben's (they are slightly modified versions of Notes C–G in *van Heijenoort 1967*; Note E is a corrected version of the original Note C, and is to appear in this revised form in the second printing of *van Heijenoort 1967*). The Note to *1928*, Note J, and Note N are by Dreben and myself, and Notes A, B, C, D, K, L, M, and O are mine, Note D based in part on Dreben's Note B in *van Heijenoort 1967*. In those Notes closely connected with Herbrand's text, Herbrand's terminology is for the most part employed; in those of a broader nature, more modern terminology is used.

Immediately preceding *1930*, *1931*, *1931b*, and *1931c* there are brief introductory notes; the last two are van Heijenoort's (the one to *1931b* appeared in French in *Herbrand 1968*, and the one to *1931c* in *van Heijenoort 1967*), the second mine, and the first is mine, in large part based on van Heijenoort's introduction to Chap. 5 in *van Heijenoort 1967*.

Footnotes not Herbrand's own are enclosed in double brackets (as are editorial clarifications in the text); in *1930*, Chap. 5, they are Dreben's, except for those numbered 4, 5, 7, 8, 18, 19, 21, 23, 36, 46, 57, 89, and 94, which are van Heijenoort's, and 1, 2, 10, 51, 55, and 86, which are mine; in *1931c*, 2 is van Heijenoort's and the rest mine (these footnotes of Dreben and van Heijenoort appeared – except for minor editorial changes – in *van Heijenoort 1967*); the remainder are all mine, but for number 4 of *1930*, Chap. 2, which is Dreben's.

I am deeply grateful to Burton Dreben for his inestimable assistance in every phase of the preparation of this volume. Jean van Heijenoort was also of great help, as was A. Paul Phillips, who suggested many improvements and did a large part of the proofreading. I would also like to thank Daniel Garber, W. V. Quine, Kenneth Ribet, Eira Ruben, Thomas M. Scanlon, Frank W. Thompson, Maria Tymoczko, and A. Thomas Tymoczko for their many helpful suggestions with regard to various parts of this volume. Moreover, in *van Heijenoort 1967* Dreben and van Heijenoort thanked Wilbur Hart III, Marc Venne, Daniel Isaacson, and Dirk van Dalen for their help with the translation of Chap. 5 of *1930*.

Work on this volume was partially supported by N.S.F. grants #GS-2615 and #GP-4032.

W. D. G.

TABLE OF CONTENTS

INTRODUCTION

Herbrand's principal concern in his logical writings was to develop a unified approach to all questions of proof theory. He based this approach on his Fundamental Theorem, which is, as Bernays has remarked (*1954*), "the central theorem of predicate logic". In addition to providing both information about the structure of logical proofs and a method for obtaining consistency and decidability results, this theorem also furnishes constructive insight into nonconstructive notions such as satisfiability. However, due in part to the difficulty of Herbrand's texts and in part to surface similarities with work of Skolem and Gentzen, Herbrand's mode of investigation is not widely understood today. In order to appreciate fully the importance of his results and their place in the history of logic, it is helpful to trace the major influences on Herbrand's work: Whitehead and Russell's *Principia Mathematica*, *Löwenheim 1915* and *Skolem 1920*, and the articles of the Hilbert school which appeared during the 1920's.

Herbrand took the *Principia Mathematica* to furnish experimental evidence that classical mathematics can in fact be codified in a formal system using a small number of primitive signs and rules of inference (*1930*, p. 48 below). The possibility of such a formalization shows the importance of metamathematical investigations. Herbrand says, "It becomes natural to study this system of signs in itself, and to pose problems regarding it. The solution of these will have an immediate echo in our general knowledge of mathematics" (p. 49 below). Herbrand begins in his thesis (*1930*) by examining the propositional calculus of the *Principia*, and then takes great pains to show that his formulation of quantification theory is equivalent to that used by Whitehead and Russell (p. 89 below). Moreover, one of the methods Whitehead and Russell use to construct quantificational logic seems to be the source of two key concepts in Herbrand, namely, those of normal identity and property *A* (see p. 4 below).

Löwenheim's paper of 1915 contains a number of ideas central to much subsequent work. He uses the notion of a universe of discourse susceptible to change, a notion coming from the Boole-Peirce-Schröder tradition. Löwenheim completely ignores syntactic considerations such as provability; rather, he assumes a naive notion of a formula's being true in a universe under a given interpretation of the predicate letters. Thus, the (set-theoretic) notions of validity and satisfiability come into play. Using them, Löwenheim proves his well-known theorem: If a formula of quantification theory with identity is satisfiable, then it is satisfiable in a denumerable universe. As we shall see, Herbrand rejects on philosophical grounds the concepts employed here; but much of his work is concerned with finding unobjectionable surrogates for them. A key notion in Löwenheim's paper is that of a quantifier-free expansion of a quantified formula; this notion was used, in various forms, in many later studies of quantification theory, including Herbrand's. However, Löwenheim's proof is very informal and difficult to follow. Löwenheim employs, without justification, several arguments (in particular with regard to infinitely long formulas) that are extensions to infinite cases of inferences applicable to finite cases. This sort of extension was common in the Schröder school, but it leaves the acceptability of Löwenheim's proof open to doubt (see, for example, *van Heijenoort 1967*, pp. 228–232). Skolem later gave several rigorous proofs; both Löwenheim's work and these improvements are discussed in greater detail below (p. 7).

The method of investigation that Herbrand adopts was essentially due to Hilbert. Partially in response to Brouwer's critiques of classical mathematics, Hilbert developed his notion of proof theory. The proof theorist's task is to examine formal systems as systems of signs, divorced from any intuitive content. The methods used must be purely finite, although this restriction is left vague. (In practice, the intuitions underlying a formal system may play an important role in obtaining results; but care must then be taken to insure that the use made of them does not involve any nonfinitistic assumptions.) The most important questions in Hilbert's metamathematics concern characterizations of provability in given formal systems; central among these are problems of consistency, completeness, and decidability. Herbrand's logical work is entirely within this framework; he agrees that arguments about formal systems must be finitistic, and is concerned with the problems Hilbert raises. In the

Introduction to *1930* and in *1930a* Herbrand explains this concept of metamathematics, but he ignores the more obscure epistemological views of Hilbert and Brouwer. Instead, he bases the restriction to finitistic reasoning on the need, in the face of critiques of infinite totalities and the law of the excluded middle, for a logical method satisfying "requirements of the most absolute rigor" (p. 208 below).

From the finitist viewpoint, the naive notion of truth is suspect; Hilbert and Herbrand ask what finite sense can be given in general to the attribution of truth in an infinite universe to a formula with quantifiers. The objection to quantifiers arises primarily from the fact that in the intuitive semantics of quantification theory, the existential quantifier is often interpreted as standing for a choice function. Indeed, in a provable formula we may not be able to replace these functions by computable functions, and hence not be able to find constructively a correct instantiation for the existentially quantified variables. To emphasize this role of the quantifier, Hilbert formulated quantification theory using the ε-symbol; the intended interpretation of the term $\varepsilon_x A(x)$ is "an object x such that $A(x)$" (see, for example, *Hilbert 1927*, p. 67 $[\![$p. 466$]\!]$ [1]).

The proof-theoretic program was based on Hilbert's insight that in any given proof only a finite amount of knowledge of this choice function is required; to prove consistency, it suffices to evaluate the ε-terms in each given proof without taking account of the evaluations given to occurrences of the same ε-terms in other proofs. If such evaluations could be found, then presumably any formula provable in the system under consideration would be reducible to a true quantifier-free one, where 'true', now restricted to quantifier-free formulas, can be given a finitistic sense. Von Neumann's consistency proof for a weak system of arithmetic (*1927*) takes this form; the quantifier-free formulas obtained are truth functions of equations between numerical terms. In Chap. 4 of *1930* (pp. 112ff. below) Herbrand presents a simpler and more powerful proof using the same underlying idea. By certain mechanical instantiations of numerals for quantified variables, he finds a quantifier-free equivalent P' for every formula P of a similar weak system of arithmetic. Further-

[1] In this Introduction, when a translation of a work cited appears in *van Heijenoort 1967*, the first page number refers to the original text and the second number (in brackets) refers to the translation.

more, P is provable in this system if and only if P' is provable in a quantifier-free subsystem. This subsystem is easily shown decidable, syntactically complete, and consistent. Hence, since if P is quantifier-free then P' is P, the original system also has these properties. Herbrand calls P' the 'réduite' (literally, reduction) of P, thus emphasizing his aim of reducing provability using quantifiers to provability without quantifiers. (The equivalent term 'Reduktion' was also used by von Neumann.) However, in keeping with current usage 'réduite' is translated 'expansion' throughout this volume, with the exception mentioned in the Preface, (p. v above) Herbrand's procedure here is a version of what is now called the "elimination of quantifiers" (see *Presburger 1929, Hilbert and Bernays 1934*, p. 234, and *Tarski 1948* and *1951*); in the case of arithmetic it turns on the existence in the formal language of terms intended to denote all members of the standard model.

Herbrand applied the approach of the Hilbert school to pure quantification theory; his goal was to analyze quantificational provability in terms of truth-functional validity. But since now there is no question of a standard model, it is difficult to see how to even approach the problem of instantiating quantified variables. Herbrand's solution to this problem arises from two ways of connecting quantified formulas with quantifier-free ones. The first is an extension of Whitehead and Russell's construction of quantified logic in *Principia Mathematica* *9, and rests on a procedure for obtaining the proof of a formula P containing quantifiers from that of a quantifier-free tautology (that is, truth-functionally valid formula) related to P in a canonical way. The second is a finitization of the model-theoretic ideas of Löwenheim and Skolem, in which with any formula P we associate certain sequences of quantifier-free formulas which in some intuitive sense are to exhibit the content of P.

In § 4 of *1930*, Chap. 2, Herbrand asks what amounts to the following question: in his formulation of quantification theory, in which the only axioms are quantifier-free tautologies, are all tautologies derivable? To obtain a partial answer, he uses the notion of *normal identity* (although he does not define this notion explicitly until Chap. 5, p. 139 below). A formula P is a normal identity if there is a prenex equivalent P' of P such that a quantifier-free tautology can be obtained from P' by (1) replacing each existentially quantified variable by either a universally quantified variable that governs it or a free variable, and (2) dropping all quantifiers. From this tautology, P can be derived. This notion was directly inspired by the arguments in *Principia Mathematica* *9 showing that certain quantified tautologies can be proved from quantifier-free tautologies. However, not all tautologies are normal identities; indeed, Whitehead and Russell had to add the axiom $\varphi(x) \lor \varphi(y) . \supset . (\exists z) \varphi(z)$ in order to show that $P \lor P . \supset P$ is provable when P contains quantifiers. Herbrand therefore develops the more general notion of *property A* to avoid this premiss. Property A turns on considering an n-fold disjunction of a prenex equivalent of S and then instantiating variables according to certain rather complex rules (p. 143 below). A formula P is said to have property A if a quantifier-free tautology results from such instantiations; furthermore, from this tautology the formula P can be deduced in a canonical way (in particular, without any applications of modus ponens; see p. 10 below). Hence, for all formulas, having property A is a sufficient condition for provability. In *1930*, Chap. 2, p. 84 below, Herbrand shows essentially that all tautologies have property A (although again he does not explicitly define the notion until Chap. 5), thereby answering his initial question. Thus, by analyzing more carefully Whitehead and Russell's "purely philosophical [[problem]], namely to show how, by means of certain primitive propositions, we can deduce the theory of deduction for propositions containing apparent variables from the theory of deduction for elementary propositions" (*Principia Mathematica*, p. 129), Herbrand succeeds in giving a rather general sufficient condition for quantificational provability. Moreover, Herbrand goes on to show that this condition, namely having property A, is also necessary for provability. To show this, Herbrand exhibits a second relation between quantificational provability and truth-functional validity, a relation based on the work of Löwenheim and Skolem.

Herbrand begins by investigating the intuition underlying the naive notion of quantificational truth: existential and universal quantifiers can be interpreted as (possibly infinite) disjunctions and conjunctions, where the quantified variables take in each conjunct or disjunct every value in the universe under consideration. For example, suppose a formula $(x_1)...(x_n) (\exists y_1)...(\exists y_m) B(x_1, ..., x_n, y_1, ..., y_m)$ is true in an infinite universe A under a given interpretation of the predicate letters appearing in B. Then for every $a_1, ..., a_n$ in A, the infinite disjunction $\sum\limits_{b_1, ..., b_m \in A} B(a_1, ...,$

$a_n, b_1, ..., b_m$) is true under this interpretation. With regard to finite universes, these considerations become finitistically acceptable; for every n we obtain the *common expansion* of a formula over a universe of n individuals by expanding the quantifiers as truth functions, and letting the quantified variables take successively the values, say, $a_1, a_2, ..., a_n$. The original formula is valid in every universe of n individuals, or *n-valid*, if this common expansion is truth-functionally valid. Herbrand defines this notion in Chap. 2 of *1930*, p. 91 below (he again uses the word 'réduite' for this expansion), and shows that if a formula is provable then it is n-valid for every n. However, as is well-known, finite validity does not provide a sufficient condition for quantificational provability. Herbrand gives an example of a formula that is n-valid for every n yet is not provable (p. 94 below). Viewed nonconstructively, the problem is that a formula may not be valid in an infinite universe although it is valid in every finite universe.

Both Löwenheim and Skolem make implicit use of the naive notion of quantificational truth in its infinitistic form. In *1920* Skolem first associates with every formula P of pure quantification theory a Skolem normal form formula P' (that is, a formula P' of the form $(x_1)...(x_n)$ $(\exists y_1)...(\exists y_m) B(x_1, ..., x_n, y_1, ... y_m)$, where B is quantifier-free) such that P is satisfiable in a universe A if and only if P' is. Now, using the axiom of choice, he argues that P' is true in A under a given interpretation of the predicate letters if and only if there are functions $f_1, ..., f_m$ defined on A such that the *functional form* $B(x_1, ..., x_n, f_1(x_1, ..., x_n), ..., f_m(x_1, ..., x_n))$ is true under the interpretation for all values of $x_1, ..., x_n$. (These functions are now called 'Skolem functions'; they enable us to find, for every $a_1, a_2, ..., a_n$, a true disjunct of $\sum_{b_1, ..., b_m \in A} B(a_1, ..., a_n, b_1, ..., b_m)$, namely, the disjunct with each $b_k = f_k(a_1, ..., a_n)$.) Let A' be the denumerable subuniverse of A comprising all elements obtained by starting with an arbitrary $a \in A$ and repeatedly applying the functions f_i. Clearly, if P' is true in A under an interpretation of the predicate letters, then P' is true in A' under the restriction of this interpretation to A'. This proves the desired theorem. (Skolem uses the procedure just described for constructing the subuniverse in the second proof in *1920*, where he deals with a countable set of formulas in Skolem normal form (p. 9 [p. 259]). In the first proof (pp. 10–11 [p. 258]), where he deals with only one formula, he takes the subuniverse to be the intersection of all subsets X of A which contain a and are closed under applications of the f_i. In *1922* (p. 220 [p. 293]), he notes that the use of intersections can be avoided, presumably by the procedure of the second proof of *1920*.)

Skolem's argument in *1922* is quite different (it also proves a weaker theorem; see *van Heijenoort 1967*, p. 253). Here Skolem interprets the n-place function signs $f_1, \ldots, f_m$ appearing in the functional form as injective number-theoretic functions. He argues that if P is satisfiable, then for every p the finite conjunction of instances $B(i_1, \ldots, i_n, j_1, \ldots, j_m)$ is truth-functionally satisfiable, where the i_k are natural numbers less than p and, for $k = 1, 2, \ldots, m$, $j_k = f_k(i_1, \ldots, i_n)$. He then shows that there is a single truth assignment verifying all such instances. This last step, although nonconstructive, does not rest on the axiom of choice; rather, Skolem proves what Quine calls the "law of infinite conjunction" (*1955*, p. 254). The infinite truth assignment under which the 'infinite conjunction' is true furnishes a verifying interpretation of P' over the natural numbers, as is obvious from the naive notion of quantificational truth.

Löwenheim's paper of 1915 contains the seeds of both these proofs. Löwenheim starts by transforming any given formula into what amounts to a functional form. (His proof that this transformation preserves satisfiability, however, involves questionable inferences regarding infinitely long formulas. It was to avoid these that Skolem introduced Skolem normal form formulas.) Löwenheim argues further that if P is satisfiable in a universe A, then there are, in effect, Skolem functions for P. Hence, his proof seems to aim at 'cutting down' the original universe A, just as in *Skolem 1920*. However, in the latter part of the proof, Löwenheim defines a sequence of finite conjunctions of instances of the functional form, thus "building up" a model for P from below, as Skolem did in *1922*. It is the latter idea that Herbrand adapts to his program of finitistic analysis (although it seems that Herbrand was familiar only with *Löwenheim 1915* and *Skolem 1920*, and not with *Skolem 1922*; see p. 12 below).

Herbrand's Fundamental Theorem turns on the use of function signs to replace certain variables. We now explain the Theorem in detail. Let P be a formula of Q_H, Herbrand's formulation of quantification theory (see p. 45 below); P may contain function signs and constants. A quantifier is said to be *restricted in P* if it is existential and governed by an even number of negation signs, or universal and governed by an odd number; otherwise, it is *general*. A variable bound by a restricted quantifier is a *restricted variable*; one bound by a general quantifier is a *general variable*. With each general variable x we associate a functional term $f_x(y_1, \ldots, y_n)$, where f_x is a new function sign and $y_1, \ldots, y_n$ are all the restricted variables governing x (n may be 0). In addition, to each free variable in P we associate a distinct 0-place function sign (that is, a constant). The *validity functional form of P* is the formula $F^V(P)$ obtained from P by replacing all free and general variables by the associated constants and functional terms and dropping all general quantifiers. The *strict validity functional* form of P is the quantifier-free formula $\mathscr{F}^V(P)$ obtained by deleting all restricted quantifiers from $F^V(P)$. (In *1931* Herbrand calls $\mathscr{F}^V(P)$ the "elementary proposition associated with P"; see p. 227 below. Herbrand twice points out that his use of function signs and Hilbert's use of the ε-symbol as a choice function are related; see p. 149 and p. 182 below.)

We now construct the canonical domains associated with P; the domain of order 1 is an arbitrary finite set (we usually choose it to contain only one element); the domain of order $p+1$ comprises all elements of the domain of order 1, plus distinct values for each distinct functional term $f(c_1, \ldots, c_n)$, where $c_1, \ldots, c_n$ are elements of the domain of order p and f is an n-place function sign appearing in $F^V(P)$. Thus, all 0-place function signs have values in the domain of order 2. The order of an element is the least p such that the element belongs to the domain of order p.

The *second expansion of P of order p* is obtained by taking the common expansion of $F^V(P)$ over the domain D of order p, and then replacing every functional term by its value.[2] Note that that is not a true common expansion, since elements which are not in D may appear in it; these are values of terms $f(c_1, \ldots, c_n)$, where f is a function sign and at least one of the c_i is of order p (such terms are replaced by their values in the canonical domain of greater order).[3] In particular, such elements can

---

[2] Herbrand also defines the 'first expansion' of a formula P; this is the common expansion of $F^V(P')$, where P' is the formula resulting from P by applications of the rules of passage in such a way that each quantifier has the smallest possible scope.

[3] Thus, to call this expansion a common expansion violates Herbrand's stipulation in *1930*, Chap. 3, p. 104 below, that in a common expansion of a formula P over a domain D, every functional term must be given a value *in D*.

appear in places originally occupied in P by general variables. Herbrand defines this expansion in *1930*, Chap. 5, p. 153 below, although he does not use this terminology and his definition is not phrased in terms of the validity functional form. A more perspicuous expansion notion is the following: the *standard expansion of P of order p* is the quantifier-free disjunction $R(P, p)$ of all instances of $\mathscr{F}^V(P)$ obtained by substituting elements of the domain of order p for the free variables (which were originally restricted variables in P), and then substituting in each disjunct the proper values for the functional terms. (Herbrand defines this expansion in *1931*, footnote 40, p. 244 below; see also *1930*, p. 161 below, and especially footnote 47. Again, the terminology is not his.) Herbrand never shows that the two notions are interchangeable; but if we take into account the associative and distributive laws, it is not hard to see that the standard expansion of a formula of order p is equivalent to the second expansion of the formula of order p. We shall use the standard expansion in our exposition of the Fundamental Theorem.

For example, if P is $(x)\,(\exists y)\,(z)\,B(x, y, z)$, B quantifier-free, then $F^V(P)$ is $(\exists y)\,B(f_x, y, f_z(y))$, and $R(P, p)$ is

$$B(c_1, c_0, c_2) \vee B(c_1, c_1, c_3) \vee B(c_1, c_2, c_4)$$
$$\vee \cdots \vee B(c_1, c_{2p-2}, c_{2p}),$$

where the domain of order p is $c_0, c_1, ..., c_{2p-2}$; c_0 is the element of order 1, c_1 is the value of f_x, and for every i the value of $f_z(c_i)$ is c_{i+2}.

We now come to the statement of the Fundamental Theorem.

(I) If a formula P is provable in Q_H, then from any given proof of P we can calculate a number p such that $R(P, p)$ is truth-functionally valid.

(II) If for some p the expansion $R(P, p)$ is truth-functionally valid, then P is provable in Q_H.

To prove (I) Herbrand proceeds by induction on proofs in Q_H. He attempts to give an *analyzing function* for each rule of inference, that is, an effectively computable number-theoretic function $\varphi(x)$ such that if P' comes from P by one application of the rule and $R(P, p)$ is truth-functionally valid, then $R(P', \varphi(p))$ is also truth-functionally valid. However, the proof contains a serious error: Herbrand argues (Lemma 3.3, p. 155 below) that the analyzing function for the rules of passage (p. 74) is the identity. This lemma fails for certain applications of one of these rules (the 'crucial applications'). In 1943 Gödel noticed a lacuna in Herbrand's argument, and wrote a note for his own use about it (but published nothing).[4] In April 1963, Dreben, Andrews, and Aanderaa published a counterexample to Lemma 3.3 (*1963*); several other notes (*Dreben 1963*; *Dreben, Andrews, and Aanderaa 1963a*; *Dreben and Aanderaa 1964*) indicate a method of correcting the argument. A detailed proof of a revised lemma was presented by Dreben and Denton (*1966*), and is also contained in Note G, p. 193 below. The failure of Lemma 3.3 also affects Herbrand's arguments for two putative corollaries: if P' is a prenex equivalent to P and $R(P, p)$ is truth-functionally valid, then so is $R(P', p)$; and if $R(P, p)$ and $R(P \supset Q, p)$ are valid then so is $R(Q, p)$. Counterexamples to Lemma 3.3 and these corollaries are given in Notes G, H, and I (pp. 193ff. below). The corrected lemma is weaker: it provides a primitive recursive analyzing function $\varphi(x, y, z)$ such that if P' comes from P by a crucial application of the rule of passage and P contains i quantifiers and j function signs, then $R(P', \varphi(i, j, p))$ is valid provided $R(P, p)$ is. (The counterexample of Note G shows that no function of p alone would work.) Analogous changes must be made in the two corollaries. Using the modified Lemma 3.3, the proof of (I) can be entirely reconstructed.

The same error infects Herbrand's proof of (II). He argues (p. 169 below) that if $R(P, p)$ is truth-functionally valid, then P has property A. (Thus he connects his notion of expansion with the sufficient condition for provability inspired by Whitehead and Russell, thereby showing that having property A is also a necessary condition for provability.) Hence P is provable in Q_H. However, his argument relies on the first false corollary to Lemma 3.3 mentioned above; but Dreben and Denton's correction can be used to reconstruct the proof. This emendation preserves the important result of Herbrand's demonstration: if $R(P, p)$ is truth-functionally valid, a proof of P in a very specific form can be given. This proof contains no applications of modus ponens. Call Q'_H the system like Herbrand's Q_H but with modus ponens and the rule of simplification (infer P from $P \vee P$) replaced by the generalized rule of simplification, where the latter is: let Q' be like Q except for containing an occurrence of a subformula P where Q contains an occurrence of $P \vee P$; then from

---

[4] This information was related by Gödel to van Heijenoort in the autumn of 1963 in conversation; see *Herbrand 1968*, p. 8.

Q we can infer Q'. (I) and (II) taken together show constructively the equivalence of Q_H and Q'_H. This is a most important result; it prefigures much work done, starting with Gentzen, on 'cut elimination' in various formal systems. Furthermore, the demonstration of the Fundamental Theorem also allows us to limit the proofs in Q'_H to those in which the rules are applied in a certain specific order (see Note F, p. 192 below).

The Fundamental Theorem thus provides the desired analysis of quantificational provability in terms of truth-functional validity, as well as furnishing a normal form theorem for quantificational proofs. However, Herbrand intends the notion of expansion to furnish more, namely, a finitistic surrogate for the model-theoretic notion of infinite satisfiability. Let us outline the grounds Herbrand has for thinking of his result in this light. For any formula P without free variables, the *satisfiability functional form of P* is the formula $F^S(P)$ obtained from $\sim F^V(\sim P)$ by dropping the two initial negation signs; in $F^S(P)$ function signs replace variables restricted in P, and the arguments of these function signs are variables general in P. The *strict satisfiability functional form of P* is the formula $\mathscr{F}^S(P)$ obtained similarly from $\sim \mathscr{F}^V(\sim P)$; note that for formulas in Skolem normal form, this is essentially the same notion that Skolem uses (above, p. 6). Further, consider $\sim R(\sim P, p)$; this expansion is equivalent to a conjunction of instances of $\mathscr{F}^S(P)$, with the functional terms replaced by their values. We call this conjunction the 'satisfiability expansion of P of order p'. The Fundamental Theorem then implies that P is irrefutable in Q_H if and only if for every p the satisfiability expansion of P of order p is truth-functionally satisfiable.

Herbrand's basic definitions are more general; we may also consider noncanonical domains in which distinct functional terms need not have distinct values. The notion of order is easily extended to such domains (*1930*, p. 165 below, and *1931*, p. 228 below). The satisfiability expansion of P over such a domain D is the conjunction of all instances of $\mathscr{F}^S(P)$ obtained by substituting elements of D for the variables and replacing each functional term by its value in D (if it has one). It is not hard to show that if the satisfiability expansion of P over a domain D of order p is truth-functionally satisfiable, then so is the satisfiability expansion of P over the canonical domain of order p. Herbrand says (*1931*, p. 229 below) that P is *true in an infinite domain* if for every p there is a domain D of order p such that the satisfiability expansion of P over D is truth-functionally satisfiable.[5] Hence the Fundamental Theorem implies that P is irrefutable in Q_H if and only if P is true in an infinite domain.

This notion of truth should be contrasted with the one Skolem uses. In *1928* (p. 133 [[p. 518]]) Skolem generalizes his earlier notion of functional form to apply to all prenex formulas (that is, he defines what we have called $\mathscr{F}^S(P)$ for all prenex P) and develops a notion of satisfiability expansion. Let $D_1, ..., D_n, ...$ be a sequence of domains (in Herbrand's sense) such that each D_i is of order i and, for all i, $D_i \subseteq D_{i+1}$. Then, for Skolem, P is satisfiable in the union of the D_i if and only if there is an infinite truth assignment that verifies every instance of $\mathscr{F}^S(P)$ over this universe. By using the law of infinite conjunction, he shows in *1929* (p. 26) that this condition is equivalent to: for all i the satisfiability expansion of P over D_i is truth-functionally satisfiable. (Skolem not only proceeds nonconstructively, but also is not concerned with provability in quantification theory. However, there are suggestions of inference rules in *1928* and *1929*; Skolem thereby implicitly indicates a formulation of quantification theory whose rules are semantically complete. More on this point appears in Dreben and van Heijenoort's introduction to *Skolem 1928* in *van Heijenoort 1967*, p. 508.) Herbrand was quite aware that nonconstructively we could obtain an infinite truth assignment, and hence a denumerable model for P, if P is true in an infinite domain (in his sense). This indicates that Herbrand's text contains a completeness proof for Q_H; see Note N, p. 265 below. However, Herbrand was apparently unaware that the model for P could be obtained without using a choice principle, and thus seems not to have been familiar with *Skolem 1922*. He says, "only a 'principle of choice' could lead us to take a fixed system of [[truth]] values in an infinite domain". (Note that such a use of a choice principle is not similar to Skolem's use of it in *1920*. There is it applied at the beginning to obtain Skolem functions on the original universe,

---

[5] In *1930*, p. 164 below, Herbrand is more explicit as to what an infinite domain itself is. It is a sequence $\Gamma_1, \Gamma_2, ..., \Gamma_n, ...$ of domains, where each Γ_i is of order i and each Γ_i is a subset of Γ_{i+1}, and, for every i, a truth assignment $\mathscr{A}_i$ to the expansion of P over $\mathscr{A}_i$. Herbrand makes a point of the fact that $\mathscr{A}_{i+1}$ is not necessarily an extension of $\mathscr{A}_i$. However, this definition is put in terms of the domains and expansions associated not with P but with the formula P' obtained from P as in footnote 2, p. 8 above.

whereas Herbrand implies that a choice principle is necessary to obtain a model from the finite expansions.) Herbrand thought the nonconstructive notion of truth in an infinite model unacceptable, due to its infinitistic nature. Hence, he sees his definition of 'truth in an infinite domain' as explicating the metamathematical content of the concept that today is called 'satisfiability in a denumerable universe'. He writes, "It is absolutely necessary to adopt such definitions if we want to give a precise sense to the words 'true in an infinite domain', words that have frequently been used without sufficient explanation, and also if we want to justify a proposition proved by Löwenheim..." (p. 166 below). Herbrand's explication of satisfiability might be likened to the explication of the intuitive notion of limit by the ε-δ method. Each satisfiable satisfiability expansion can be seen as a finite approximation to a model for the formula; what prevents the expansions from merely providing finite models is that terms of greater order can appear in place of restricted variables (these arise from the functional terms) than can appear as substituents for the general variables. Thus Herbrand's explication equates satisfiability in a denumerable universe with having arbitrarily large finite approximations to a model. Herbrand merely stops short of the usual nonconstructive final step of showing that P has a model in the infinitistic sense if and only if P has these arbitrarily large finite approximations.

If, for all n, $R(P, n)$ is not truth-functionally valid, then obviously for every n the satisfiability expansion of $\sim P$ of order n is truth-functionally satisfiable; hence $\sim P$ is 'true in an infinite domain'. Nonconstructively speaking, the truth assignments falsifying $R(P, n)$ provide, as n increases, successive approximations to a denumerable model for $\sim P$. This procedure of successive approximation will break down only if some $R(P, n)$ is truth-functionally valid. Hence Herbrand says that P is 'false in an infinite domain' when it has no truth-functionally valid standard expansion. Now the Löwenheim-Skolem Theorem is equivalent to "P is not valid if and only if there is a denumerable interpretation falsifying P". The Fundamental Theorem furnishes a finitistic correlate: "P is not provable in Q_H if and only if there is an infinite domain such that P is false in this domain (in Herbrand's sense)". Herbrand himself calls his theorem "a more precise statement of the well-known Löwenheim-Skolem theorem" (p. 289 below; see also p. 175 below). His comparison of the two theorems seems to rely not only on his finitistic explication of falsifiability in a denumerable universe, but also on the replacement of validity by provability. Again, the set-theoretic notion of validity makes no sense finitistically, and provability is the natural proof-theoretic notion with which to replace it. (The situation is somewhat more complex. Herbrand calls the formulas provable in Q_H *identités de deuxième espèce*. It seems clear that he took his terminology from Zaremba (*1926*), and for Zaremba the use of the phrase 'identité' reflects a special analysis of validity; see the Note to *1928*, p. 32 below.)

One of the principal applications of the Fundamental Theorem is to consistency proofs. A set of axioms is consistent if and only if every conjunction $\mathscr{H}$ of axioms in the set is irrefutable in Q_H. Hence, to constructively prove consistency we must show that for every n there is a domain D of order n such that the satisfiability expansion of $\mathscr{H}$ over D is truth-functionally satisfiable (see *1930*, Chap. 5, p. 179 below). Here it is usually more convenient to deal with noncanonical domains, for then we can use our intuitions regarding the standard model for the axioms. We can take finite parts of the universe of the standard model as the domains and try to evaluate the function signs in them in such a way that instances of the satisfiability functional form of $\mathscr{H}$ come out true under some constructively specifiable truth-assignment to quantifier-free formulas whose arguments are all elements of this finite part. Thus, such a proof proceeds by constructively building approximations to the standard model. (Bernays remarks in *1934a*, p. 71, that even in simple cases where we have an effective model for the axioms, in the absence of the Fundamental Theorem or some similar result we cannot be sure of consistency; for in proofs from these axioms we can use the principle of the excluded middle with respect to quantified formulas, and other questionable inference procedures. See also the works cited in footnote 78, p. 179 below.) Herbrand's difficult consistency proof in *1930*, Chap. 5, p. 185 below, for a fragment of arithmetic can be put into this form, and even extended to full arithmetic (*Dreben and Denton 1968*; *Dreben, Denton, and Scanlon 1972*). Such Herbrand-style consistency proofs bear great similarity to Hilbert's original idea of evaluating ε-terms; for the idea is to evaluate the function signs appearing in expansions over finite domains, and these functions signs are essentially choice operators. (In *1931c*, Herbrand gives a simpler consistency proof for the same fragment of arithmetic; this proof, however, cannot be extended to stronger systems. It turns on reducing the system to one whose axioms contain no restricted variables, but rather only number-theoretic functions which can be evaluated in the domains. Here Herbrand presents an idea which, after considerable clarification by Gödel, became the notion of 'general recursive function'; see p. 283 below.)

Another important use of the Fundamental Theorem is in applications to decision problems of quantification theory. On the one hand, it furnishes a constructive method for proving that certain classes of formulas are reduction classes with respect to the decision problem for Q_H. The classical method of showing a class K to be a reduction class is to associate with each formula P a formula P' in K such that P is satisfiable if and only if P' is. The Fundamental Theorem provides a uniform way of reconstructing such proofs finitistically, with respect to the finitistic form of the decision problem, that is, that of deciding whether any given formula is refutable. We merely need to show that, for all n, P has a truth-functionally satisfiable satisfiability expansion of order n if and only if P' does. Herbrand carries out several such proofs in *1931* (p. 237 below). On the other hand, the Fundamental Theorem also provides a uniform way of showing that various classes of formulas are decidable; we show that for every formula P in the class under consideration we can calculate a number n such that if the satisfiability expansion of P of order n is satisfiable, then so is the satisfiability expansion of P of any order. (Such proofs furnish solutions for special cases of the finitistic decision problem. Prior to Herbrand's work, all solutions for special cases dealt with the model-theoretic form of the problem, that is, for deciding questions of satisfiability or validity of quantificational formulas; for example, *Ackermann 1927* and *Bernays and Schönfinkel 1928*. The Fundamental Theorem provided the first method for attacking the finitistic form of the problem, and was used for this purpose not only by Herbrand but also, for example, in *Schütte 1933* and *1934*.) Decidability proofs resting on the Fundamental Theorem furnish nonconstructive insight into the nature of models for the formulas in the class: for these proofs turn on the possibility of defining periodic truth assignments to the conjuncts of an arbitrary expansion of P, based on the truth assignment verifying the expansion of order n (see *Dreben 1961* and *Dreben, Denton, and Scanlon 1972*). Thus the model for P obtained by considering an 'infinite expansion' has certain periodic properties. (Herbrand actually furnishes decision procedures for provability; that is, he shows that from P we can calculate an n such that $R(P, n)$ is truth-functionally valid if there is an m such that $R(P, m)$ is. See *1931*, pp. 246ff. below.)

Finally, Herbrand considers the Fundamental Theorem to provide an arithmetization of mathematical theories. He uses the term 'arithmetization' in three senses. First, in studying a theory with regard to consistency (or equivalently, according to Herbrand's explication of truth and the Fundamental Theorem, the axioms' truth in an infinite domain) we need consider only denumerable domains, that is, whether the axioms have arbitrarily large approximations to a denumerable model. Hence we need consider only a denumerable number of terms. (This is another aspect of what Herbrand means in calling the Fundamental Theorem a finitistic correlate to Löwenheim-Skolem. See p. 253 below.) Secondly, the Fundamental Theorem reduces quantificational provability to a combinatorial problem regarding the existence of certain truth assignments on the expansions. Herbrand shows that this is equivalent to an arithmetical problem (the exact form of which depends on the syntactical structure of the formula under consideration); this is stated in detail in *1929b*, p. 41 below, and *1931*, p. 245 below. (Analogously, Skolem saw that his notion of expansion provides an arithmetical way of viewing satisfiability; see *Skolem 1928*, p. 133 [[p. 518]].) Arithmetization in the third sense – today, the most usual sense – was not carried out by Herbrand. This is the arithmetization of syntax, developed by Gödel (*1931*), where numbers are assigned to formulas so that syntactic properties (like provability) are correlated with properties of numbers. Herbrand uses the word 'translation' to describe the effects of both Gödel's arithmetization and his own (p. 258), and thus obscures the important differences between the two. Herbrand's method merely provides, for any given formula P of Q_H, a sentence of arithmetic equivalent to 'P is provable'. Gödel's arithmetization, on the other hand, furnishes a uniform way of translating *all* syntactic considerations about formulas into number theory.

The Fundamental Theorem has numerous additional applications to problems of pure quantification theory, number theory, algebra, and other areas. Several of these can be found in *Dreben, Denton, and Scanlon 1972*, along with references to many more.

Herbrand's work had an immediate impact on the Hilbert school. Bernays wrote, in the Foreword to *Hilbert and Bernays 1934*, "the appearance of the works of Herbrand and Gödel have altered proof theory" (see also the Foreword to *Hilbert and Bernays 1939*). However, Herbrand's argument for the theorem was considered "difficult to follow" (*Hilbert and Bernays 1939*, p. 158, note 1), and both Gentzen and Bernays, within a few years after 1930, gave simpler proofs of similar theorems.

In *1934* Gentzen proved his *Hauptsatz*, which asserts that every sequent provable in his formulation of quantification theory as a sequential calculus is provable without cut (that is, in essence, without modus ponens). For classical logic Gentzen derives from the *Hauptsatz* a *verschärfter Hauptsatz*, which states that all provable sequents whose constituent formulas are prenex can be proved using a two-part cut-free demonstration: the first part is truth-functional and terminates in a quantifier-free 'midsequent', and the second part derives the original sequent from the midsequent. This normal form for proofs is very close to that resulting from the Fundamental Theorem (see Note F). Gentzen called the Fundamental Theorem a "special case" of the *verschärfter Hauptsatz* (*Gentzen 1934*, p. 409, note 6) because he thought Herbrand's work applied only to prenex formulas (apparently a common misconception among the German logicians). However, there is no such restriction in the Fundamental Theorem, so it is in fact Gentzen's result that is the special case, since it applies only to sequents of a particular form. Moreover, the Fundamental Theorem yields an expansion theorem, which provides a straightforward mechanical procedure for generating quantifier-free expansions, as well as a normal form theorem. The *verschärfter Hauptsatz* does not furnish directly such detailed information on the midsequent.

This last contrast is a reflection of the deep difference in the modes of proof of the two theorems. Gentzen's demonstration relies on syntactic manipulations of proofs in the sequential calculus: a proof is subjected to certain reduction rules so as to eliminate cuts, and then it is shown that these reductions always terminate in a normal form proof. There is no concept, as there is in Herbrand, of making finitistic the model-theoretic intuitions underlying quantification theory. (On the other hand, the absence of this concept in Gentzen's work permits him to derive more general results: the *Hauptsatz* applies to nonclassical logics which, of course, do not have the same model-theoretic underpinnings as classical logic.) As we have seen, Herbrand's demonstration uses the notion of an analyzing function. These functions provide a finitistic measure of the strengths of the laws of quantificational logic; they show the effect an inference step has on the length of the procedure necessary to defeat any approximation to a model falsifying the provable formula. Deriving such information is part of the program of constructively analyzing the power of the laws of quantificational logic in terms of truth functions; it is entirely different in spirit from Gentzen's work, where a proof is viewed as a whole, that is, individual inference steps are considered only in the context of a proof.

Both approaches to proof theory can be found in the works of the Hilbert school. As mentioned above, consistency proofs resting on the Fundamental Theorem are similar to those based on Hilbert's original *Ansatz* (approach), in which the ε-terms are evaluated finitistically; see, for example, *Ackermann 1924, von Neumann 1927, Ackermann 1940*. (Moreover, some of the ideas arising from the *Ansatz* can be used to obtain an argument for the Fundamental Theorem differing from Herbrand's; this proof proceeds by using an evaluation technique to find an analyzing function for modus ponens, and then deriving most of the other analyzing functions from this one. See *Dreben, Denton, and Scanlon 1971*. In addition, Dreben and Denton's revision of Herbrand's original argument also borrows from the *Ansatz*; the notion of an *A*-resolvent in Note G is related to that of a resolvent in *Hilbert and Bernays 1939*, p. 95.) However, some time before 1932, Ackermann, basing his work on another idea of Hilbert, uses a different proof-theoretic approach to eliminate ε-terms (*Bernays 1932*, p. 343 and *1935*, p. 213). This elimination approach turns on carrying out various syntactic transformations and substitutions in proofs. It results in the First and Second ε-Theorems (*Bernays 1936, Hilbert and Bernays 1939*). From these Bernays obtains his analogue to the Fundamental Theorem.

The First ε-Theorem states that if a formula *B* without bound variables (that is, without either quantifiers or ε-symbols), but possibly containing function signs, is provable in the ε-calculus from a set of axioms also without bound variables, then *B* is provable from these axioms in the elementary (free variable) calculus, using only the rules of truth-functional logic and substitution for variables. The argument is roughly as follows:

by substituting different functional terms for an ε-term in different copies of the original proof of B from the axioms, and then making some simple modifications in the resulting sequences of formulas, we can obtain a proof of B from the axioms with no occurrences of this particular ε-term. If substitutions of this kind are carried out in an appropriate order (which is necessary because an ε-term may contain other ε-symbols), we eventually obtain a proof of B completely without bound variables.

This proof also yields the Extended First ε-Theorem: if a purely existential formula, that is, a formula of the form $(\exists x_1)\dots(\exists x_n) B(x_1,\dots, x_n)$, where B contains no bound variables, is provable from axioms without bound variables, then there are terms $t_{1,\,1},\dots, t_{1,\,n},\dots, t_{m,\,1},\dots, t_{m,n}$ such that

$$B(t_{1,\,1},\dots, t_{1,\,n}) \vee \cdots \vee B(t_{m,\,1},\dots, t_{m,\,n})$$

is derivable from these axioms in the elementary calculus. Now if a prenex formula P is derivable in pure quantification theory (that is, without any special axioms), then $F^V(P)$ is also derivable, and $F^V(P)$ is purely existential. Hence, if P is derivable then a quantifier-free disjunction of instances of $F^V(P)$ is provable in the elementary calculus, that is, is a tautology. Bernays thus derives the expansion result of the Fundamental Theorem for prenex formulas from the Extended First ε-Theorem (*Bernays 1936*, p. 94, *Hilbert and Bernays 1939*, pp. 149–158).[6] Again, since this proof relies on syntactic manipulations of entire proofs, rather than separate consideration of each inference rule, no information is given directly on the relation between the length of the tautology and the steps used in the original proof of P.

Conversely, the analogue to the First ε-Theorem for Q_H is an easy consequence of the Fundamental Theorem (see Note J, p. 201 below). The analogue states that if a quantifier-free formula B is derivable from quantifier-free axioms, then a proof can be found which does not use quantifiers. Indeed, such an argument provides a normal form for the proof of B eventually obtained. However, it is perhaps more natural to view the First ε-Theorem as the more basic result in the context of Hilbert's program (this seems to be Bernays' view). For the First ε-Theorem shows

---

[6] Moreover, he derives the normal form result of the Fundamental Theorem from the Second ε-Theorem (see *Bernays 1936*, p. 97 and *Hilbert and Bernays 1939*, pp. 133–137 and 158).

that the system obtained by adding axioms for quantifiers to axioms containing no bound variables is a conservative extension of the system without quantifiers. Hence, at least in this special case, the theorem supports Hilbert's idea that 'ideal elements' (reflected in the formalism by the use of quantifiers and ε-symbols) are helpful but not essential aids for organizing the 'real' data (see *Hilbert 1925*, p. 166 [[p. 372]]).

The syntactic manipulation technique has been greatly extended. Gentzen used it to obtain a consistency proof for arithmetic (*1938*)[7], and more recently it has been applied to systems with infinite proofs and infinitely long formulas (see, for example, *Schütte 1960* and *Feferman 1967*), so as to provide consistency proofs for much stronger formalisms.

On the other hand, the use of quantifier-free formalisms to provide an analysis of provability in formal systems with quantifiers has also been extended in recent work in proof theory. (This is the basis of Kreisel's general notion of interpretation. See his *1951*.) As we saw, one of Herbrand's goals was to carry this out for quantification theory in terms of truth function theory. Moreover, the Fundamental Theorem also provides such an analysis for the system of arithmetic without induction: If a formula P is provable in this system, then there is a standard expansion of P which is provable in the quantifier-free fragment of this system. However, no such result applies to full first-order arithmetic; Kreisel showed (*1952*) that full arithmetic does not possess such an *Herbrand interpretation*. For the analysis of arithmetic and stronger formal systems, different quantifier-free systems must be employed. For example, Kreisel's *no counterexample interpretation* (*1951*) uses a system of ordinal recursive functionals mapping number-theoretic functions to numbers (see *Tait 1965* and *1965a*); and Gödel's interpretation of number theory (*1958*) uses a system of primitive recursive functionals of all finite types. The Gödel interpretation approach has also been extended to much stronger systems (see *Spector 1961*).

Cambridge, Massachusetts   WARREN D. GOLDFARB
July 1970

---

[7] However, it should be noted that here, underlying Gentzen's techniques for manipulating proofs, is the notion of finding a finitistic interpretation of nonfinitistic number-theoretic formulas. This aspect of Gentzen's work is even more pronounced in his *1936*.

BIOGRAPHICAL NOTE ON
JACQUES HERBRAND

CLAUDE CHEVALLEY and ALBERT LAUTMAN

(1931)

HERBRAND, Jacques: born in Paris on 12 February 1908; died at La Bérarde (Isère) on 27 July 1931.

Jacques Herbrand died in a mountaineering accident at La Bérarde on 27 July 1931. He was only 23 years old, but as Professors Helmut Hasse and Richard Courant wrote to his father, he was already counted among the greatest mathematicians of the younger generation. He was the only child of parents who recognized his precocious genius and endeavored to assure its full development by their love and support. He was never anything but the first everywhere: in the *Concours Général*, in the examination of the *École Normale Supérieure* when he was 17, and in the *Agrégation* in 1928. In 1930 he received his doctorate with highest honors; the same year he received a Rockefeller Prize to travel to Germany, where his studies in Berlin and Hamburg earned him a place on the honor roll of higher education.

His work was perfect in abstractness and rigor; but for him the life of mathematical creation was not a spiritual one which is led apart from the concrete life of a man; it was the only expression he could give to the interior drama of his impassioned soul. He lived constantly absorbed in the analysis of the conflicts and duties which gave birth to an inescapable sensitivity within him. It seemed that only the most brilliant successes could be worthy of this life spent in spiritual solitude. The finest works of music and poetry contained for him thoughts close to his own; the unceasing work of his will was no less a matter of conscience to him.

It was always necessary for him to unite the elements of an idea or a sensation in a finished construct in order to savor them in advance and to see them come at his will. Thus, the lifelong interest he had in mathematical logic was perhaps born of the wondrous hope of anticipating the future by means of finite calculi and combinations.

From his days at the *École*, he read and assimilated the material in Whitehead and Russell's *Principia Mathematica*, and intended to introduce into France the study of the new axiomatic logics which were being developed at Göttingen around Hilbert. During the year of his *Agrégation* he obtained the results which would constitute his thesis: a new proof, the simplest known to date, of the consistency of arithmetic, and a new criterion, very general and completely formal, for the truth of propositions. These investigations, through which he became well-known among the mathematicians at the *Collège de France* and in particular by Hadamard, were at first considered with little favor at the Sorbonne: to the eyes of the French analysts, they seemed to contain more philosophical than mathematical interest, and Herbrand had difficulty in finding a panel willing to approve them. He owed much at this point to the confidence which Vessiot had in him; and he found in the director of the *École* a thesis director who bestowed the greatest praises on him after a rather lively dialogue, in which different conceptions of mathematics confronted each other. In face of the 'constructivists', for whom mathematical truth resided in the reality of a construction or a calculus, Herbrand tried to show the validity of formalisms and explained the fundamental problem here: to set up a calculus of propositions such that 'true' and 'false' could be considered to be predicates. Several months later, moreover, he was pleased to clear up the nature and significance of 'metamathematics' in an article he published in the *Revue de métaphysique et de morale* [1930a].

In fact, he loved philosophy very much: first of all the philosophy of the sciences, but also, and especially, philosophy dealing abstractly with the feelings and desires of the soul. He did not seek in it a system of man. Practical problems did not interest him; he did not speak of them nor did he ever debate them. He was occupied in an unceasing labor of introspection, and sought in this attitude of constant moral tension the difficult rigor which was the constant desire of his being. His thought always retained the same ideal, whether he recited to himself the "prose for des Esseintes"[1] or he applied himself to the study of arithmetic or modern algebra.

In fact, it was to these disciplines, the most abstract in mathematics, that he devoted himself during his year in Germany. He linked himself in friendship with the young German mathematicians, and produced a whole series of articles, most of which have not yet been published, on the simplification of class-field theory and its application to Fermat's theorem. He intended, on the other hand, to point out more completely various analogues to the theory of number- and algebraic-function fields. He also wished to attack the problem of inverse functions of an integral function; finally, he continued his study of recent theories of mathematical physics. His knowledge extended to all areas of mathematics, and he was considered among his peers to be one who could judge beforehand the results to expect from a new investigation.

This practice, always followed by rigorous thought, was in everyone's opinion going to give to the scholarly world one of its great spirits. But sometimes it seemed to Herbrand that it dragged his consciousness into a world as sterile as the emptiness he occasionally felt upon the deepest self-analysis. He suffered from the hard law that bound him without respite in this abstraction, in which he felt his being disappear as in death. It was in the hope of full internal harmony that he formed the goal of a heroic life in which to sustain the genius of his spirit; and it was in the powerful emotion of the high mountains that he approached most closely to this fullness of joy and ardor of which he sometimes believed himself to be eternally deprived. He died in an ascent; he would no longer pursue the ideas he formed and the feelings he experienced. But his friends had understood enough of the sublime beauty of these ideas and feelings that they will never be able to turn away from the paths which this beloved soul showed to them.

---

[1] [[Des Esseintes is the decadent and esthetic hero of the novel *A rebours* by J.-K. Huysmans (1884).]]

THE ACCIDENT

We have just learned from Le Bérarde that a new accident has occurred on the Pelvoux plateau: a young man, part of a three-man company from Lyons, has fallen to his death. (*Le Temps*, 29 July 1931.)

MOUNTAINEERING ACCIDENTS: We mentioned yesterday that a young man, part of a company of Alpinists climbing in the area of Le Bérarde, fell to his death. He was M. Jacques Herbrand, residing at 10 rue Viollet-le-Duc, Paris. M. Herbrand departed Sunday with three comrades, MM. Jean Brille, Pierre Delair, and Henri Guigner, to ascend the Baus. During the descent, the *piton* to which the line was attached gave way, carrying with it a small platform on which M. Herbrand was situated, and fell into the chasm. A rescue party has left to seek the body, which it hopes to reach today. (*Le Temps*, 30 July 1931.)

ON HERBRAND'S THOUGHT

CLAUDE CHEVALLEY

(Lecture at the Colloquium on Mathematical Logic, organized by the University of Geneva, in June 1934)

Jacques Herbrand was born in 1908. In 1925, at the end of his secondary studies, he took first place at the *École Normale Supérieure*. I entered the *École* myself in 1926, and immediately noticed the entirely special place he occupied among his comrades, due to the vigor and universality of his spirit. In 1928, he took first place in the *Agrégation*, and was able to stay a fourth year at the *École*, during which he completed his thesis, which contains the work in mathematical logic that he had been pursuing for two years. In 1929–1930 he did his military service; during that year he published two notes on the units of algebraic number fields. These notes form the basis of the new methods in class-field theory. He also finished the article *1931*, which was a continuation of his thesis. He spent the academic year 1930–1931 in Germany: first in Berlin with von Neumann, where he continued his work in logic, notably comparing his results to those of Gödel (see *Herbrand 1931c*); then he went to Hamburg and finally to Göttingen. He returned to France at the end of July and left immediately to indulge in his favorite sport, mountaineering. There he died in a fall, on July 27. Thus passed one whom a mathematician described as "one of the greatest of his generation".[1]

Jacques Herbrand expressed himself rather little on the philosophical

---

[1] From a letter of Prof. Courant to Herbrand's father: "During his short stay in Göttingen and even before this from his works, we have come to respect your son as one of the most promising and, because of the results he had already obtained, prominent young mathematicians of the world."

ideas relating to the problems of mathematical logic (see, however, the Introduction to his thesis and *1930a*). This is why I have eagerly taken the opportunity afforded by the University of Geneva to deliver several remarks on his ideas. I draw them from memories of the many conversations I had with him. One should remember that 1 have no other source and, having myself thought about these questions, my own opinions could have unconsciously infected my recollections. Given the agreement which there was in general between us, I hope that the distortions I might thus have involuntarily introduced will be minimal.

In our attempt to penetrate Herbrand's system of thought, we shall rely on the following quotation (*1930a* [p. 212 below]): "But it should not be hidden that perhaps the role of mathematics is merely to furnish us with arguments and forms, and not to find out which of these apply to which objects. Just as the mathematician who studies the equation of wave propagation no longer has to ask himself whether waves satisfy this equation in nature, so no longer in studying set theory or arithmetic should he ask whether the sets or numbers of which he intuitively thinks satisfy the hypotheses of the theory he is considering. He ought to concern himself with developing the consequences of these hypotheses and with presenting them in the most suggestive manner; the rest is the role of the physicist or the philosopher."

When we refer to the distinctions that Bernays and Fraenkel formulated very clearly in their lectures [*Bernays 1934* and *Fraenkel 1934*] between Platonist and intuitionist (or Aristotelian) mathematicians, I believe that this quotation allows us to conclude immediately that there are no Platonist inclinations to be found in Herbrand's thought. Indeed, Platonism, no matter what form it appears in, always admits the existence of a given world ruled by purely rational laws. Consequently mathematics is quite naturally considered to be knowledge of this world by man. Its role is precisely to find the human arguments which fit this world and which let us penetrate its structure. It was this that Herbrand called into question.

If one abandons the Platonist view, one must admit that mathematical objectivity, no longer a sign of the existence of a rational world, is created by man. The processes of axiomatization and the formalist method are the most extreme points of this movement towards the objective. This is to say, and I believe that this is what Herbrand thought, that objectivity is attained only in a pure symbolism, in emptying symbols completely of all meaning. Objectivity and concrete reality, far from being synonyms, exclude each other.

We can now understand why Herbrand's thought, although not Platonist, was not intuitionist either. In fact, the Intuitionists do not disallow treating in mathematics objects that are simultaneously rational and real. Undoubtedly they do not believe that such objects are given *a priori*. But they construct these objects starting from an intuition, namely, temporal intuition, so that mathematical assertions represent for them the assertions one can make regarding intuitions about time. Only the assertions that can be translated in this manner are valuable. For Herbrand, such restrictions were without foundation, for he believed that no reasoning whatsoever concerning something given and concrete would be valuable from a purely mathematical point of view, nor all the more that it was necessary to limit oneself to such reasoning.

The same considerations apply to logic. Logic comprises a schema which is objective only insofar as it is purely formal. Were one to give a sense to the symbols appearing in the formulas of logic, were one to consider them as representing operations of thought, one could cause logic to lose its objectivity. This is why it is not surprising that different thinkers have different opinions on the value of the axioms of logic. If the system of forms of classical logic is repugnant to Brouwer's thought, for example, this does not mean that this logic is denuded of value; it is an assertion about Brouwer's thought. If Heyting's formalism agrees with Brouwer's thought, this means that this formalism is suitable for describing the datum that his thought comprises. But in any case a human thought remains incongruous in any formalism; there is the same relationship between a formal logic and a mode of thought as between a mathematical equation and a physical phenomenon.

In regard to this, let us recall another quotation from Herbrand (*1930*, Introduction [p. 51 below]): "It can be said that many of the obscurities and discussions that have arisen in regard to the foundations of mathematics have their origin in a confusion between the 'mathematical' and the 'metamathematical' senses of terms." These difficulties spring from one's wanting to treat purely symbolic formulas of the domain of mathematics as assertions relating to something given. They are not of a different nature from those which engendered the birth of the infinitesimal calculus, which one wished to exclude for philosophical reasons because one wanted to see a 'real' object in the differential. Similarly, today, certain people wish to exclude the principle of the excluded middle because they wish to see 'real' assertions in the propositions.

From the preceding considerations we must not conclude that a mathematical act was for Herbrand a 'gratuitous' sort of act. Undoubtedly it is possible to carry out mathematics with any axioms and any rules of reasoning whatsoever; but in reality, and Herbrand liked to insist on this point, rigor has in a sense two complementary faces: if it is first the requirement of formalism, with respect to the 'rules of the game', it is also, in the sense given it by Leonardo da Vinci, an attempt at an ever more perfect description of something given. This description comes about by interpreting the axioms by means of experimental concepts. Mathematical physics already shows that one approaches positivist schemata (the direct interpretation of sensation) only at the price of an increasing abstraction, which one can compare to a sort of magic by which man dominates the domain of sensation only in first completely leaving it and in passing to the pure world of mathematics.

Just as mathematical physics permits us to penetrate further and further into the structure of matter, logic allows us to describe something nearer yet to man than his sensations: his intellectual thought. Herbrand said to me one day, "I would like to construct a system that contains all present-day thoughts". This is the greatest demand one could make on a formal logic: it leads us to the very center of the drama of Herbrand's thought, balancing between an investigation always more concrete and a formalism always more abstract. This drama was enacted in Herbrand's thought with a poignant intensity. Could it perhaps be a necessity of fate that where the spirit attains such a degree of violent purity, there death would be closest?

I

ON PROOF THEORY

(1928)

I

The theory of deduction, insofar as it uses only logical symbols such as $\vee$ (or), $\sim$ (not), and $\supset$ (implies), whose role is to bind propositions together, can be based, for example, on Russell's primitive propositions and the following rule of implication:

> If p and $p \supset q$ are true, then q is true.

From these we deduce propositions which are true,[1] no matter what the logical values [valeurs logiques] (cf. *Zaremba 1926*, p. 7) of the letters (atomic propositions) which appear in them. These propositions are called propositional identities of the first kind [identités propositionnelles de première espèce].[2] We can *prove* (in the sense of Hilbert) that

(1) This theory is consistent; that is, P and $\sim P$ cannot both be true;

(2) Every proposition whose logical value is 'true', no matter what the logical values of the letters which appear in it, is a propositional identity whose proof we can find, and conversely.

II

We can now introduce propositions containing variables (which can be of different sorts) and the new symbols $(\exists x)$[3] (there exists an x such that)

---

[1] [[Rather, propositions which have the logical value 'true'. Herbrand is here confusing his use of 'true' to mean 'provable' with his use of 'true' for the logical value.]]

[2] [[Regarding the use of the term 'propositional identity', see the Note, p. 33 below.]]

[3] [[In the French texts of this and the three notes immediately following, Herbrand uses '(Ex)' rather than '$(\exists x)$' and '.' rather than '&'.]]

and (x) (for all x). The theory of these can be set up in different ways, independently of the theory of types; the simplest of these, from the practical point of view, is the following: We retain both the primitive propositions of the theory of propositional identities of the first kind[4] and the rule of implication, and add the following rules:

RULE 1: If $\Phi(x)$ is true, then $(x).\Phi(x)$ is true.

RULE 2: If $\Phi(xx)$ is true, then $(\exists y).\Phi(yx)$ is true.

RULE 3: If

$$\Phi(x_1x_1x_2\ldots x_n) . \vee . \Phi(x_2x_1x_2\ldots x_n)$$
$$. \vee . \cdots . \vee . \Phi(x_nx_1x_2\ldots x_n)$$

is true, then $(\exists y).\Phi(yx_1x_2\ldots x_n)$ is true.

RULE 4: In a true proposition we can replace $\sim:(x).\Phi(x)$ by $(\exists x):\sim.\Phi(x)$; $\sim:(\exists x).\Phi(x)$ by $(x):\sim.\Phi(x)$; $p . \vee . (x) \Phi(x)$ by $(x):p . \vee . \Phi(x)$; and $p . \vee . (\exists x).\Phi(x)$ by $(\exists x):p . \vee . \Phi(x)$, whatever the propositions $\Phi(x)$ and p are, and conversely.[5]

Let us call the true propositions thus obtained 'propositional identities' of the second kind [[de deuxième espèce]].[2] We can prove that this method is equivalent to that of Russell and Whitehead (even if Rule 3 is used only when $n=2$), and that it is consistent.

Let us call the identities which can be obtained without using the rule of implication 'normal identities'.[6]

(1) We can tell whether a proposition is a normal identity or not; and if it is, we can prove the proposition.

(2) If in a propositional identity of the first kind $A(p_1, p_2, \ldots, p_n)$, p_1, $p_2, \ldots, p_n$ are replaced by any propositions whatever, then the result is a normal identity.

(3) For every propositional identity P there exists a normal identity Π such that $\Pi . \supset . P$ is a normal identity.

Any mathematical theory can be obtained by replacing the atomic propositions by propositions of a determinate nature which satisfy a finite or an infinite number of primitive propositions. If P is a theorem

---

[4] [[See footnote 1 to *1929a*, p. 38 below.]]

[5] [[p cannot contain the real variable x.]]

[6] [[See the last paragraph of the Note, p. 34 below.]]

true in a theory, then there exists a normal identity Π and a certain number of primitive propositions $H_1, H_2, ..., H_n$ of the theory such that

$$\Pi \ \& \ H_1 \ \& \ H_2 \ \& \ ... \ \& \ H_n \ . \supset . \ P$$

is a normal identity.

III

A particular mathematical theory is obtained by considering variables of different types (individuals, classes of individuals, relations between individuals, classes of classes, etc., as in Russell) and by using the atomic propositions $x \in \alpha$ (x is in the class α) and xRy (x bears the relation R to y), where the variables can be of different types. The primitive propositions are of the form

$$(\exists \alpha)::(\beta):.(\lambda): \beta \in \lambda . \supset . \ \alpha \in \lambda : \supset . \ (x).x \in \beta \equiv \Phi(x)$$
$$(\exists R)::(S):.(\lambda): S \in \lambda . \supset . \ R \in \lambda : \supset . \ (xy).xSy \equiv \Phi(xy)$$

in which $\Phi(x)$ and $\Phi(xy)$ are replaced by arbitrary propositions containing the ⟦real⟧ variables x (and x and y, respectively). We thus obtain a theory equivalent to Russell's but without the axiom of reducibility,[7] which can easily be proved consistent. We can also add the axiom of choice to the primitive propositions (the theory remains consistent), and the axiom of infinity.[8]

Let us call this theory ⟦with the axiom of infinity⟧ R_1. We could just as well replace the ordinary axiom of infinity by another which requires, for every n, the existence of classes of cardinality greater than $\aleph^{(n)}$, where we set

$$\aleph^{(0)} = \aleph_0, \qquad \aleph^{(n+1)} = 2^{\aleph^{(n)}}.$$

Let us call this theory R_2. We can prove that Zermelo's axioms without the axiom of infinity admit an interpretation into R_1, and with the axiom

---

[7] ⟦⟦This is what is now called the simple theory of types.⟧⟧

[8] ⟦⟦Of course, once the axiom of infinity is added, the system can no longer 'easily be proved consistent'.⟧⟧

of infinity into R_2; and that R_1 admits an interpretation into Zermelo's axioms with the axiom of infinity.[9]

NOTE

The reference in this, the first of Herbrand's papers, is the only explicit reference to Zaremba in Herbrand's writings. Nevertheless, *Zaremba 1926* appears to be the immediate source of several of Herbrand's key terms and poses the first questions in logic Herbrand answers. The reference here to p. 7 of *Zaremba 1926* is to Zaremba's Definition IV: "The truth [[vérité]] or falsity [[fausseté]] of a proposition constitutes what we call its *logical value [[valeur logique]]*." More important, though, is Zaremba's Definition XLIX on p. 29:

"The assertion that a proposition *P* is a *proposition of logic of the first kind [[proposition de logique de première espèce]]*, or, as we prefer to say, a *propositional identity [[identité propositionnelle]]* means that:

(1) *P* is a combination of a finite number of indeterminate propositions $p_1, ..., p_n$ formed solely by means of the [[truth-functional]] operations...

(2) *P* remains true whatever the logical values (Def. IV, p. 7) of the propositions $p_1, ..., p_n$.

The propositions of logic other than the propositional identities are called *propositions of logic of the second kind [[propositions de logique de deuxième espèce]]*."

(For Zaremba, a proposition of logic is "a proposition dealing exclusively with other propositions and logical functions [[that is, propositional functions]], which themselves belong to a totally indeterminate scientific domain" (p. 23). Zaremba implies on p. 42 that pp. 132–195 of *Principia Mathematica*, Vol. I deal with propositions of logic of the second kind. These pages cover Whitehead and Russell's theory of identity and general theory of classes, as well as quantification theory.)

Immediately after this Definition XLIX, Zaremba says (p. 30):

"The choice of the term 'propositional identity' is prompted by the following analogy: just as an algebraic identity tells us nothing but a property of the four algebraic

---

[9] [[These results are not mentioned elsewhere in Herbrand's published writings. Skolem (*1922*) first remarked that in Zermelo's set theory with the axiom of infinity, one cannot obtain a set of cardinality greater than all $\aleph^{(n)}$ (we use Herbrand's notation). However, other evidence indicates that Herbrand was probably not familiar with this paper of Skolem (see the Introduction, p. 12 above). Moreover, no work Herbrand cites deals with the relations between the theory of types and Zermelo's set theory.]]

operations, without telling us anything about the numerical values of the variables of which it is composed, so a propositional identity expresses a property of the [[truth-functional]] operations ... without informing us about the logical values of the propositions of which it is composed."

Herbrand retains the term 'identité' throughout his work, but not in strict accord with Zaremba's usage. Herbrand calls the formulas provable in his formulation of the propositional calculus "identités propositionnelles de première espèce" and those provable in his formulation of quantification theory "identités propositionnelles de deuxième espèce". (Thus, while Herbrand broadens the use of 'propositional identity', he restricts the use of 'second kind' to pure quantification theory.) Although these terms are purely proof-theoretic in Herbrand, their adoption from Zaremba suggests a certain view of logical validity, not unlike that of Wittgenstein in the *Tractatus*. Indeed, in *1930a* Herbrand says, "[[The propositional identities]] are in some sense the ones [[propositions]] which are true no matter what atomic propositions they are formed from" (p. 207 below). This reads – especially when its context is taken into account – as if Herbrand were extrapolating to all provable quantificational formulas Zaremba's justification for calling provable truth-functional formulas 'identités'.

On p. 38 Zaremba places among the "fundamental problems of deductive logic" the following two: "To develop the theory of propositional identities..." and "To develop the theory of propositions of logic of the second kind (Def. XLIX, p. 29)." Herbrand's assertion in section I of this note – his proof appears in Chap. 1 of *1930* – that Russell's axiomatization of the theory of propositional identities of the first kind is complete with respect to truth-functional validity is a direct response to Zaremba's claim on p. 41 that no published work has established such a result. (Zaremba adds that this lacuna has been filled by Sleszynski in a Polish work as yet unpublished; both Zaremba and Herbrand are unaware of *Post 1921*, as indeed are Hilbert and Ackermann when they give the same result in *Hilbert and Ackermann 1928*. Also, all four are certainly unaware of Kolmogorov's assertion that "Hilbert's system [[of the propositional calculus in *1922a*]] is complete: no new independent axiom can be added without contradiction"; see *Kolmogorov 1925* in *van Heijenoort 1967*, p. 418.) Again, it is not unduly speculative to suggest that Herbrand's Sections II and III are – at least in part – Herbrand's response to Zaremba's remarks on pp. 42–43 that the inadequacies of Whitehead and Russell's treatment of propositions of logic of the second kind result from the 'untenability' of their theory of types. In these sections Herbrand sharply distinguishes pure quantification theory from the theory of types by calling the latter a "particular mathematical theory"; presents quantification theory in an original and unusual way that reflects Whitehead and Russell's concerns in *9 of

Principia (see the Introduction, p. 4 above, and *1930*, pp. 79–85 below); asserts that Russell's theory of types is equivalent to what today is called the simple theory of types; and then states some interpretability results between his formulations R_1 and R_2 of the theory of types and Zermelo's set theory.

The notion of normal identity in this note must not be confused with that introduced in *1930*, Chap. 5, p. 139 below. The latter notion corresponds to provability using only the Rules 1, 2, and 4 given here, and hence is weaker than the former notion. In *1930*, Chap. 2, p. 84 below, Herbrand proves that all quantified tautologies are normal identities in the former sense (that is, he proves assertion (2) of Section II, p. 30 above); see the last paragraph of Note B, p. 100 below. The proof there also shows implicitly that all quantified tautologies have a special case of property A (defined in *1930*, Chap. 5, p. 143 below); see Note D, p. 189 below. Indeed, property A itself would seem to be the outgrowth of Herbrand's attempt to improve the normal form for proofs he gives above in assertion (3) of Section II; see Note F, p. 192 below for the final version of this normal form.

THE CONSISTENCY OF THE AXIOMS OF ARITHMETIC

(1929)

For the specification of the signs we use and the rules for combining them, we refer the reader to our previous note ⟦above, p. 29⟧. Following Russell, we shall call variables appearing in the signs (x) and $(\exists x)$ 'apparent variables', and the other variables 'real variables'.

In the following we consider two mathematical theories that deal with individuals called numbers,[1] among which there is a particular one denoted by 0, and for which there exists a 'descriptive function' $a+1$ which associates with every number a another number. We also have the atomic proposition $a=b$, which is to be considered as a propositional function of the individuals a and b. We shall consider the following five axioms (or primitive propositions):

$$a = a, \quad a = b . \supset . b = a, \quad a = b \ \& \ b = c . \supset . a = c$$
$$a + 1 = b + 1 . \equiv . a = b, \quad \sim .a + 1 = 0$$

to which we add all those of the form

$$\sim .a = a + 1, \quad \sim .a = a + 1 + 1,$$
$$\sim .a = a + 1 + 1 + 1, \ldots .$$

We call Theory 1 (abbreviated Th. 1) the theory not using apparent variables which is obtained by starting with all propositions obtained from these by substituting any definite expressions for a, b, and c. We call Theory 2 (abbreviated Th. 2) the theory using apparent variables which is obtained by starting with these primitive propositions. Hence-

---

[1] ⟦The results announced in this note are proved in Chap. 4 of *1930*, pp. 112ff. below.⟧

forth, we shall call any individual 0, 0+1, 0+1+1, etc., a 'numeral'.

(1) It is easy to prove that Th. 1 is consistent (see, for example, *von Neumann 1927*, p. 25).

(2) The consistency of Th. 2 was proved by von Neumann by means of a rather complicated method. We shall indicate the fundamentals of a simpler proof.

We note first of all that the truth or falsity of a proposition of Th. 1 can be decided by a definite algorithm. In particular, we can tell whether or not two propositions are equivalent; moreover, we can prove that if two propositions are not equivalent, then we can actually find the numerals which make one of the propositions true and the other false. Now with every proposition of Th. 2 we associate a proposition of Th. 1, called its expansion, by means of the following rules: if with P and Q we have associated the expansions p and q, then we associate $p \vee q$ with $P \vee Q$ and $\sim p$ with $\sim P$. Then we define the expansion of $(\exists x).\Phi(xy_1y_2\ldots \ldots y_n)$ on the basis of that of $\Phi(xy_1y_2\ldots y_n)$ in such a way that a necessary and sufficient condition for a system of numerals replacing $y_1, y_2, \ldots, y_n$ to make the new expansion true is that, in the original expansion, x can be replaced by a numeral such that with the same system of numerals substituted for $y_1, y_2, \ldots, y_n$, the expansion becomes true in Th. 1. Furthermore, the expansion of $(x).\Phi(x)$ is, by definition, the same as that of $\sim : (\exists x). \sim \Phi(x)$.

Then we can quite easily prove that for a proposition to be true in Th. 2 it is necessary for its expansion to be true in Th. 1. This entails the consistency of Th. 2 (since the expansion of $0 \neq 0$ is $0 \neq 0$). Then we can prove that if the new axiom

$$x = 0 . \vee . (\exists y).x = y + 1$$

(which satisfies the above condition and hence is not inconsistent with the axioms of Th. 2) is added to the axioms, our condition becomes sufficient.[2]

(3) To arrive at arithmetic, it would be necessary to introduce definitions by recursion and the axiom of mathematical induction. Our method

---

[2] We can easily see that this axiom, as well as those of the form $\sim .a = a + 1$, $\sim .a = a + 1 + 1$, etc. which were used above, are consequences of the axiom of mathematical induction.

does not allow us to prove the consistency of this system, any more than does von Neumann's. However, it should be noted that if the axiom of mathematical induction is introduced without definitions by recursion, it becomes a consequence of the preceding axioms, and hence is not inconsistent.

ON SEVERAL PROPERTIES OF TRUE PROPOSITIONS AND THEIR APPLICATIONS

(1929a)

For the specification of the terms and symbols we use, as well as of the rules for combining them, we refer to a previous note.[1] We recall that every proposition that has been proved true by means of the rules which are indicated there is said to be an *identity*; and that the variables which appear in a quantifier (x) or $(\exists x)$ are *apparent variables*, and the other variables are *real variables*. Finally, the *matrix* of a proposition P is the proposition without apparent variables which is obtained from P by omitting all quantifiers (x) and $(\exists x)$. (We assume here that every variable of P is designated by a different letter.) We can assume in the following that the propositions may contain descriptive functions (that is, individuals which can appear as arguments of atomic propositions and which are functions of other individuals, which can in turn also be such functions or variables. An example of a descriptive function is the function $x + 1$ in arithmetic.) This extension obviously necessitates a modification, easy to imagine, in Rules 2 and 3 of the note cited above.

It is easy to study propositions in finite domains, that is, under the assumption that the variables appearing in them can take only a finite number of values $a_1, a_2, ..., a_n$, so that we consider $(\exists x).\Phi(x)$ as standing

---

[1] *Herbrand 1928*. Regarding the rules of reasoning enumerated there, we note that it is necessary to use the primitive propositions of the theory of identities of the first kind only in cases where the letters appearing in these are replaced by propositions *without apparent variables*.

for $\Phi(a_1) \vee \Phi(a_2) \vee \cdots \vee \Phi(a_n)$, and $(x).\Phi(x)$ for $\Phi(a_1) \& \Phi(a_2) \& \cdots \& \Phi(a_n)$.[2] On the other hand, we have also sought to study propositions in domains composed of an infinite number of individuals $a_1, a_2, \ldots, a_p, \ldots$ (infinite domains). We have succeeded in giving a precise definition to the notion of a 'proposition true in an infinite domain' (but which is not the most natural of the definitions imaginable), and in proving the following two theorems:[3]

THEOREM I: *If a proposition P is an identity, then $\sim P$ cannot be true in an infinite domain.*

THEOREM II: *If a proposition P is not an identity, then we can construct an infinite domain in which $\sim P$ is true.*

Analogous considerations had been developed by Löwenheim (*1915*), but in a way which seems to us to be insufficient. He gave an intuitive sense to the notion of truth in an infinite domain, so that his proof of Theorem II is not, it seems to us, of sufficient rigor. As for Theorem I, he seems to admit this as obvious; indeed, it is precisely this theorem whose proof gave us the greatest difficulties, and which moreover leads us to the most important consequences.

To arrive at this result, we were obliged to study in a thorough manner certain properties of propositions which lead to canonical forms of proof. Among other consequences, we deduce from these considerations the following results:[4]

(1) The result of Löwenheim (*1915*), from which it follows that the resolution of the *Entscheidungsproblem* (that is, the problem consisting of finding a method of deciding whether or not a given proposition is an identity) can be reduced to the case of propositions containing only atomic propositions of two arguments, and which relies at bottom on Theorems I and II, is completely justified by our results. We can even go further and prove that the problem can be reduced to the case in

---

[2] $p \& q$ signifies 'p and q' (that is, $\sim . \sim p \vee q$) [[rather, $\sim . \sim p \vee \sim q$]].

[3] [[*1930*, Chap. 5, pp. 148ff. below. See also the Introduction, p. 11 above.]]

[4] [[(1) and (2) are proved in *1931*, Chaps. 2 and 3, pp. 237ff. below, (3) in *1930*, Chap. 5, and (4) in *1930*, Chap. 5, 6.7.]]

which there is no more than one atomic proposition of three arguments or three of two arguments.

(2) Aside from the already known cases of the *Entscheidungsproblem*, we have solved the case of propositions whose matrix is a disjunction of terms which are atomic propositions or negations of atomic propositions (even when the propositions contain descriptive functions).

(3) The rule of implication can be eliminated from the rules of reasoning (see *1928*), provided that Rule 3 is replaced by the following:

If within a true proposition $P \vee P$ is replaced by P, then the result is another true proposition.

Hence we see that the rule of implication (which basically has its origin in the classical theory of the syllogism) is useless in logic, but it remains indispensable in mathematical theories (in which there are hypotheses).

(4) Theorem I furnishes us with a general method for studying the consistency of mathematical theories, in particular of those theories which are verifiable in denumerable domains. In this way, the consistency of the axioms of arithmetic[5] is an immediate consequence. We can also prove that arithmetic remains consistent when the use of definitions by recursion is allowed. As for the axiom of mathematical induction, which entails considering all propositions of the form

$$\Phi(0) \,.\&. \, (y)\,\Phi(y) \supset \Phi(y+1) :\supset. \, (x)\,\Phi(x)$$

as true, we have succeeded in showing only that it can be admitted without risk of inconsistency when $\Phi(x)$ does not contain any apparent variables.

---

[5] With regard to this subject, see *1929*.

ON THE FUNDAMENTAL
PROBLEM OF MATHEMATICS

(1929b)

I

We could consider the fundamental problem of mathematics to be the following:[1]

PROBLEM A: *What is the necessary and sufficient condition for a theorem to be true in a given theory having only a finite number of hypotheses? If this theorem is true, what is its proof?*

We can in fact always contrive to construct all classical mathematical theories within theories having only a finite number of hypotheses[2] (an example of this is the theory of von Neumann, which furnishes a new axiomatization of set theory; see *von Neumann 1925*). Moreover, even in a theory having an infinity of hypotheses, only a finite number are used to prove any particular theorem; but we do not know beforehand which ones.

The results already indicated in a previous note permit us to show that this problem is equivalent to the following:[3]

---

[1] We refer to *1928* and *1929a*, which we designate by A and B, respectively.

[2] Most ordinary mathematical theories have hypotheses containing indeterminate propositions, which give rise to an infinity of particular hypotheses when these propositions are made determinate (for example, the axiom of mathematical induction; or the axioms by which the axiom of reducibility can be replaced when we want to formalize it; see A). But in practice, if we like, we could always replace these theories by others having only a finite number of hypotheses.

[3] [[*1931*, p. 244 below.]]

PROBLEM B: *Consider a denumerable set of elements $a_0, a_1, a_2, ..., a_n, ...$ and a finite number of functions $f_i(x_1 x_2 ... x_{n_i})$ $(i = 1, 2, ..., p)$ whose arguments and values are elements of this set. Suppose that*

1. $f_i(a_{m_1} a_{m_2} ... a_{m_{n_i}})$ *and* $f_j(a_{r_1} a_{r_2} ... a_{r_{n_j}})$ *can be equal only if* $i = j$, $m_1 = r_1$, $m_2 = r_2, ..., m_{n_i} = r_{n_j}$;

2. *Every element is the value of a function obtained by combining our functions by substitution, and all of whose arguments are a_0.*[4]

Given any collection composed of a finite number of systems of n elements $a_{i_1}, a_{i_2}, ..., a_{i_n}$, can we associate with each system one of the numbers $1, 2, ..., k$ in such a way that certain determinate conditions of the following form are satisfied?

Let $b_1, b_2, ..., b_n$ and $c_1, c_2, ..., c_n$ be two of the systems, either identical or different. If a given system of equalities of the form

$$f_i(b_{j_1} b_{j_2} ... b_{j_{n_i}}) = c_m \quad \text{or} \quad f_i(c_{j_1} c_{j_2} ... c_{j_{n_i}}) = b_m \quad \text{or} \quad b_i = c_j$$

is satisfied, then the numbers associated with $b_1, b_2, ..., b_n$ and $c_1, c_2, ..., c_n$ can form only certain given pairs of numbers.

If the desired correspondence is impossible for a certain collection, what is this collection?[5]

We can then consider this latter problem as the most important of those which exist at present in mathematics. We can realize its difficulty by noting that it suffices to particularize the conditions in order to arrive at the problem of actually solving any arbitrary diophantine equation. But now at least we are faced with a definite problem that is purely mathematical. However, it must be noted that to be of value, the study of this problem should use only "metamathematical" modes of reasoning, which are characterized by the fact that it is possible to repeat them in each individual case while using only elements which we can actually recognize and properties whose truth or falsity we can actually verify.

---

[4] We can satisfy these conditions by supposing that a_n is the integer n and the f_i are suitable polynomials. From this we see that our problem is a direct generalization of the diophantine problem.

[5] We can always verify whether this association is possible or not for any particular collection.

However, we could study this problem by using all the methods of a definite mathematical theory, as long as we have proved beforehand metamathematically that this theory is consistent.

II

Now suppose that the above problem has been resolved. We designate by *R* the theory that Russell and Whitehead develop in *Principia Mathematica* with the supposition that the multiplicative axiom and the axiom of infinity are true. (In the following, we could also replace this theory by others that are less extensive.)

(a) In the study of Problem A, we obviously supposed that only ordinary procedures of reasoning were used; namely, the ones we enumerated in Note A (see an erratum in Note B), and the ones deducible from them. Suppose that furthermore new rules of reasoning are used. Then we can prove that *R* becomes inconsistent.[6] (However, it has not yet been proved that *R* with the ordinary rules of reasoning is consistent.)

(b) Moreover, suppose that *R* has been proved consistent; then we can deduce a general result of which the following is a special case: If an arithmetical theorem has been proved by using incommensurable numbers or analytic functions, then it can also be proved by using only purely arithmetical elements (integers and functions defined by recursion). Examples of this are Dedekind's theorem on prime numbers, and class field theory.

---

[6] [[See *1931*, p. 256 below, and Note N, p. 265 below.]]

INVESTIGATIONS IN PROOF THEORY

(1930)

⟦This paper is Herbrand's thesis. The date given at the end is 14 April 1929, but the defense at the Sorbonne did not take place until 11 June 1930 (in October 1929 Herbrand was drafted for a year of service in the French army). There is no indication that he introduced revisions into the text between April 1929 and June 1930; his *1931*, which is dated September 1929, contains emendations to the thesis, and this shows, it seems, that the text remained unchanged after April 1929.

The thesis is divided into five chapters. Chapter 1 presents the classical propositional calculus, including an elegant proof of the completeness of his axiom system with respect to truth-functional validity. Chapter 2 is devoted to Herbrand's formulation of quantification theory; he proves here that it is equivalent to several other standard formulations. Chapter 2 also contains results regarding finite validity, obtained by using the notion of common expansion (see p. 6 above), including some applications to cases of the decision problem. Chapter 3 consists of general remarks on formalizations of mathematical theories. Herbrand here extends his system of quantification theory to include function signs, with an extended rule of existential generalization. This system, which we call Q_H, is used throughout Chapters 4 and 5. Chapter 4 contains investigations of several weak systems of arithmetic, yielding various consistency and decidability results. Finally, in Chapter 5 Herbrand states and attempts to prove the Fundamental Theorem. This is preceded by studies of three properties (*A*, *B*, and *C*) of provable formulas, and followed by applications of the theorem to decision problems and consistency proofs.

Herbrand's statement of the formation rules of Q_H lacks precision and is not always consistent with his usage. The notation used frequently allows confusion between use and mention, although in practice this confusion does not create any basic difficulties. To assist the reader, we shall now outline his symbolism, omitting a great many details.

For each $n \geqslant 0$ there is a finite or denumerable supply of n-place function signs. An *elementary descriptive function* (*fonction descriptive élémentaire*) is either a 0-place function sign or, for $n > 0$, an n-place function sign followed by parentheses enclosing n variables separated by commas and called the *arguments* of the function. (Herbrand also calls such functions fundamental descriptive functions. In the French text, commas and parentheses are not used; the translators have found it convenient to reestablish them.) The *descriptive functions* are obtained from the elementary descriptive functions by iterated substitution of descriptive functions for arguments. A function in which no variable occurs is a constant; a 0-place function sign is a *primitive constant* (*constante fondamentale*; in *1931* Herbrand uses the expression *constante élémentaire*). Variables and descriptive functions are *individuals* (*individus*). Herbrand uses f sometimes as a syntactic variable ranging over functions and sometimes as a syntactic variable ranging over function signs.

For each $n \geqslant 0$ there is a denumerable supply of n-adic predicate letters (these are left unspecified). An *atomic proposition* (*proposition-élément*) is either a 0-adic predicate letter, or, for $n > 0$, an n-adic predicate letter followed by parentheses enclosing n individuals. (Again, in the original text, parentheses are not used.) A *proposition* is a well-formed formula of Q_H; it is constructed from atomic propositions by means of connectives and quantifiers. The primitive connectives are negation ($\sim$) and disjunction ($\vee$); conjunction ($\&$), the conditional ($\supset$) and the biconditional ($\equiv$) are defined in terms of these two. (In his text Herbrand uses groups of dots for conjunction.) Both the universal and the existential quantifiers, (x) and $(\exists x)$, are taken as primitive. The former is sometimes written $(+x)$ and the latter $(-x)$. A quantifier left indeterminate is written $(\pm x)$. As in *Principia Mathematica*, a bound variable is said to be *apparent* and a free variable *real*. A quantifier-free proposition is said to be *elementary* (*élémentaire*). Herbrand uses 'fonction propositionnelle' in two senses: (1) A proposition P is said to be a *propositional function* of its real variables; (2) a proposition P is said to be a *propositional function* of any atomic proposition occurring in P; it is *of the first kind* if it is quantifier-free, and *of the second kind* otherwise. (More generally, Herbrand occasionally says P is a proposition function of a not necessarily atomic proposition Q; what he means then is that Q is a well-formed part of P.) The letters Φ and Ψ are used both as syntactic variables ranging over atomic propositions and as syntactic variables ranging over all propositions, and they are used together with variables when Herbrand wishes these variables to be exhibited (the variables shown need neither actually occur nor be all of the real variables in the proposition denoted). An occurrence of a subproposition A in a proposition P (written in terms of the primitive connectives $\vee$ and $\sim$) is said to be *positive* if this occurrence of A lies within the scopes of an even number of negation signs of P; it is negative if the number is odd.

Finally, we note that Herbrand says a proposition P is *true* if it is provable in quantification theory, and P is *true in a theory* if it is provable in the theory.]

TABLE OF CONTENTS

INTRODUCTION

One of Russell and Whitehead's great accomplishments in their fundamental work *Principia Mathematica* was to have shown, following the point of view originated by the logicists of Peano's school, that every mathematical proposition could be translated into combinations of a small number of signs, and that the laws of reasoning ultimately reduced to several simple rules for combining these signs. Hence, in a certain sense this system of signs can be considered as equivalent to the totality of mathematics.

Toward this end, a certain number of signs are used which translate either the simplest logical operations and concepts (one sign means 'or', another 'not', another 'and', etc.) or definite relations between certain objects. From the beginning of this work, we shall study these signs in detail. We shall give a certain number of laws, which are of two sorts:

(a) Some indicate that certain combinations of signs are propositions;

(b) The others indicate procedures that allow the formation of new combinations of signs that are propositions, starting from a certain number of combinations already known to be such.

A suitable choice of these signs and laws succeeds in effecting the translation of propositions into signs. Furthermore, it must be noted that this first step is but the least important; for the statement of a proposition in words of any definite language can be considered as a collection of signs representing the proposition. Our symbolism is basically only a shorthand, which, moreover, allows us to give more uniformity and precision to the statement of mathematical propositions. This was the only goal of the logicists.

The laws of reasoning must now be studied. We can establish that within any theory these reduce to several very simple laws, of the following two sorts:

(a) Some indicate that certain propositions are to be considered true;

(b) The others indicate procedures which allow the deduction of new propositions, which are then to be considered true, from propositions already known to be true. These are the 'rules of reasoning'.

As will be seen further on, the statement of these rules is such that every combination of signs called a proposition is actually the translation of a proposition of ordinary language, and that a sequence of propositions which, according to these rules, are to be considered as true corresponds to a mathematical proof. But we may still wonder whether there are propositions that the system of signs will not be able to translate, and proofs that are not captured by these rules.

It must not be concealed that this is only an experimental result (whose validity cannot fail to be confirmed by a philosophical dialectic); its proof lies wholly in the fact that Russell and Whitehead succeeded, in the three volumes of *Principia Mathematica*, in reproducing all the arguments regarding the foundations of mathematics and the theory of sets. That all reasoning that can actually be done by a rational mathematician is immediately translatable into the system of signs studied can be considered as one of the most perfectly verified facts of our logical knowledge of the world. It is possible, however difficult it seems to us, that some day this framework will be broken; yet perhaps, by a more precise comprehension of what this symbolic logic is, we will convince ourselves that undoubtedly even then it will suffice to modify slightly the initial rules regarding the signs' use in order to absorb these new theories.[1]

Once the absolute parallel between mathematical reasoning and the combinations of these signs has been discovered, it becomes natural to study this system of signs in itself, and to pose problems regarding it. The solution of these will have an immediate echo in our general knowledge of mathematics (and this is how the consistency of certain theories can be proved). We shall pose problems of the following kind: Do all propositions have such-and-such a property? or: Do all true propositions have such-and-such a property? We could just as well seek a criterion permitting us to recognize with certainty if a given proposition is true in a definite theory; the discovery of such a criterion in a sufficiently general case would obviously be of considerable theoretical importance.

It is necessary for us, however, to find a method of attacking these problems. We can rather easily convince ourselves that there is only one such method that is unobjectionable; and this is the one usually designated by the name 'the method of recursion'.

For example, let us suppose that we want to prove that every true proposition of a given theory has a property A. We must first show that all propositions admitted as true at the start in this theory have this property. Then we must show that if some true propositions have this property, the situation is the same for every proposition deducible from them by the use of one of the rules of reasoning. We would then be certain that for every proof put into signs that we could have before our eyes, we could attempt to verify that the conclusion possesses property A by repeating the above argument for each step of the proof; and we could be sure beforehand that this verification would succeed. This is a certainty of an intuitive, experimental nature. It is the consciousness we have that we can argue thus which permits us to know that we will eventually verify that the conclusion of each particular proof has property A by repeating the argument a sufficient number of times – and

---

[1] The intuitionist logics, as far as their manner of reasoning can be determined, limit themselves to prohibiting certain methods of reasoning, and hence do not risk going beyond the framework of the theory which we consider.

we can determine this number beforehand by looking at the particular proof under consideration.

This recursion which 'stops in the finite' has such an intuitive certainty that the most rigorous mind could not refuse to acquiesce to it; for an argument which relies on it is basically only a description of the operations which are to be executed in each particular case; it is a manual of operations which permits us to verify property A for the conclusion of any proof translated into signs that we can actually construct.

This point of view has been developed vigorously during the past years by Hilbert, who, in a series of articles, has indicated the foundations of his view and the results he deduced from it (the most important of these is the consistency of ordinary arithmetic).[2]

The properties to which we shall apply reasoning by recursion are such that one can always recognize whether or not they hold with regard to any particular proof or proposition (for example, the property of containing, or not containing, a given sign). It is certain that a criterion enabling us to recognize if a property satisfies this condition cannot be given, but in each particular case that this is so will easily be seen to be true. To avoid this appeal to intuition, it would be necessary to do work for this logic analogous to that which permits the axiomatization of ordinary mathematics; but this is perhaps yet premature.

This work will systematically use the method of recursion in three different ways:

(1) To show that every proposition possesses a certain property, say A, we shall show successively: (*a*) that the collections of signs explicitly indicated as being propositions by the rules allowing the construction of propositions have property A; and (*b*) that if some propositions have property A then so do all those which can be derived from them by applying one of the rules allowing the construction of new propositions from old ones. We shall then be sure that every proposition we can construct will have property A. Such a proof will be said to proceed by *recursion on the construction of the proposition.*

---

[2] In his communication to the Bologna Congress (*1928*), Hilbert in fact includes among the problems which exist at the present time certain of the results which he had previously announced (and which, it seems, correspond to the consistency of ordinary mathematics and of the continuum hypothesis).

(2) Similarly, to show that every true proposition of a theory has a property A, we shall show successively that the propositions admitted as true at the start in this theory have property A; and that, if several propositions have property A, so do those which are deducible from them by the application of one of the rules of reasoning. Such a proof will be said to proceed by *recursion on the proof of the proposition*.

(3) Sometimes we shall also have to consider series of propositions, each of which is derived from the preceding one by a definite operation; in which case these propositions can be enumerated with numerals. Suppose that we have proved that the first proposition of the series has property A, [[and that if a proposition in the series has property A, then]] so does the following one. We would then be certain that every time we actually pick a proposition from the series, it will have property A (for it would suffice to repeat the argument imagined above for each of the steps which lead from the first proposition of the series to the one of which we are thinking).

It must be carefully noted that there is a certain difference between the manner in which we employ reasoning by recursion here and the manner in which it is sometimes employed in mathematics. Here, it is never anything but an indication, in a single formula, of a procedure which must be employed a certain number of times in each particular case. In mathematics, on the other hand, it can happen that this reasoning is used in the case of concepts for which a material representation is not possible, as opposed to our signs; as, for example, for the set of integers or of real numbers. That is why it will not be tautologous for us to prove later on that reasoning by recursion, in its use in arithmetic, is consistent.

In general, it can be said that many of the obscurities and discussions that have arisen in regard to the foundations of mathematics have their origin in a confusion between the 'mathematical' and the 'metamathematical' senses of terms. (The latter is the expression used by Hilbert to designate his logic.) The former sense is used when we *make* a mathematical argument; the latter when we *talk about* mathematical arguments. Many questions are now easily made clearer: for example, concerning reasoning by recursion, the excluded middle (in the mathematical sense, this is the possibility of using in an argument the fact that a proposition is either true or false; in the metamathematical sense, this is the possibility of always being able to prove the negation of a theorem in a given theory, if not the theorem itself); the question of the objects which can actually be constructed (given a set, to know whether it can actually be ordered is a metamathematical question; to know if the proposition 'there is an ordering' is true is a mathematical question); the Borel paradox about the objects definable in a finite number of words (the paradox results from the illegitimate application of a mathematical argument to a metamathematical question), etc. It must not be forgotten that the study of metamathematical reasoning could furnish us with a new theory of which it would be the object, and this ladder of metamathematics of different 'types' could be pursued indefinitely. But these considerations far exceed the framework which we have set up for ourselves.

In reading this work, one could if one wished divorce the signs used from their intuitive meaning and consider us to be studying a certain system of objects (i.e., the signs employed) which we subject to certain rules. The study of such a system then becomes as legitimate as that which concerns only some other system as, for example, a group, a field, or a ring. Such a point of view will perhaps be of some utility to avoid confusions between the properties which we instinctively attribute to the signs when we recall their meaning, and those which we attribute to them in reality. But from time to time it will not be without interest to remember this meaning in order to justify the route taken, the view with which we are concerned, and the goal which it would be desirable to attain.

This work is divided into three parts, comprising five chapters.[3] In the first part (Chaps. 1 and 2), we shall exhibit the systems of signs we employ and the rules governing their use. We have adopted here a system of rules which differs somewhat from those used until now, but which nonetheless is connected to one of the methods of Russell and Whitehead (cf. Chap. 2). The reasons which have prompted us to adopt this system are first, that it is one of those in which the number of propositions admitted as true is smallest, and second, that it permits us better than any other to study in detail those fundamental properties of propositions that are either necessary or sufficient for their truth. Moreover, we shall show in detail its equivalence to the methods of Russell and Whitehead, as it is

---

[3] The principal results of this article were summarized in three notes: *1928*, *1929*, and *1929a*.

necessary to do in accordance with the point of view explained above.

In the second part, which comprises Chaps. 3 and 4, we shall show how to construct systems of signs corresponding to a mathematical theory; in order to do this it will be necessary to generalize the symbolism of the preceding chapters slightly. Chap. 4 is devoted to the study of a particularly simple mathematical theory corresponding to the beginnings of classical arithmetic, and for which a new method will lead to precise and interesting results.

Finally, the third part comprises a study of conditions necessary and sufficient for the truth of a proposition. It begins with the study of sufficient conditions, then goes on to prove a fundamental theorem which can be considered as the basis of a general method regarding the theory to which this work is devoted. One of the simplest applications of this method will yield the consistency of the axioms of arithmetic and definitions by recursion.

BIBLIOGRAPHY

Without trying to be at all complete, we note here the works which we used in the course of this work. A complete bibliography can be found in the work numbered 2.

1. *Whitehead and Russell 1910, 1912*, and *1913, 1925, 1927*, and *1927a*. (We refer to the first edition, and denote this work by the initials *PM*.)
2. *Hilbert and Ackermann 1928*. (We denote this work by *HA*.)
3. *Hilbert 1922, 1922a, 1925*, and *1927*.
4. *von Neumann 1927*
5. *Löwenheim 1915*

CHAPTER 1

THE THEORY OF IDENTITIES OF THE FIRST KIND

1. SIGNS

1.1. In this chapter,[1] each letter will be called a proposition, and can

---

[1] In regard to the first five sections of this chapter, see *Hilbert and Ackermann 1928*, Chap. 1, where this theory is developed in an analogous manner, and *Whitehead and Russell 1910* §§ 1–5.

be replaced, if desired, by groups of letters and signs which form a proposition according to the rules below.

We shall use the two signs $\sim$ and $\vee$; $\sim p$ is read 'not p' and is a new proposition called the *negation* of p. $p \vee q$ is read 'p or q' and is a new proposition called the *disjunction* of p and q. We also call it the *logical sum*, or the *sum*, of p and q.

1.2. We define new signs on the basis of these two. For example, to use a notation due to Russell and Whitehead,

$$p \supset q. =. \sim p . \vee q \qquad Df\,^2$$

defines the sign $\supset$ (that is, every time the left side appears in an expression, where p and q are definite propositions, it should be replaced by the right side in order to obtain the meaning of the expression under consideration). $p \supset q$ is read 'p implies q' (that is, if p is true then q is true).

$$p \& q. =. \sim [\sim p \vee \sim q] \qquad Df.^3$$

$p \& q$ means 'p and q are simultaneously true' and is called the *logical product* (or just the *product*) of p and q.

$$p \equiv q. =: p \supset q .\&. q \supset p \qquad Df.$$

$p \equiv q$ means 'p and q are simultaneously true or simultaneously false'. It is read 'p and q are *identical*'.

1.3. A collection of letters, signs, and dots formed from the signs $\sim$ and $\vee$ by use of the preceding rules and those below in 1.4 is called a *proposition*.

The letters which appear here are called *atomic propositions*, and the expression is said to be a *propositional function* of the letters appearing in it.

1.4. Every sign appearing in a proposition relates to one or two parts of the proposition, called its *scopes*, which are marked out by dots or groups of dots. Thus, the scope of the $\sim$ sign in $\sim p$ is p, and the scopes

---

² The letters *Df* signify definition.

³ [[In the French text, Herbrand uses groups of dots to indicate conjunctions; we replace these by the sign '&'. Hence, there are no longer any dots of the first sort (1.4); those dots to the right or left of '&' are of the third sort.]]

of the signs $\lor$, $\&$, $\supset$, and $\equiv$ in $p \lor q$, $p \& q$, $p \supset q$, and $p \equiv q$ are in each case p and q.

The dots will be considered as of three different sorts, distinguished by their place in the proposition. Those of the first sort indicate logical products, and consequently play a different role from the others.[3] Those of the second sort are situated to the right of a $\sim$ sign. Those of the third sort are to the right or left of the other signs. We say that the dots of the third sort are *stronger* than those of the other two sorts, and that those of the second sort are *stronger* than those of the first. The scope of the $\sim$ sign or the scopes of one of the other signs are limited by groups of dots either of a greater number or of the same number and stronger than every group of dots appearing in this part of the proposition. Furthermore, if several $\sim$ signs follow one another in such a way that the scope of each extends exactly as far as the scope of all those signs situated to its right, then the dots between each of the $\sim$ signs are deleted. Also, we add that a group of dots may contain no dots at all. (These rules are almost the same as those in *Whitehead and Russell 1910*, p. 9.)

For example, the proposition

$$p \supset . q \lor r$$

means p implies q or r.

$$p \supset q . \lor r$$

means either p implies q or else r.

$$\sim \sim . p \& q . \supset r$$

means the negation of the negation of the product $p \& q$ implies r.

1.41. We shall use the following very important convention throughout the course of this work: we shall always consider propositions in which the letters represent arbitrary propositions, and must be replaced by definite propositions in each particular case. However, we shall use dots as if these letters represented atomic propositions, with the understanding that, when the letters are replaced by definite propositions, the number of dots must consequently be increased in such a way that the scopes of all the signs remain the same.

We shall use the same convention in general, when in any proposition the atomic propositions are replaced by other propositions.

Thus, the proposition $p \supset q$ becomes

$$q \vee r . \supset q$$

when p is replaced by $q \vee r$.

The same convention must be used when a sign is replaced by its definition. Thus, $p \, \&. \, p \equiv q$ is nothing but

$$p . \& : p \supset q . \&. q \supset p .$$

1.42. REMARKS. 1. Hence, from now on a logical product may be designated not only by one dot, but by a group of dots.[3] Thus, we may write

$$\sim p \vee p . \& : p \supset q . \vee q .$$

2. It should be understood that certain groups of dots (except for dots of the first sort) may contain no dots at all and yet the above rules continue to hold (there are some groups of no dots stronger than others).

3. We may use more dots than are necessary, if we judge this to be clearer.

4. Certain collections of signs have no meaning if the dots are not used in a suitable manner. Thus

$$p \vee q \supset p$$

means nothing; it is necessary to write, for example,

$$p \vee . q \supset p$$

or

$$p \vee q . \supset p .$$

2. RULES OF REASONING

2. We shall say that certain propositions are *true*, according to the following conventions.[4]

First, we consider as true the following five propositions (which are called *primitive propositions*, indicated by writing the letters Pp after

---

[4] It should be understood that when we say a proposition is not true, that does not mean that $\sim p$ is true (hence an atomic proposition is never true).

them), as well as all those which can be deduced from them by replacing the letters which appear by other letters or by non-atomic propositions (1.3).

1.	$p \lor p . \supset p$	Pp
2.	$q \supset . p \lor q$	Pp
3.	$p \lor q . \supset . q \lor p$	Pp
4.	$p \lor . q \lor r : \supset : q \lor . p \lor r$	Pp
5.	$q \supset r . \supset : p \lor q . \supset . p \lor r$	Pp

Then we admit the

RULE OF IMPLICATION: *If $p \supset q$ and p are true propositions, then so is q.*

To indicate that a proposition is true, following Russell we shall write the sign ⊢(*Whitehead and Russell 1910*, p. 8) before it, followed by dots of the second sort. The scope of this sign is the entire true proposition.

2.1. A true proposition in which there appear only the signs introduced so far (or others defined from them) will throughout this work be said to be a *propositional identity of the first kind* (or, if no ambiguity is to be feared, an *identity*).[5]

The series of intermediate propositions necessary to obtain a true proposition is called the *proof* of this proposition.

2.11. This method of presenting the theory of identities of the first kind is due to Russell and Whitehead (*1910*, § 1). In the next few sections, we shall refer to *PM* in order to establish that a given proposition is true, without reproducing the proof here.

2.2. Nicod (*1916*) has simplified this theory. First, he shows that primitive proposition 3 may be omitted if the second one is replaced by

$$\vdash . q \supset . q \lor p \qquad Pp.$$

But a further simplification is possible. We start with the fundamental sign $|$. $p|q$ is a proposition read 'p and q are incompatible'.[6] Starting from this, the original signs are defined as follows:

[5] [[Regarding the use of the term 'propositional identity', see the Note to 1928, p. 32 above.]]

[6] $p|q$ can be defined from the original signs as $\sim p \lor \sim q$.

$$\sim p \ . = . \ p|p \qquad Df$$
$$p \lor q \ . =: \ \sim p|\sim q \qquad Df$$
$$p \supset q \ . = . \ p|\sim q \qquad Df$$
$$p \ \& \ q \ . = . \ \sim . \ p|q \qquad Df$$

There is one primitive proposition:

$$\vdash :: . \ p \ \big| . \ q \big| r :\big| :: t \ \big| . \ t \big| t :\big| :. \ s \big| q \ . \big| : p \big| s \ . \big| . \ p \big| s \qquad Pp$$

and one rule: If $p \ . \big| . \ q \big| r$ and p are true, then so is r.

By starting with these, he proves the five primitive propositions of Russell and Whitehead and the rule of implication.[7]

3. CONSEQUENCES

We shall deduce several consequences of this theory.

3.1. Let $A(p_1, p_2, ..., p_n)$ be a true proposition formed from the atomic propositions $p_1, p_2, ..., p_n$. *If $p_1, p_2, ..., p_n$ are replaced by other propositions, then this proposition remains true.*

In fact, the proof of the new proposition is obtained by replacing p_1, $p_2, ..., p_n$ by their new values throughout the proof of the original proposition.

This rule for obtaining true propositions is called the *rule of substitution.*

3.2. We say that two propositions p and q are equivalent (or identical) if $\vdash . p \equiv q$. This relation is symmetrical and transitive, since $\vdash . q \equiv p$ can be deduced from $\vdash . p \equiv q$ (*PM* 4.21 and 3.26), and $\vdash . p \equiv r$ can be deduced from $\vdash . p \equiv q$ and $\vdash . q \equiv r$ (*PM* 4.22 and 3.26).

3.21. *When two propositions are equivalent, the truth of one is necessary and sufficient for the truth of the other.*

For, if $\vdash p$ and $\vdash . p \equiv q$, that is (from 1.2) $\vdash : p \supset q \ . \&. \ q \supset p$, then we can deduce $\vdash p \supset q$ (*PM* 3.26); hence, from the rule of implication, $\vdash q$. The same argument works when p and q are interchanged.

3.22. We say p *implies* q if $\vdash . p \supset q$.

3.3. *Let $f(r)$ be a propositional function* (1.3) *containing r as well as*

---

[7] It is useful to note that any system of primitive propositions $p_1, p_2, ..., p_n$ can always be reduced to a system of three primitive propositions, which are, using the notation of 3.41, $\vdash . p_1 \ \& \ p_2 \ \& \ ... \ \& \ p_n$, $\vdash . p \ \& \ q \ . \supset p$, and $\vdash . p \ \& \ q \ . \supset q$.

other atomic propositions, and let p and q be two (not necessarily atomic) equivalent propositions. Then f(p) and f(q) are equivalent.

Here we are going to find the first example of reasoning by recursion in the particular form of which we spoke in the Introduction, where we demonstrated its validity. Let us begin by noting that, if the theorem is true for $f(r)$, then it is true for $\sim.f(r)$. This results from the fact that if $\vdash.p \equiv q$, then also $\vdash.\sim p \equiv \sim q$ (from Theorems 4.11 and 3.26 of *PM*, and the rule of implication).

Similarly, if the theorem is true for $f(r)$ and $g(r)$, then it is also for $f(r) \vee g(r)$. For, if $\vdash.p \equiv q$ and $\vdash.p' \equiv q'$, then also $\vdash.p \vee p'. \equiv .q \vee q'$ (*PM* 4.37).

Now let us suppose that we have before us a propositional function $f(r)$, constructed from atomic propositions by combining them with the signs $\sim$ and $\vee$; since $\vdash.r \equiv r$ (*PM* 4.2), it suffices to repeat one or the other of the two proofs above as many times as there are operations performed in the construction of $f(r)$, in order to conclude the desired theorem.

3.31. In particular, since $\vdash.p. \equiv .p \vee p$ (*PM* 4.25), in a true proposition $p \vee p$ can always be replaced by p, and conversely.

3.4. GENERALIZED SUM AND PRODUCT. The following propositions are provable:

$$p \vee q. \equiv .q \vee p$$
$$p.\vee.q \vee r: \equiv :q.\vee.p \vee r \qquad (PM\ 4.31,\ 4.33).$$

Hence, we see that in a ⟦true⟧ proposition, $p \vee q$ can be replaced by $q \vee p$ and $p.\vee.q \vee r$ by $q.\vee.p \vee r$ without the proposition's ceasing to be true. This permits us to generalize the use of the disjunction sign. We set

$$p \vee q \vee r. =:p \vee.q \vee r \qquad Df$$
$$p \vee q \vee r \vee s. =:p \vee.q \vee r \vee s \qquad Df$$

and, in the general case, we define $p_1 \vee p_2 \vee ... \vee p_n$ from step to step as follows:

$$p_1 \vee p_2 \vee \cdots \vee p_n. =:p_1.\vee.p_2 \vee p_3 \vee \cdots \vee p_n \qquad Df.$$

For any well-determined number n, we thus have the definition of $p_1 \vee p_2 \vee ... \vee p_n$. Hence, if $p_1, p_2,..., p_n$ are propositions, then so is $p_1 \vee p_2 \vee ... \vee p_n$, which is read '$p_1$ or p_2 or ... or p_n' and is called the *disjunction*, or *logical sum*, of $p_1, p_2, ..., p_n$ (which are called its *terms*). In such a generalized disjunction, we may always permute the order of the terms arbitrarily. Furthermore, from the above remarks, this disjunction is 'associative'; thus

$$\vdash:. p \vee q . \vee . r \vee s: \equiv . p \vee q \vee r \vee s.$$

3.41. Since also

$$\vdash: p \,\&\, q . \equiv . q \,\&\, p$$
$$\vdash:. p .\&. q \,\&\, r: \equiv : q .\&. p \,\&\, r \qquad (PM\ 4.3\ and\ 4.32),$$

we can define a generalized product $p_1 \,\&\, p_2 \,\&\, ... \,\&\, p_n$ in the same way.

3.42. We can give a definition of the generalized product in terms of the generalized sum. In fact, we have

$$\vdash: p_1 \,\&\, p_2 \,\&\, \cdots \,\&\, p_n . \equiv . \sim . \sim p_1 \vee \sim p_2 \vee \cdots \vee \sim p_n. \qquad (1)$$

To prove this for any definite value of n, it suffices to prove it stepwise, by supposing it proved for n and deducing it for $n+1$ from this supposition.

That is, $p_1 \,\&\, p_2 \,\&\, ... \,\&\, p_n$ is identical to $p_1 .\&. p_2 \,\&\, ... \,\&\, p_n$ and hence to $\sim : \sim p_1 . \vee . \sim . p_2 \,\&\, ... \,\&\, p_n$ by definition, which, after we recall that $\vdash . \sim \sim a . \equiv . a\ (PM\ 4.13)$, yields the desired result.

Moreover, we see that

$$\vdash: \sim . p_1 \,\&\, p_2 \,\&\, \cdots \,\&\, p_n . \equiv . \sim p_1 \vee \sim p_2 \vee \cdots \vee \sim p_n. \qquad (2)$$

This results from formula (1) and from the result, which we have already cited,

$$\vdash . p \equiv q . \supset . \sim p \equiv \sim q \qquad (PM\ 4.11).$$

Furthermore, if $\sim p_1, \sim p_2, ..., \sim p_n$ are substituted for $p_1, p_2, ..., p_n$, respectively, in formula (1), we obtain

$$\vdash: \sim . p_1 \vee p_2 \vee \cdots \vee p_n . \equiv . \sim p_1 \,\&\, \sim p_2 \,\&\, \cdots \,\&\, \sim p_n. \qquad (3)$$

3.43. REMARK 1. Since

$$\vdash p \,\&\, q . \supset p \qquad (PM\ 3.26)$$

and

$$\vdash p \supset : q \supset . p \,\&\, q \qquad (PM\ 3.2),$$

we can easily deduce that the necessary and sufficient condition for $p_1 \,\&\, p_2 \,\&\, ... \,\&\, p_n$ to be true is that $p_1, p_2, ..., p_n$ are all true.

3.44. REMARK 2. In what follows we shall have occasion to speak of products and sums that have only one term p. We stipulate that this is to be p itself. This convention permits us to use formulas (1), (2), and (3) even in the case $n=1$.

3.45. REMARK 3. Further on we shall need the following property, which we generalize in 5.34.

The proposition a_1 & a_2 & ... & a_n . $\vee$. b_1 & b_2 & ... & b_p is equivalent to the product of all propositions $a_i \vee b_j$, where i and j take all possible values.

By recalling that A & B . $\vee$. C is equivalent to A & C . $\vee$. B & C (*PM* 4.4), this is proved without any difficulty: first for $p=1$ by recursion on n, and then by recursion on p.

4. LOGICAL VALUES

4. We are going to prove that the theory developed so far is consistent, that is, among the true propositions cannot be found both a proposition and its negation.

Let us suppose that we have a demonstration that leads to both $\vdash p$ and $\vdash . \sim p$.

4.1. Let us set up a correspondence between each of the letters which appear in this demonstration and one of two signs that we may designate, for example, by T and F. Then with every proposition formed from these letters and the signs $\sim$ and $\vee$, we can associate either T or F in a way that we shall indicate. When the sign T is associated with a proposition, we say that the proposition has the *logical value 'true'*; and when the sign F is associated to it, that it has the *logical value 'false'*.[8]

If T is associated with p, then we stipulate that F is to be associated with $\sim p$; and if F is associated with p, then T is to be associated with $\sim p$.

---

[8] [[In the French text, Herbrand uses 'le vrai' and 'le faux' for the logical values, to distinguish this use of the words from that of 'vrai' and 'faux' as meaning 'provable' and 'refutable'. In this translation, we use quotation marks around 'true' and 'false' when they refer to the logical values. In addition, Herbrand uses the letters V and F rather than T and F (this is also the case in *1931*, p. 225 below and *1931c*, p. 286 below).]]

We stipulate that F is associated with $p \lor q$ if and only if F is associated with both p and q.

By proceeding as in an argument above (3.3), we can see that these two rules suffice to determine uniquely the logical value of every proposition.

4.2. Let us prove that every true proposition has the logical value 'true' [[whatever the logical values of the atomic propositions appearing in it]] (the converse is not obviously correct). For, every proposition obtained by replacing p, q, and r by other propositions in the primitive propositions (§ 2) has the logical value 'true'. This is verified directly by supposing successively that each of the eight possible cases of logical values of p, q, and r is realized. We see that in all these cases each of the primitive propositions has the logical value 'true'.

Furthermore, if $p \supset q$ and p both have the logical value 'true' then q has it as well. For otherwise, if p had the logical value 'true' and q the logical value 'false', then according to its definition $p \supset q$ would have the logical value 'false'.

When we have before us a demonstration starting with a certain number of primitive propositions and using the rule of implication a certain number of times, it suffices, in this particular case, to repeat our argument the same number of times in order to conclude that the conclusion of the demonstration has the logical value 'true'. (This is the first example of 'recursion on the proof of a proposition', of which we spoke in the Introduction.)

In summary, we have the

THEOREM. *For a proposition to be true, it is necessary that it have the logical value 'true' no matter what logical values its atomic propositions have.*

In particular, p and $\sim p$ cannot both be true, and this justifies the assertion made above [[§ 4]].

4.31. The following is a particular case of the theorem. If p and q are equivalent, then p and q have the same logical value for any assignment of logical values to the atomic propositions. (For it is only in this case that $p \equiv q$ will have the logical value 'true'. See the definition of $p \equiv q$ (1.2).)

We shall now show that this condition is sufficient. We shall permit ourselves to abbreviate our arguments slightly – they are all on the same model as those above – by not showing the validity of reasoning by recursion in every particular case. The legitimacy of its use can easily be seen in each case by recalling what we said in the Introduction.

5. THE TWO NORMAL FORMS OF A PROPOSITION

5. We say that a proposition is *simple* if it is an atomic proposition or the negation of one.

5.1. *Given a proposition, we shall furnish a procedure permitting us to find two propositions equivalent to it, one of which is a sum of products of simple propositions (disjunctive normal form) and the other of which is a product of sums of simple propositions (conjunctive normal form).*

When this procedure is applied, we shall say that the proposition is put into (conjunctive or disjunctive) normal form.

1. An atomic proposition is obviously of both forms.

2. If p can be put into one of these forms, $\sim p$ can be put into the other. This results from the following three facts, which show that the negation of a normal form of p immediately furnishes a normal form of $\sim p$.

(a) The negation of a disjunction is equivalent to the product of the negations of the terms of the disjunction (3.42).

(b) The negation of a product is equivalent to the disjunction of the negations of the terms of the product (3.42).

(c) $\sim \sim .p$ is equivalent to p (*PM* 4.13).

3. If p and q can be put into the first form, $p \lor q$ obviously can also. If p and q can be put into the second form, then Remark 3.45 allows us immediately to put $p \lor q$ into the second form.

Hence, by proceeding step by step, we can put every proposition into one or the other of these two forms.

Thus, we have

$$p \lor \sim q .\&. \sim p \lor q$$

in conjunctive normal form, and

$$p \& \sim q .\lor. \sim p \& q^9$$

in disjunctive normal form.

---

[9] [[Rather, the proposition in disjunctive normal form equivalent to $p \lor \sim q .\&. \sim p \lor q$ is $p \& q .\lor. \sim p \& \sim q.$]]

Finally, we note that a proposition can be equivalent to several normal propositions. For example, $p \& q \& r . \lor . p \& q \& \sim r$ and $p \& q$ are equivalent.

5.11. REMARK. We shall need the following remark. We call the places that an atomic proposition p occupies in a propositional function $f(p)$ the *occurrences* of p in $f(p)$. Thus, we say that p has two occurrences in the proposition $\sim p . \lor . p \lor q$. With each occurrence we associate one of the signs $+$ or $-$. This association is defined by recursion in the following manner:

(a) The sign of the occurrence of p in the proposition p is $+$;

(b) The sign changes when we pass from p to $\sim p$;

(c) The sign is the same in p and in $p \lor q$.

(In short, the sign of an occurrence depends on the parity of the number of $\sim$ signs in whose scopes the occurrence appears.) We shall also say that an occurrence is positive or negative when the sign $+$ or $-$, respectively, is associated with it. Hence, in $\sim p . \lor . p \lor q$, one of the occurrences of p is positive, the other is negative, and that of q is positive.

Suppose then that all occurrences of p in a proposition P have the same sign. We see immediately that the signs of the occurrences do not change when we apply any of the operations, indicated in 5.1, that permit us to construct normal forms. Hence, in at least one of the normal forms of each sort of P, p will appear either always preceded or never preceded by the $\sim$ sign, according to whether its occurrences in P are negative or positive.

5.2. Let us consider a proposition put into conjunctive normal form; for the original proposition to be true, it is necessary and sufficient that its normal form be true (3.21), and hence that each of the terms of the product be true (3.43). Let us consider one of these terms; suppose there is an atomic proposition which appears in it (at least) twice, once not preceded by a $\sim$ sign, and the other time preceded by $\sim$. Then this term is a true proposition, since $\vdash . p \lor \sim p$ (*PM* 2.11), and if a is true so is $a \lor b$ (from the second primitive proposition (§ 2)).

Hence, if this circumstance is the case for every term of the product, then the proposition under consideration is an identity. We shall show that this condition is necessary and sufficient for the truth of the proposition. (Hence, this furnishes a criterion for recognizing whether or not a proposition is true.)

Let us suppose that this condition does not hold for one of the terms of the product. We assign the logical value 'false' to the atomic propositions appearing there never preceded by $\sim$, the logical value 'true' to the atomic propositions appearing there always preceded by $\sim$, and any logical value at all to the atomic propositions not appearing in this term. Then the term under consideration has the logical value 'false', and hence from 4.3 the proposition under consideration cannot be true.

5.21. At the same time, this argument proves the

THEOREM. *The necessary and sufficient condition for a proposition to be true is that it have the logical value 'true' for any assignment of logical values to the atomic propositions appearing in it. We have indicated in the above a procedure for proving the proposition if the condition holds.*[10]

We note moreover that we can tell whether or not the proposition is an identity from a simple inspection of the conjunctive normal form.

5.22. In particular, if a proposition is a disjunction of simple propositions (§ 5), then it is in a canonical conjunctive form. Then, for it to be true, it is necessary and sufficient that it be of the form

$$p \vee \sim p \vee A$$

CONSEQUENCES

5.31. (a) The theorem permits us to reduce to a single sort all the proofs of Russell and Whitehead in Section A of the first part of *Principia Mathematica. In what follows, we shall no longer refer to this work to verify that a proposition is an identity of the first kind.*

5.32. (b) The theorem easily furnishes a new proof of the axiom of substitution (3.1) and of the theorem stated in 3.3.

5.33. (c) *A necessary and sufficient condition for two propositions to be identical is that they have the same logical value no matter what*

[10] [[Hilbert and Ackermann, in *1928*, pp. 11–29, essentially prove the completeness of their axiom system for the propositional calculus by using conjunctive and disjunctive normal forms. However, their text does not contain a precise definition of the notion of truth-functional validity; they seem to rely on a more intuitive notion of 'always true' (p. 11). Hilbert and Ackermann, as well as Herbrand, seem to be ignorant of *Post 1921*, wherein the truth-table method is defined and the completeness of Russell's rules for the propositional calculus is proved.]]

logical values are assigned to the atomic propositions appearing in them.

For $p \equiv q$, which is nothing but $p \supset q$.&. $q \supset p$ (1.2), has the logical value 'true' only when p and q have the same logical values, as can easily be seen.

5.34. (d) *Distributivity of logical products and sums.*

A proposition that is the product of logical sums is equivalent to the sum of all products obtained by taking one and only one term from each term of the original product.

This is a generalization of 3.45. For example,

$$\vdash:.p \lor q .\&. r \lor s: \equiv :p \& r . \lor . p \& s . \lor . q \& r . \lor . q \& s.$$

Indeed, we see that for the first proposition to have the logical value 'true', it is necessary and sufficient that for every possible system of logical values there is a term with logical value 'true' in each term of the product, and this is also a necessary and sufficient condition for the second proposition to have the logical value 'true'.[11]

Similarly, by finding out when the proposition in question has the logical value 'false', we can verify that

A proposition that is a sum of products is equivalent to the product of all the sums obtained by taking one and only one term from each term of the original sum.

Thus,

$$\vdash:. p \& q . \lor . r \& s: \equiv :p \lor r .\&. q \lor r .\&. p \lor s .\&. q \lor s.$$

These two propositions allow us to pass directly from one normal form to the other.

5.35. (e) *Law of duality. If, in a true proposition containing only the signs $\sim$ and $\lor$, $p \lor q$ is replaced by $p \& q$ wherever the $\lor$ sign appears, a new proposition is obtained whose negation is true.*

In order to apply this transformation, it is necessary in every case to replace each sign by its definition. Hence, this transformation changes

---

[11] [[Rather, the first proposition has the logical value 'true' under a given assignment of logical values to the atomic propositions if and only if the assignment is such that within each term of the product there is a term having the logical value 'true'. This is also a necessary and sufficient condition for the second proposition to have the logical value 'true' under an assignment.]]

$$p \supset q \quad \text{into} \quad \sim.q \supset p$$

$$p \mathbin{\&} q \quad \text{into} \quad p \vee q$$

$$p \equiv q \quad \text{into} \quad \sim.q \equiv p.$$

Let us assign logical values to the atomic propositions of P and of its transform $\bar{P}$, such that the same atomic proposition has different log'cal values in P and in $\bar{P}$. Then P and $\bar{P}$ will have different logical values. This is proved by 'recursion on the construction of P'.

(a) If it is true for P and $\bar{P}$, it is true for $\sim P$ and $\sim\bar{P}$.

(b) If it is true for P and $\bar{P}$ and for Q and $\bar{Q}$, then it is true for $P \vee Q$ and $\bar{P} \mathbin{\&} \bar{Q}$ (since $\bar{P} \mathbin{\&} \bar{Q}$ has the same logical value as $\sim.\sim\bar{P} \vee \sim\bar{Q}$, and hence as $\sim.P \vee Q$).

In particular, if P and Q have as their transforms $\bar{P}$ and $\bar{Q}$, then from $\vdash.P \equiv Q$ can be deduced $\vdash.\bar{P} \equiv \bar{Q}$.

Hence, from the truth of one of the theorems stated in 5.34 can be deduced the truth of the other.

5.36. (f) As can easily be seen, we can always construct a propositional function of the atomic propositions $p_1, p_2, ..., p_n$ in either one or the other normal form such that its logical value agrees with a value fixed beforehand for each system of logical values of the p_i.

Thus, given a propositional function $A(p_1, p_2, ..., p_n)$ of the atomic propositions $p_1, p_2, ..., p_n$, we can construct another propositional function $B(p_{\alpha_1}, p_{\alpha_2}, ..., p_{\alpha_m})$ no longer containing certain atomic propositions $p_{\beta_1}, p_{\beta_2}, ..., p_{\beta_r}, p_{\gamma_1}, p_{\gamma_2}, ..., p_{\gamma_s}$, and such that its logical value is the same as that of the original proposition when the latter atomic propositions have previously agreed upon logical values. If this logical value is 'true' for the p_{β_i} and 'false' for the p_{γ_i}, then to obtain B it suffices to replace in A each p_{β_i} by $r \vee \sim r$ and each p_{γ_i} by $r \mathbin{\&} \sim r$, where r is one of the other letters. r can also be a new atomic proposition; this has the advantage (which we shall use further on) of not changing the sign of the occurrences of any of the p_i.

6. AN ALGEBRAIC CRITERION

In this section we shall use the two signs 0 and 1 instead of T and F; letters will denote one or the other of these signs. We define

$$0 + 0 = 0 \qquad 0 \cdot 0 = 0$$
$$0 + 1 = 1 \qquad 0 \cdot 1 = 0$$
$$1 + 0 = 1 \qquad 1 \cdot 0 = 0$$
$$1 + 1 = 0 \qquad 1 \cdot 1 = 1 \, .$$

This permits us to write the combinations $a + b$ and $a \cdot b$, where a and b are two letters. We note that these rules of calculation are the rules of the field of remainders modulo 2 in ordinary arithmetic. Hence, all the rules of the ordinary algebraic calculus hold (we shall also use the same terminology as in algebra).

To express that a polynomial $A(p_1, p_2, ..., p_n)$ is zero whatever the values of the letters appearing in it, we shall use the usual notation $A(p_1, p_2, ..., p_n) \equiv 0 \pmod 2$.

Let us replace every proposition by a polynomial by considering the letters appearing in it as designating 0 or 1, $\sim p$ as standing for $1 + p$, and $p \vee q$ as standing for $p \cdot q$. Then for a proposition to be true it is necessary and sufficient that the polynomial corresponding to it always be 0, whatever the values of the letters appearing in it.

In fact, it suffices to verify that if logical values are assigned to the atomic propositions of a proposition, and each letter is replaced by 0 or 1 according to whether its logical value is 'true' or 'false', then the logical value of the proposition is 'true' or 'false' according to whether the corresponding polynomial becomes 0 or 1 with these values. Indeed, this can be proved immediately by recursion on the construction of the proposition, when the definition of logical value (4.1) is recalled.

How can it be determined whether a polynomial is always 0 mod 2? We start by using the congruence $p^n \equiv p \pmod 2$ to reduce the polynomial to a sum of mononomials containing no exponent greater than 1. *It is then necessary that all coefficients be even* (and this obviously suffices).

Indeed, let us suppose that this is proven for a polynomial in $n - 1$ variables, and let us prove it for n variables. We write the polynomial as

$$a_1 \varphi_1 (a_2, a_3, ..., a_n) + \varphi_2 (a_2, a_3, ..., a_n) \, .$$

For a system of values of $a_2, a_3, ..., a_n$, let us give a_1 the values 0 and then 1. We see that it is necessary that

$$\varphi_1 (a_2, a_3, ..., a_n) \equiv 0 \qquad (\mathrm{mod}\ 2)$$

and $\quad \varphi_2(a_2, a_3, \ldots, a_n) \equiv 0 \quad$ (mod 2).

This proves our theorem (since it is obvious for a polynomial of degree 0).

Hence, we see that to find out whether a proposition is true, we replace it by a polynomial and seek to reduce this polynomial by using the rules

$$p^n \equiv p \quad \text{(mod 2)}$$
$$1 + 1 \equiv 0 \quad \text{(mod 2)}$$

This method, which gives an arithmetical interpretation to our logical signs, leads to a rather convenient calculus. (For example, we can always change a sign or replace an even number by 0.)

For example, let us prove

$$\vdash : . p \supset q . \supset : p \vee r . \supset . q \vee r$$

We replace this by $[(1+p)\cdot q+1]\cdot(p\cdot r+1)\cdot q\cdot r$. But $q[(1+p)\cdot q+1]\equiv$ $\equiv(1+p)\cdot q^2+q\equiv q\cdot(1+p+1)\equiv p\cdot q$ (mod 2) (since $q^2\equiv q$ (mod 2)). We then have $pqr(pr+1)$. But $pr(pr+1)\equiv p^2r^2+pr\equiv pr+pr\equiv 0$ (mod 2).

7. TRANSFORMATION OF THE PRIMITIVE PROPOSITIONS INTO RULES

7.1. We note that already in the very simple case we have just treated, the choice of primitive propositions and rules is very arbitrary. We shall give an example in which all the primitive propositions but one are replaced by rules.

In the following, it is understood that the letters may be replaced by arbitrary propositional functions.

As the only primitive proposition we have

$$\vdash . p \vee \sim p \qquad Pp,$$

and we have the following four rules:

Rule 1. $\vee$ is associative and commutative.

Rule 2. In a propositional identity $p \vee p$ may be replaced by p, and conversely.

Rule 3. If $\vdash . p$ then $\vdash . p \vee q$.

Rule 4. If $\vdash . p \vee q$ and $\vdash . r \vee \sim q$, then $\vdash . p \vee r$.

These rules cannot lead to false propositions, as the theory of logical values and 3.3 show.

Conversely, the original primitive propositions and the rule of implication can be deduced from these rules.

1. $\vdash: p \lor p . \supset p$ results from $\vdash . p \supset p$, which is nothing but $\vdash : \sim p \lor p$, by use of Rule 2.

2. $\vdash : q \supset . p \lor q$ is nothing but $\vdash . \sim q . \lor . p \lor q$, which results from the new primitive proposition and Rule 3.

3. $\vdash : p \lor q . \supset . q \lor p$ and $\vdash : . p . \lor . q \lor r : \supset : q . \lor . p \lor r$ result from Rule 1 and the primitive proposition.

4. $\vdash : . q \supset r . \supset : p \lor q . \supset . p \lor r$ is proved as follows. We have $\vdash : \sim . q \supset r . \lor . \sim q \lor r$ from the primitive proposition, and $\vdash : \sim . p \lor q . \lor . p \lor q \lor r$ from the primitive proposition and Rule 3. Hence, from Rule 4, $\vdash : \sim . q \supset r . \lor . r . \lor . \sim . p \lor q . \lor . p \lor r$, from which we can deduce the desired proposition by using Rule 2.

5. If $\vdash . p \supset q$ and $\vdash p$, the $\vdash q$. In fact, we then have $\vdash . \sim p \lor q$ and $\vdash . p \lor q$, from which we obtain $\vdash . q \lor q$ using Rule 4, and $\vdash . q$, using Rule 2.

Thus, the method of Russell and Whitehead may be obtained again, using this new method.

7.2. We could base the entire theory presented in this chapter by taking the property expressed by Theorem 5.21 as the definition of propositional identity. This method would be very quick, but has the drawback of not permitting the proof that the theory of Russell and Whitehead is equivalent to it.

CHAPTER 2

THE THEORY OF IDENTITIES OF THE SECOND KIND

1. SIGNS

In this chapter we shall use two sorts of letters. The first (always lower case Roman letters with or without indices) are called *variables*. Henceforth we shall consider the same letter with two different indices, such as x_1 and x_2, to be in reality two different letters. The second sort (either Greek letters, upper case Roman letters, or even lower case Roman letters where no ambiguity is possible) are always accompanied by a certain number of variables.[1] These letters are called *atomic propositional functions* of the variables, and the variables are called the *arguments* of the function. The letters are considered to be propositions, and are the *atomic propositions* of the theory we are going to consider.

We shall also consider propositions without variables, which can be viewed as propositional functions of 0 arguments. It should henceforth be understood that when we write a propositional function $\Phi(x)$, it may contain other real variables which are omitted (unless there is a formal indication to the contrary).

1.1. By using the logical signs $\sim$ and $\vee$ to combine our atomic propositions according to the rules set up in the preceding chapter, we form new propositions with these atomic propositions. We call these new propositions *elementary*. For example,

$$\Phi(xy) \vee \Phi(xz) \quad \text{and} \quad \sim\Phi(xy) \vee \Psi(z)$$

are elementary propositions.

1.2. We use two new logical signs of the forms (x) and $(\exists x)$, where x is a variable. We shall indicate their meanings below. Let us say at once that these signs are called *quantifiers*; the variables of a proposition occurring in such signs are said to be *apparent*, and the other variables *real*. Thus, all the variables of an elementary proposition are real.

In the following, the sign $\times$ designates a group of dots whose number will be determined in 1.5.

1. If $\Phi(x)$ is a collection of signs and letters making up a proposition of which x is a real variable, then $(x) \times \Phi(x)$ is considered to be a new proposition which is read '*whatever x is, $\Phi(x)$*'.

2. If $\Phi(x)$ is a collection of signs and letters making up a proposition of which x is a real variable, then $(\exists x) \times \Phi(x)$ is considered to be a new proposition which is read '*there exists an x such that $\Phi(x)$*'.

1.21. For more generality, we allow $\Phi(x)$ in the preceding two rules not to contain x at all; x will then be said to be a *fictitious variable*. (From what follows it will result that $(x).p$ and $(\exists x).p$ are equivalent to p if p does not contain x.)

From the point of view of the meaning of the signs introduced, when

---

[1] This number is always the same for a definite letter; it can even be zero for certain letters.

we consider them as translating mathematical relations, we note that $\Phi(x)$ means that the particular object x (although perhaps indeterminate) has the property Φ, whereas $(x) \times \Phi(x)$ means that every object x has property Φ, and $(\exists x) \times \Phi(x)$ means that there is (at least) one object having this property.

1.3. Hence we see that from now on a proposition can be constructed from atomic propositions by combining them using the signs $\sim$ and $\vee$, according to the rules of the previous chapter, and the signs of the form (x) and $(\exists x)$, according to the rules which we have just indicated. Hence, from now on in order to carry out a proof by recursion on the construction of a proposition, it will be necessary to take these four methods of formation into account. However, a little further on we shall see two ways in which this method may be modified.

1.4. A proposition is said to be a *propositional function* of its real variables. Henceforth a collection of signs like $\Phi(x)$ will represent a propositional function of x, not necessarily atomic.

1.41. A proposition containing a definite atomic proposition is said to be a *propositional function* of this atomic proposition. If this atomic proposition is replaced by another proposition, then the result is a propositional function of this other proposition. A propositional function is of the *first kind* if it contains no quantifiers (hence if it is formed only from letters and the signs $\sim$ and $\vee$); otherwise it is said to be of the *second kind*.

For example, $(x)\,\Phi(xy)$ is a propositional function of the second kind of $\Phi(xy)$; $\Phi(xy) \vee \sim\Phi(xy)$ is a propositional function of the first kind of $\Phi(xy)$.

We note that there are two senses of the words 'propositional function', according to whether it is a function of a variable or of a proposition. We can define a propositional function of several propositions in a similar fashion. We shall denote a propositional function of the propositions $p_1, p_2, ..., p_n$ by a notation such as $A(p_1, p_2, ..., p_n)$.

1.5. As in the preceding chapter, the part of a proposition to which a quantifier relates is called the *scope* of the quantifier.[2] To mark out this scope, we utilize the same rules as in the preceding chapter by considering

---

[2] That is, $\Phi(x)$ in $(\exists x) \times \Phi(x)$ and $(x) \times \Phi(x)$. [[Herbrand also calls this scope the "scope of the apparent variable x".]]

the dots which follow quantifiers to be of the second level of strength. Here, just as always, when several quantifiers or $\sim$ signs follow each other so that the scope of each comprises exactly the scope of all those situated to its right, then the dots between each of these signs are omitted. For example,

$$(x)(\exists y).\Phi(xy) \vee \sim\Psi(xz)$$

means: whatever x is, there exists a y such that $\Phi(xy)$ or $\sim\Psi(xz)$. (In this proposition, x and y are apparent variables and z is a real variable, according to the definition given in 1.2.)

Similarly,

$$\sim(\exists x).\Phi(x)$$

means: it is false that there is an x such that $\Phi(x)$.

We also adopt the following conventions:

(a) We shall sometimes write

$$\begin{aligned} (+x) \quad &\text{instead of} \quad (x),\\ (-x) \quad &\text{instead of} \quad (\exists x). \end{aligned}$$

(b) We shall write

$$\begin{aligned} (xy).\Phi(xy) \quad &\text{instead of} \quad (x)(y).\Phi(xy),\\ (xyz).\Phi(xyz) \quad &\text{instead of} \quad (xy)(z).\Phi(xyz), \end{aligned}$$

etc.,

$$\begin{aligned} (\exists xy).\Phi(xy) \quad &\text{instead of} \quad (\exists x)(\exists y).\Phi(xy),\\ (\exists xyz).\Phi(xyz) \quad &\text{instead of} \quad (\exists xy)(\exists z).\Phi(xyz), \end{aligned}$$

etc.

(c) When we use the notation $(+x)$ and $(-x)$ and we have several quantifiers following each other satisfying the conditions under which we said the dots could be omitted, then we shall also omit the intermediary parentheses. We shall write

$$(+x-y).\Phi(xy) \quad \text{instead of} \quad (+x)(-y).\Phi(xy).$$

(d) It is understood that the letter which designates a variable can be changed into another without any trouble (in particular, it does not matter which letter is used for an apparent variable), with the condition that two variables can be designated by the same letter only in case they are both apparent and their scopes have no sign in common. Hence, we can write

$$(x)\Phi(x) \lor (\exists x)\sim\Phi(x)$$

(whatever x is, $\Phi(x)$, or there is an x such that $\sim\Phi(x)$) instead of

$$(x)\Phi(x) \lor (\exists y)\sim\Phi(y).$$

(e) We shall write $(\pm x)$ in a proposition when we could have $(+x)$ or $(-x)$, according to the particular case which we are imagining.

2. RULES OF REASONING

2. The rules of reasoning can be stated in several different ways. In this section we shall set forth one of these methods; further on we shall indicate other methods and show their equivalence to the first one.

Certain propositions are considered true, according to the following rules:

1. *Those elementary propositions* (1.1) *are true which, considered as propositional functions of the first kind* (1.41) *of their atomic propositions, are identities of the first kind.*

2. RULES OF PASSAGE. *If within a true proposition* $\sim(x) \Phi(x)$ *is replaced by* $(\exists x)\sim\Phi(x)$, *or* $\sim(\exists x) \Phi(x)$ *by* $(x)\sim\Phi(x)$, *or vice versa; or* $(x) \Phi(x) . \lor p$ *by* $(x).\Phi(x) \lor p$, *or* $(\exists x) \Phi(x) . \lor p$ *by* $(\exists x).\Phi(x) \lor p$, *or vice versa (where* p *denotes any proposition not containing x and* $\Phi(x)$ *a proposition which can contain x), the result is another true proposition.*[3]

For example, here is a common use of these rules of passage: If $(x).\Phi(x) \supset p$, that is, $(x).\sim\Phi(x) \lor p$, is true, then we can deduce from it that $(x).\sim\Phi(x) . \lor p$, hence that $\sim :(\exists x).\Phi(x) : \lor p$, and finally that $(\exists x).\Phi(x) . \supset p$ are all true. Similarly, if $(\exists x).\Phi(x) \supset p$ is true, we can deduce that $(x).\Phi(x) . \supset p$ is true.

3. FIRST RULE OF GENERALIZATION. *If a proposition* $\Phi(x)$ *containing the real variable x, among others, is true, then the proposition* $(x).\Phi(x)$ *is true.*

4. SECOND RULE OF GENERALIZATION. *If a proposition* $\Phi(xy)$ *containing the real variables x and y, among others, is such that* $\Phi(xx)$ *is true, then the proposition* $(\exists y).\Phi(xy)$ *is true.*

---

[3] [[This list of the rules of passage is incomplete. See *1931*, p. 225 below.]]

We give the sense of these two rules of generalization:

(a) The first signifies that a real variable x can be made apparent by putting (x) in front of the proposition.

(b) The second signifies that in certain of the places where a real variable x appears in a proposition, it can be changed into y by putting $(\exists y)$ in front of the proposition.

5. RULE OF SIMPLIFICATION. *If $P \vee P$ is true then so is P, where P denotes any proposition.*

6. RULE OF IMPLICATION. *Let P and Q denote propositions. If $P \supset Q$ and P are true, then Q is true.*

We see that in this method, the primitive propositions of the preceding chapter apply *a priori* only to elementary propositions. But we shall prove a little further on that it results from the other rules of reasoning that they apply to all propositions without exception.

2.1. The fundamental problem of mathematical logic consists in finding a procedure that always allows us to recognize whether or not a proposition is true. This is what the Germans call the *Entscheidungsproblem*.[4] This problem has been resolved in the particular case of the first chapter; further on we shall see other particular cases for which it is resolved.

As in Chap. 1 (§ 2), we indicate that a proposition is true by writing the sign $\vdash$ in front of it. We then say it is a *propositional identity* (which we say is of the *second kind* if we wish to note that it contains apparent variables) and, for short, an *identity*.[5]

Equivalence of two propositions is defined as in Chap. 1, 3.2.

The collection of operations necessary to show that a proposition is true, and the intermediate true propositions whose introduction this involves, are called the *proof* of the proposition.

2.2. REMARK 1. Henceforth when we wish to prove properties of true propositions, it will be necessary for us to take every new rule of reasoning

---

[4] [[*"The Entscheidungsproblem must be termed the main problem [[Hauptproblem]] of mathematical logic"* (*Hilbert and Ackermann 1928*, p. 77; the italics are theirs). "The central problem [[zentrale Problem]] of mathematical logic ... is the *Entscheidungsproblem"* (*Bernays and Schönfinkel 1928*, p. 342). Compare Herbrand's remarks on p. 41 above, p. 218 below, and p. 273 below.]]

[5] [[Regarding the use of the term 'propositional identity', see the Note to 1928, p. 32 above.]]

into account; we shall have to show that the envisaged property is true for the elementary propositions which are propositional identities, and that if it holds for some propositions then it holds also for those which can be deduced from them by applying any one of the rules of reasoning. As in the preceding chapter, we shall then be sure that whenever we have in front of us a particular proof, we shall actually be able to verify that its conclusion has the stated property.

2.3. REMARK 2. We stipulate that the rules of generalization can be applied even when the propositions $\Phi(x)$ and $\Phi(xy)$ do not actually contain these variables.

Thus, if p does not contain x, we can deduce $\vdash:(x).p$ and $\vdash:(\exists x).p$ from $\vdash.p$. Conversely, from $\vdash.p \supset p$ we can deduce (by utilizing the rules of passage conjointly) $\vdash:(x).p .\supset p$ and $\vdash:(\exists x).p .\supset p$.

2.4. REMARK 3. The preceding rules lead to the following, which constitutes a *third rule of generalization*: If $\Phi(xyz)$ is a proposition containing the real variables x, y, and z, among others, and $\Phi(yyz) \vee \Phi(zyz)$ is a true proposition, then so is $(\exists x).\Phi(xyz)$.

In fact, from

$$\vdash.\Phi(yyz) \vee \Phi(zyz)$$

we can easily deduce, by applying the second rule of generalization and the rule of passage,

$$\vdash:(\exists x).\Phi(xyz).\vee.(\exists x).\Phi(xyz),$$

and hence $\vdash:(\exists x).\Phi(xyz)$ by the rule of simplification.

We could also show that this new rule could replace the rule of simplification.

3. CONSEQUENCES

3. We shall now develop some consequences of this theory.

3.1. Given a proposition (in which we suppose that every apparent variable is represented by a different letter), we call the *matrix* of this proposition the elementary proposition obtained by omitting all quantifiers and the dots which accompany them. (We can see immediately that we do thereby obtain a proposition.) For example, the matrix of $(\exists x).\Phi(x)$ $.\vee.(y).\sim\Phi(y)$ is $\Phi(x).\vee.\sim\Phi(y)$. An elementary proposition is its own matrix. We can easily see that the matrix of a proposition does not change when this proposition is transformed by the rules of passage.

3.101. A proposition is said to be in *prenex form* [de forme normale] if it is of the form

$$(\pm x_1 \pm x_2 \ldots \pm x_n).M(x_1 x_2 \ldots x_n),$$

where $M(x_1 x_2 \ldots x_n)$ is an elementary proposition (1.1) (and is the matrix of the proposition).

By applications of the rules of passage, *every proposition can be put into prenex form (that is, an equivalent proposition in prenex form can be found). A proposition of this form can even be found such that the quantifiers appear in it in the same order, left to right, as in the original proposition P. This prenex proposition will be said to be 'tied to P'.*

This is proved by recursion on the construction of P; in fact we can see immediately that if it is true for P, then it is also for $\sim P$; that if it is true for P and for Q, it is for $P \vee Q$; and that if it is true for $\Phi(x)$, then it is for $(\pm x)\,\Phi(x)$.

For example, the proposition in prenex form tied to the proposition of the above example is

$$(\exists x)(y).\Phi(x) \vee \sim\Phi(y).$$

Another proposition in prenex form which is equivalent to the original proposition is

$$(y)(\exists x).\Phi(x) \vee \sim\Phi(y).$$

An apparent variable is said to be restricted in a proposition P if, in the prenex proposition tied to P, it appears in a quantifier $(\exists x)$, and is said to be general if it appears in a quantifier (x).

3.102. Let us recall the definition of the sign of an occurrence (Chap. 1, 5.11). We retain this definition and complete it as follows: the sign of an occurrence does not change in passing from $\Phi(x)$ to $(\pm x).\Phi(x)$. We note with respect to this that if the apparent variable x appears in a quantifier (x) in a positive occurrence then it is general (3.1), and if in a negative occurrence then it is restricted. The situation is reversed if x appears in a quantifier $(\exists x)$. (This can be seen immediately by recursion on the construction of the proposition.)

3.11. We can see that in order to construct any prenex proposition, it suffices to start with an elementary proposition and to apply successively in a unique manner the following two construction procedures:

1. Going from $\Phi(x)$ to $(x).\Phi(x)$;
2. Going from $\Phi(x)$ to $(\exists x).\Phi(x)$

(without any use of the procedures of construction of Chap. 1). This allows us to simplify proofs that proceed by recursion on the construction of a proposition.

3.12. REMARK. Let $A(p_1, p_2, ..., p_n)$ be a propositional function of the first kind. By application of the rules of passage, $A((\pm x).\Phi(x), p_2, ..., p_n)$ can be given a prenex form such that x is the variable whose quantifier is situated leftmost. This is readily proved by recursion on the construction of $A(p_1, p_2, ..., p_n)$.

3.2. We shall now prove a theorem which generalizes that of Chap. 1, 3.3.

THEOREM: *Let $F(p)$ be a propositional function of the proposition p, in which all occurrences of p have the same sign (3.102). If the occurrences of p in $F(p)$ are positive, then*

$$\vdash : p \supset q . \supset . F(p) \supset F(q).$$

If the occurrences of p in $F(p)$ are negative, then

$$\vdash : p \supset q . \supset . F(q) \supset F(p).^6$$

We prove this theorem by recursion on the construction of $F(p)$, which we assume to be in prenex form. The rules of passage then lead immediately to the general case. We have seen (3.11) that in order to construct this propositional function we can proceed as follows: start with an elementary proposition and then perform operations like passing from $\Phi(x)$ to $(x). \Phi(x)$ or to $(\exists x).\Phi(x)$. Thus, it suffices to prove the following four assertions.

1. The theorem is true for atomic propositions. This is obvious.
2. It is true for elementary propositions; for these are formed by

---

[6][[The theorem is incorrect as stated. Its conclusion should read: If the occurrences of p in $F(p)$ are positive, then from $\vdash p \supset q$ we can deduce $\vdash F(p) \supset F(q)$; if they are negative, then from $\vdash p \supset q$ we can deduce $\vdash F(q) \supset F(p)$. See Note A, p. 98 below.]]

starting with atomic propositions and combining them with the signs ~ and ∨. Our assertion then results from the identities of the first kind

$$\vdash : p \supset q \mathbin{.} \supset \mathbin{.} \sim q \supset \sim p$$
$$\vdash :. p \supset q \mathbin{.} \supset : p \vee r \mathbin{.} \supset \mathbin{.} q \vee r.$$

3. If the theorem is true for $F(p)$, where $F(p)$ contains the real variable x, then it is true for $(x).F(p)$, for by using the rules of generalization and passage, we have successively

$$\vdash : p \supset q \mathbin{.} \supset \mathbin{.} F(p) \supset F(q)$$

(we assume for the sake of argument that the occurrence of p in $F(p)$ is positive [rather, the occurrences are positive]), then

$$\vdash :. p \supset q \mathbin{.} \supset : (x).F(p) \mathbin{.} \supset F(q)$$
$$\vdash :. p \supset q \mathbin{.} \supset : (x).F(p) \mathbin{.} \supset (x).F(q).$$

We proceed similarly if the occurrence of p is negative.

4. It is proved in a similar fashion that the theorem is true for $(\exists x).\Phi(x)$. This proves the theorem.

4. CONNECTION WITH THE THEORY OF IDENTITIES OF THE FIRST KIND

4. THEOREM. *If, in a propositional identity of the first kind, the letters which appear are replaced by nonelementary propositions, then the resulting proposition is an identity of the second kind.*

4.1. We shall prove this theorem first in the special case in which each of the atomic propositions of the identity of the first kind has at most only one occurrence of each sign. Then from this we shall deduce a number of consequences which will allow us to prove the theorem for the general case.

Let $p_1, p_2, \ldots, p_n$ be all the atomic propositions of the propositional identity of the first kind $A(p_1, p_2, \ldots, p_n)$ (each p_i has only one occurrence of each sign).

Let us replace $p_2, p_3, \ldots, p_n$ by $\Phi_2, \Phi_3, \ldots, \Phi_n$ (which can be nonelementary), and p_1 by $(\exists x).\Phi_1(x)$ or $(x).\Phi_1(x)$, where $\Phi_1(x)$ is a proposition containing the real variable x.

We shall prove that the proof of the proposition thus obtained can be reduced to that of the proposition obtained by replacing $p_1, p_2, ..., p_n$ by $\Phi_1(x), \Phi_2, ..., \Phi_n$. Hence, in any given case we can repeat this operation a certain number of times, each time transforming an apparent variable into a real one, until we have to replace $p_1, p_2, ..., p_n$ only by propositions without apparent variables, in which case the truth of the proposition results from the rule of substitution (Chap. 1, 3.1).

We assume for the sake of argument that p_1 is replaced by $(\exists x).\Phi_1(x)$ (the other case is treated in exactly the same way). We indicate explicitly the two occurrences of $(\exists x).\Phi_1(x)$; the proposition to be proved can be written

$$A((\exists x).\Phi_1(x), (\exists y).\Phi_1(y), \Phi_2, ..., \Phi_n).{[7]}$$

$(\exists x).\Phi_1(x)$ occurs positively, and $(\exists y).\Phi_1(y)$ negatively. From 3.12, the proof of this proposition reduces to that of

$$(y)(\exists x).A(\Phi_1(x), \Phi_1(y), \Phi_2, ..., \Phi_n).$$

Now let us assume that

$$\vdash.A(\Phi_1(y), \Phi_1(y), \Phi_2, ..., \Phi_n)$$

has been proved. Then successively we can deduce

$$\vdash:(\exists x).A(\Phi_1(x), \Phi_1(y), \Phi_2, ..., \Phi_n)$$

by the second rule of generalization, and

$$\vdash:(y)(\exists x).A(\Phi_1(x), \Phi_1(y), \Phi_2, ..., \Phi_n)$$

by the first rule of generalization.

We have thus proved the desired result; we shall now draw several of its consequences.

4.2. COROLLARY 1. From $\vdash.p \equiv q$ can be deduced

$$\vdash.F(p) \equiv F(q)$$

for every propositional function F.[8]

---

[7] [[The French text has $A((\exists x).\Phi_1(x), (\exists y).\Phi_1(y), p_2, ..., p_n)$, which is an oversight.]]

[8] [[This proof must be altered in view of the change necessary in Theorem 3.2 (footnote 6 above). For this we first need Corollary 2, so that from $\vdash p \equiv q$ we can deduce $\vdash p \supset q$ and $\vdash q \supset p$, and from these $\vdash F(p, p) \supset F(q, p)$ and $\vdash F(q, p) \supset F(q, q)$, by 3.2. Then, starting with the identity of the first kind $A \supset B :\supset: B \supset C .\supset. A \supset C$, which satisfies the condition of 4.1, replacing A by $F(p, p)$, B by $F(q, p)$, and C by $F(q, q)$, and finally applying the rule of implication twice, we obtain $\vdash F(p, p) \supset F(q, q)$. Symmetrically, $\vdash F(q, q) \supset F(p, p)$. Hence, by Corollary, 2, $\vdash F(p, p) \equiv F(q, q)$.]]

We use $F(q, r)$ to denote the proposition obtained from $F(p)$ by replacing p by q in its positive occurrences and by r in its negative occurrences.

From 3.2,

$$\vdash: p \supset q .\supset. F(p, p) \supset F(q, p)$$
$$\vdash: q \supset p .\supset. F(q, p) \supset F(q, q).$$

In the identity of the first kind

$$\vdash:: A \supset. B \supset C :\supset:. A' \supset. C \supset D :\supset D :\supset: A \& A'$$
$$.\supset.B \supset D,$$

in which every letter has only one occurrence of each sign, we replace B, C, and D by $F(p, p)$, $F(q, p)$, and $F(q, q)$, respectively, A by $p \supset q$, and A' by $q \supset p$; we can then deduce, using the rule of implication,

$$\vdash: p \equiv q .\supset. F(p, p) \supset F(q, q).$$

Hence we have $\vdash.F(p, p) \supset F(q, q)$. Similarly, we can prove $\vdash.F(q, q) \supset F(p, p)$. By reasoning as in Corollary 2, we can deduce from this $\vdash.F(p, p) \equiv F(q, q)$.

4.3. COROLLARY 2. We have

$$\vdash:. p \supset: q \supset. p \& q$$

for any propositions p and q, since this proposition has only one occurrence of each sign. Hence from $\vdash.p$ and $\vdash.q$ we can obtain $\vdash.p \& q$. Similarly, $\vdash: p \& q .\supset p$; hence from $\vdash.p \& q$ we can obtain $\vdash.p$, and similarly $\vdash.q$.

4.4. COROLLARY 3. Similarly, we have

$$\vdash: p \vee q .\supset. q \vee p$$
$$\vdash: q \vee p .\supset. p \vee q.$$

Hence (from Corollary 2)

$$\vdash: p \vee q. \equiv. q \vee p.$$

Similarly, we can prove

$$\vdash:. p .\vee. q \vee r: \equiv :q .\vee. p \vee r.$$

These results, in conjunction with Corollary 1, lead to the legitimacy of using the generalized disjunction, just as in Chap. 1 (3.4). Hence, we shall use it from now on; all its properties are preserved. Similarly, we can justify the use of the generalized product.

4.5. COROLLARY 4. We introduce the following notation: if n is a numeral (1, 2, 3, etc.), then nP denotes the disjunction

$$P \lor P \lor \cdots \lor P \qquad \text{(with } n \text{ } P\text{'s)}.$$

Hence, we can define nP by recursion in the following way:

$$nP. =:(n-1)P . \lor . P \qquad Df$$
$$1P. =. P \qquad\qquad\quad Df.$$

THEOREM. $\vdash.P$ can be deduced from $\vdash.nP$.

This constitutes a generalized rule of simplification. We prove it by recursion on n. Suppose we have shown that $\vdash.P$ can be deduced from $\vdash.(n-1) P$. In the identity

$$A \lor B .\&. A \supset P .\&. B \supset Q :\supset. P \lor Q,$$

which has only one occurrence of each sign, we replace A by $(n-1) P$, B by P, and Q by P. We can then conclude that from $\vdash.nP$ we can deduce $\vdash.P \lor P$ (since $P \supset P$ is an identity with one occurrence of each sign), and hence, from the rule of simplification, $\vdash.P$.[9]

As in 2.4, the following rule can be derived from this theorem and the rules of passage; this rule generalizes the second rule of generalization. From

$$\vdash.\Phi\left(x_1 x_1 x_2 \ldots x_n\right) \lor \Phi\left(x_2 x_1 x_2 \ldots x_n\right)$$
$$\lor \cdots \lor \Phi\left(x_n x_1 x_2 \ldots x_n\right)$$

---

[9] [[This proof is fallacious in that the induction assumption needed is $\vdash(n-1) P \supset P$, whereas the induction step yields the weaker statement 'If $\vdash nP$ then $\vdash P$'. Hence either we must amend the induction argument so that we need only assume 'If $\vdash(n-1) P$ then $\vdash P$'; or else we must prove the stronger theorem $\vdash nP \supset P$ by induction, and then derive 4.5 by the rule of implication. We shall do the latter.

We have $\vdash P \supset P$ from 4.1. Assume $\vdash(n-1) P \supset P$. By 3.2, $\vdash(n-1) P \lor P . \supset . P \lor P$, that is, $\vdash nP . \supset . P \lor P$. Since $P \lor Q . \supset P :\lor: R \lor S . \supset Q$ is an identity of the first kind satisfying the condition of 4.1, we obtain $\vdash P \lor P . \supset P :\lor: P \lor P . \supset P$ by replacing Q, R, and S by P. Hence by the rule of simplification $\vdash P \lor P . \supset P$. Starting with the identity $A \supset B :\supset: B \supset C . \supset . A \supset C$, which also satisfies the condition of 4.1, replacing A by nP, B by $P \lor P$, and C by P, and using the above two results and the rule of implication, we can conclude $\vdash nP \supset P.$]]

we can conclude

$$\vdash : (\exists y) . \Phi(y x_1 x_2 \dots x_n).$$

4.6. COROLLARY 5. Here are several other consequences of the preceding results. From $\vdash . \Phi(xy) \supset \Phi(xy)$ we can deduce, by the rules of generalization and passage,

$$\vdash : (\exists x)(y) . \Phi(xy) . \supset . (y)(\exists x) . \Phi(xy).$$

Furthermore, by using 4.3 we obtain

$$\vdash : (xy) . \Phi(xy) . \equiv . (yx) . \Phi(xy)$$
$$\vdash : (\exists xy) . \Phi(xy) . \equiv . (\exists yx) . \Phi(xy).$$

By using 4.2 and 3.2, we can deduce quite easily from this that a prenex proposition (3.1) is equivalent to those obtained from it by permuting two ⟦successive⟧ quantifiers of general variables or two ⟦successive⟧ quantifiers of restricted variables, and that it implies (Chap. 1, 3.22) those obtained by moving a quantifier of a restricted variable to the right, or by moving a quantifier of a general variable to the left.

4.7. COROLLARY 6. *Proving $\Phi(x)$ and proving $(y) \Phi(y)$ amount to the same thing.*

For, (a) we can go from the former to the latter by using the first rule of generalization.

(b) We can go from the latter to the former by noting that

$$\Phi(x) \supset \Phi(x)$$

is an identity, true according to 4.1. Hence we can deduce

$$\vdash : (\exists y) . \Phi(y) \supset \Phi(x)$$

by using the second rule of generalization, and hence also

$$\vdash : (y) . \Phi(y) . \supset \Phi(x)$$

by using the rules of passage.

5. CONTINUATION OF THE PRECEDING SECTION

We are now able to begin the complete proof of the theorem of the preceding section. We use the same notation as above, and in $A(p_1, p_2, \dots, p_n)$

we replace $p_1, p_2, ..., p_n$ by $(\exists x).\Phi_1(x), \Phi_2, ..., \Phi_n$, respectively. (The argument is the same when p_1 is replaced by $(x).\Phi_1(x)$.)

We shall show that the proof of the proposition thus obtained reduces to the proof of the proposition obtained from another identity of the first kind that also contains n atomic propositions $p_1, p_2, ..., p_n$ by replacing $p_1, p_2, ..., p_n$ by $\Phi_1(x), \Phi_2, ..., \Phi_n$. This then leads to the truth of the theorem under consideration, for the same reason as earlier (4.1).[10]

Assume that p_1 occurs α times positively and β times negatively in $A(p_1, p_2, ..., p_n)$, which we now write as

$$A\,(\underbrace{p_1, p_1, ..., p_1}_{\alpha \text{ times}};\ \underbrace{p_1, p_1, ..., p_1}_{\beta \text{ times}};\ p_2, p_3, ..., p_n)$$

in order to exhibit these occurrences (the first α ones being the positive occurrences, the next β ones being the negative).

It is necessary to prove

$$\vdash.A\,[(\exists x_1).\Phi_1(x_1), ..., (\exists x_\alpha).\Phi_1(x_\alpha);$$
$$(\exists x_{\alpha+1})\,\Phi_1(x_{\alpha+1}), ..., (\exists x_{\alpha+\beta}).\Phi_1(x_{\alpha+\beta});\ \Phi_2, ..., \Phi_n]$$

or else

$$\vdash:(x_{\alpha+1}, ..., x_{\alpha+\beta})\,(\exists x_1 ... x_\alpha).A\,[\Phi_1(x_1), ..., \Phi_1(x_\alpha);$$
$$\Phi_1(x_{\alpha+1}), ..., \Phi_1(x_{\alpha+\beta});\ \Phi_2, ..., \Phi_n],$$

which is equivalent to the first proposition by the rules of passage, as can be seen from 3.12. It suffices to prove that

$$(\exists x_1 ... x_\alpha)\,A\,[\Phi_1(x_1), ..., \Phi_1(x_\alpha);$$
$$\Phi_1(x_{\alpha+1}), ..., \Phi_1(x_{\alpha+\beta});\ \Phi_2, ..., \Phi_n]$$

is a propositional identity, from the first rule of generalization; and hence it even suffices to prove that the disjunction of the propositions $A\,[\Phi_1(x_i), ..., \Phi_1(x_i);\ \Phi_1(x_{\alpha+1}), ..., \Phi_1(x_{\alpha+\beta}), \Phi_2, ..., \Phi_n]$ for every value of i from $\alpha+1$ to $\alpha+\beta$ is a propositional identity, for then the preceding proposition would also be a propositional identity, because of the second rule of generalization and the generalized rule of simplification (4.5).

Let us show that the latter proposition is an identity of the first kind.

---

[10] [[Herbrand's proof contains many errors in subscripts; these have all been corrected without special note. There are more serious mistakes in the proof, however; see Note B, p. 98 below.]]

It suffices to show that the disjunction of $A[a_i, ..., a_i; a_{\alpha+1}, ..., a_{\alpha+\beta}, b_2, ..., b_n]$ for all values of i from $\alpha+1$ to $\alpha+\beta$ is an identity of the first kind, given that

$$A[a_1, ..., a_1; a_1, ..., a_1; b_2, ..., b_n]$$

is one also.

For this we study the logical value of A. Let us give definite logical values to all the atomic propositions $b_2, ..., b_n$. $A(c, ..., c; a_{\alpha+1}, ..., a_{\alpha+\beta}; b_2, ..., b_n)$ then becomes equivalent to a proposition $B(c; a_{\alpha+1}, ..., a_{\alpha+\beta}; r)$ obtained by using the method of Chap. 1, 5.36, to replace the b_i by $r \vee \sim r$ or $r \mathbin{\&} \sim r$, where r is a new letter. We know that

1. In B, c has only positive occurrences and the a_i only negative occurrences.

2. $B(c; c, ..., c; r)$ is an identity.

It is necessary to prove that for any definite logical values of the a_i (and whatever that of r), if we replace c by $a_{\alpha+1}, a_{\alpha+2}, ...,$ and $a_{\alpha+\beta}$, then one of the B's obtained will have the logical value 'true'.

In a suitable conjunctive normal form of $B(c; a_{\alpha+1}, ..., a_{\alpha+\beta}; r)$, each term of the product is a disjunction of propositions of the form a_i, $\sim c$, r, or $\sim r$ (from property 1 and Chap. 1, 5.11). In those terms which do not contain both r and $\sim r$ (the others are identities) there actually appear propositions of each of the first two forms, from the second property and the criterion of truth of Chap. 1, 5.21. Hence each of these terms is equivalent to a term of the form

$$a_{i_1} \vee a_{i_2} \vee \cdots \vee a_{i_p} \vee M,$$

where M has one of the forms $\sim c$ or $\sim c \vee N$, N containing only the letter r.

Then, for definite logical values of $a_{\alpha+1}, ..., a_{\alpha+\beta}$, either all the a_i have the logical value 'true' and B can be seen to have the same logical value whatever that of c, or else a_i has the logical value 'false'; then, by replacing c by a_i, B acquires the logical value 'true'.

We have thus proved the desired theorem.

5.1. The following is a consequence and generalization of the theorem:

RULE OF SUBSTITUTION. *If a proposition is true, other true propositions can be obtained from it by replacing the atomic propositional functions by arbitrary propositional functions with the same arguments.*

(This is so because this substitution can be made throughout the proof of the true proposition; in particular, from the preceding theorem, in the propositional identities without apparent variables with which the proof begins.)

6. ANOTHER METHOD

6. We shall now indicate some other methods on which the theory of identities of the second kind may be based. These will differ from the preceding one only in their rules of reasoning and not in the signs employed.

6.1. We start by indicating the form of the proof of a lemma which will be necessary in the study of each method. A special case of this lemma has already been proved in the method used until now (4.2).

LEMMA. *If $F(p)$ is a propositional function of the proposition p, then*

$$\vdash : p \equiv q . \supset . F(p) \equiv F(q) .^{11}$$

This is proved by recursion on the construction of F. We assume that we are working in a method in which the identities of the first kind are true even if they contain non-elementary propositions, and which contains the rule of implication.

(1) If the lemma is true for $F(p)$ and $\Phi(p)$, then it is also for $\sim F(p)$ and $F(p) \vee \Phi(p)$, from the identities of the first kind

$$\vdash : a \equiv b . \supset . \sim a \equiv \sim b$$
$$\vdash : a \equiv b \ \& \ c \equiv d . \supset : a \vee c . \equiv . b \vee d$$

and the rule of implication.

(2) If the lemma is true for $F(p)$ (where $F(p)$ contains x), then it will be true for $(x).F(p)$ if from $\vdash . \Phi(x) \equiv \Psi(x)$ can be deduced

$$\vdash : (x) . \Phi(x) . \equiv . (x) . \Psi(x)$$

---

[11] [[This Lemma will not in general be correct when p or q contains real variables which become apparent in $F(p)$ and $F(q)$. For example, $\Phi(x) \equiv p . \supset . (x) \Phi(x) \equiv (x) p$ is not an identity of the second kind. However, Corollary 4.2 is enough for Herbrand's purpose of showing the equivalence of the different methods. In fact, when he claims to have established Lemma 6.1 in each of these methods, what he does establish is Corollary 4.2, by showing that a proof of Theorem 3.2 analogous to that contained in Note A can be carried out in the method under consideration.]]

(or, as can easily be seen, even only

$$\vdash:(x).\Phi(x).\supset.(x).\Psi(x)).$$

(3) Under the same hypotheses as in (2), the lemma is true for $(\exists x).\Phi(x)$ if we can deduce

$$\vdash:(\exists x).\Phi(x).\equiv.(\exists x).\Psi(x)$$

(or even only $\vdash:(\exists x).\Phi(x).\supset.(\exists x).\Psi(x))$ from

$$\vdash.\Phi(x)\equiv\Psi(x).$$

Hence in each method we must look to see if this lemma can be proved (in the methods where the quantifier (x) is defined from other symbols, the second part of the proof is not used; where the quantifier $(\exists x)$ is so defined, the third part is not used).

6.2. The first of these new methods holds a practical interest for future proofs (we shall always call it 'the second method'). It consists in considering quantifiers (x) as defined from quantifiers $(\exists x)$, in the following manner:

$$(x).\Phi(x).=:\sim:(\exists x).\sim\Phi(x)\qquad Df$$

(as always, the right side gives the meaning of the left side). The rules of inference are as follows:

1. All identities of the first kind furnish true propositions *when the atomic propositions appearing in them are replaced by arbitrary propositions.*

2. The following rules of passage: *Within a proposition, $(\exists x).\Phi(x)\vee p$ can be replaced by $(\exists x).\Phi(x).\vee p$ and conversely, and $(\exists x).\Phi(x)$ & p by $(\exists x).\Phi(x).\& p$ and conversely,* where $\Phi(x)$ is a proposition which can contain the variable x, and p is a proposition not containing x.

3. *The same two rules of generalization as in the first method, and the rule of implication.*

6.21. To prove Lemma 6.1 in the second method, it suffices to show that $\vdash:(\exists x).\Phi(x).\supset.(\exists x).\Psi(x)$ can be deduced from $\vdash.\Phi(x)\supset\Psi(x)$, that is, from $\vdash.\sim\Phi(x).\vee.\Psi(x).$

Indeed, from $\vdash.\sim\Phi(x).\vee.\Psi(x)$ can be deduced

$$\vdash:\sim\Phi(x).\vee.(\exists y).\Psi(y)$$

(rules of generalization and passage); but this proposition implies the following, in virtue of an identity of the first kind:

$$\vdash:.\sim\!\Phi(x)\ \vee:\ \sim\sim:(\exists y).\Psi(y).$$

From this can be deduced

that is,

$$\vdash::(x):.\sim\!\Phi(x).\vee:\ \sim\sim:(\exists y).\Psi(y),$$

$$\vdash::\sim(\exists x)\sim:.\sim\!\Phi(x).\vee:\ \sim\sim:(\exists y).\Psi(y),$$

or

$$\vdash:.\sim(\exists x):\Phi(x)\ \&\ \sim(\exists y).\Psi(y).$$

From this we can infer, using a rule of passage,

$$\vdash:.\sim:(\exists x).\Phi(x)\ .\&.\ \sim(\exists y).\Psi(y),$$

which implies, in virtue of an identity of the first kind,

$$\vdash:(\exists x)\Phi(x)\ .\supset.\ (\exists y).\Psi(y).$$

Thus, we have proved the desired result.

6.22. *Every proposition true in the second method is true in the first.* This results from the fact that all the rules of the second method are also rules of the first, and from the following remark: in the second method we can replace $\sim(\exists x)\sim\!\Phi(x)$ by $(x)\,\Phi(x)$ and conversely; while in the first method, from

$$\vdash:(x)\Phi(x).\equiv.\sim.(\exists x)\sim\!\Phi(x)$$

and the lemma of 6.1, it results that we can do this as well.

Every proposition true in the first method is true in the second. The only rules of the first method which are not in the second are in fact the following:

(a) The rule of simplification, which results in the second method from the identity $P \vee P .\supset P$ and the rule of implication.

(b) The rules of passage. In the second method, the rules of passage involving the $\sim$ sign result from the definition of $(x).\Phi(x)$ and the identity $\vdash.\sim\sim p\equiv p$ as well as the lemma of 6.1.

For the rules of passage involving the $\vee$ sign, it suffices to note that $(x).\Phi(x) \vee p$ is, in the second method,

$$\sim(\exists x)\sim.\Phi(x) \vee p.$$

Hence it is identical to

$$\sim (\exists x) : \sim \Phi (x) .\&. \sim p,$$

and hence to

$$\sim (\exists x) \sim \Phi (x) .\&. \sim p,$$

and hence to

$$\sim : \sim (x) \Phi (x) .\&. \sim p,$$

and finally to $(x) \Phi(x) . \lor p$ (all by iterated applications of the rules of reasoning and Lemma 6.1).

6.23. In the second method, in order to argue by recursion on the construction of a proposition, it is not necessary to take quantifiers (x) into account. There are only three methods of constructing propositions: by using the signs $\lor$, $\sim$ and signs of the form $(\exists x)$.

Similarly, proofs by recursion on proofs are modified because of the changes in the rules of inference.

7. THE METHODS OF RUSSELL AND WHITEHEAD

We shall now study the methods of Russell and Whitehead. They employ two different methods of basing the theory under consideration.

7.1. The first, shown in PM *10, is alone employed in the rest of that work. Hence it is essential, following the point of view expressed in the Introduction, to show its equivalence to our previous methods.

Here, $(\exists x).\Phi(x)$ is defined by

$$(\exists x). \Phi (x) := : \sim (x) \sim . \Phi (x) \qquad Df,$$

and the following are admitted as primitive propositions:

(1) The propositional identities of the first kind,
(2) $\vdash :(x).\Phi(x) \supset . \Phi(y)$ *Pp (PM* 10.1),
(3) $\vdash :.(x).p \lor \Phi(x) . \supset : p \lor . (x).\Phi(x)$ *Pp (PM* 10.12),
(4) $\vdash :(xy).\Phi(xy) . \supset . (yx).\Phi(xy)$ *Pp (PM* 11.07),

and the following two rules:

If $\vdash.\Phi(y)$, where y is a real variable, then $\vdash :(x) \Phi(x)$ (PM, 10.11),
If $\vdash.p \supset q$ and $\vdash.p$, then $\vdash.q$.

In all these rules and propositions, the letters p, q, and Φ can be replaced by any propositions or propositional functions whatsoever.

The following propositions are provable:

(5) $\vdash:.(x).p \vee \Phi(x).\equiv :p \vee .(x).\Phi(x)$　　　$(PM\ 10.2)$,

(6) $\vdash:.(\exists x).p \vee \Phi(x).\equiv :p \vee .(\exists x).\Phi(x)$　　　$(PM\ 10.36)$.

We note first of all that by looking at the use that Russell and Whitehead make of the second primitive proposition, we can see that it should be written

$$\vdash:(x).\Phi(xy).\supset \Phi(yy).$$

From this, by replacing Φ by $\sim\Phi$, we can deduce

$$\vdash:(x).\sim \Phi(xy).\supset. \sim\Phi(yy),[12]$$

that is

$$\vdash:(\exists x).\Phi(xy).\vee. \sim\Phi(yy);$$

hence

$$\vdash:\Phi(yy) \supset. (\exists x)\Phi(xy).$$

From this we infer that the second rule of generalization is true in this method.

Lemma 6.1 can then be proved easily; for, $\vdash.(x).\Phi(x).\supset. (x).\Psi(x)$ can be deduced from $\vdash.\Phi(x) \supset \Psi(x)$ by using the two rules of generalization and the third primitive proposition.

We shall now show that this method is equivalent to our first method.

1. *Every proposition true in the new method is true in the first one.* In fact, we can prove that in our first method the following are true:

(a) The identities of the first kind (§ 4).

(b) Primitive propositions 2, 3, and 4; which can be deduced immediately by the rules of passage and generalization from the following three identities of the first kind, respectively:

$$\vdash.\Phi(y) \supset \Phi(y),\quad \vdash:p \vee \Phi(z).\supset. p \vee \Phi(z),\quad \vdash.\Phi(zt) \supset \Phi(zt).$$

(c) $\vdash:(\exists x).\Phi(x).\equiv.\sim(x)\sim\Phi(x)$; for we can prove $\vdash:(\exists x).\Phi(x) .\supset.$ $\sim(x)\sim\Phi(x)$ and $\vdash:\sim(x)\sim\Phi(x).\supset. (\exists x).\Phi(x)$ by the rules of generalization and of passage, and it then suffices to use 4.3.

It is then enough to use the theorem of 4.2 to see that every true prop-

---

[12] [[The French text has $\vdash:(x).\sim \Phi(xy).\supset. \Phi(yy)$, which is an oversight.]]

osition obtained in the new method by the use of the definition of $(\exists x).\Phi(x)$ can also be obtained in our original method.

2. *Every proposition true in the original method is true in the new one.* This results from the fact that in this new method we can prove:

(a) The rules of passage, by using the Lemma of 6.1, propositions 5 and 6, and the *Df*;

(b) The rule of simplification, which results from the identity

$$\vdash :P \vee P . \supset P.$$

The other rules of reasoning of the first method are already included among those of the new one.

We note that the fourth primitive proposition of the theory is a consequence of the others. In fact, it was not used in this last part of the proof, and we saw that it could be derived in our first method.

7.2. We shall not explain the second method of Russell and Whitehead. Indeed, it is rather incompletely explained in PM *9, and is very close to our original method; for in it we can obtain the rules of passage immediately, and in it propositional identities of the first kind are admitted as true only when the atomic propositions are replaced by elementary propositions (1.1). We can even consider that the arguments necessary to obtain our result of § 4 in this method can be entirely replaced by the proof we gave of it.

8. FINITE DOMAINS

8. In order to study the properties of propositions, we shall use the following procedure several times: With every proposition we associate another one, called its *expansion* [[*réduite*]], and it is this expansion that we study. It is defined in the following way: We define the expansion of an atomic proposition, and stipulate that if the expansion of P is p, then that of $\sim P$ is $\sim p$; if the expansions of P and Q are p and q, then that of $P \vee Q$ is $p \vee q$, and finally we specify how to find the expansion of $(\exists x).\Phi(x)$ if we know what the expansion of $\Phi(x)$ is.

All propositions in the second method (6.2) are constructed by starting from atomic propositions and combining them with the signs $\sim$, $\vee$ and $(\exists)$; hence these rules permit us to find the expansion of any given proposition.

8.1. Let us apply this to an example. Consider n variables, designated by $a_1, a_2, ..., a_n$ (n is any determinate number). We stipulate that the expansion of an atomic proposition is itself, and that if the expansion of $\Phi(x)$ is $\varphi(x)$, then that of $(\exists x).\Phi(x)$ is $\varphi(a_1) \vee \varphi(a_2) \vee ... \vee \varphi(a_n)$.[13] We shall prove:

THEOREM. *If $\Phi(y_1 y_2 ... y_p)$ is a true proposition in which $y_1, y_2, ..., y_p$ are the only real variables, then the expansion of $(y_1 y_2 ... y_p).\Phi(y_1 y_2 ... y_p)$ (which no longer contains apparent variables) is a propositional identity of the first kind of its atomic propositions.*

8.10. In the proof of this theorem, we need not consider whether a variable actually appears in Φ or not, for if a 'fictitious' variable of Φ (1.2) is under consideration, then this ⟦that is, forming the expansion⟧ amounts to replacing Φ by $\Phi \vee \Phi \vee ... \vee \Phi$; i.e., the two propositions are equivalent.

8.11. We note that the propositions whose expansions are true are in some sense those which are true when there are only n different individuals $a_1, a_2, ..., a_n$ which the variables can represent.

8.12. We note moreover that the expansion of $(x).\Phi(x)$ is by definition the same as that of $\sim(\exists x)\sim.\Phi(x)$ (see 6.2). Hence, if the expansion of $\Phi(x)$ is $\varphi(x)$, then that of $(x).\Phi(x)$ is $\varphi(a_1) \& \varphi(a_2) \& ... \& \varphi(a_n)$ (Chap. 1, 3.42). Hence, if the expansion of $\Phi(y_1 y_2 ... y_p)$ is $\varphi(y_1 y_2 ... y_p)$, then that of $(y_1 y_2 ... y_p).\Phi(y_1 y_2 ... y_p)$ is the product of the propositions obtained from $\varphi(y_1 y_2 ... y_p)$ by replacing $y_1, y_2, ..., y_p$ by $a_1, a_2, ..., a_n$ in all the different ways. It is necessary and sufficient for the truth of the expansion that all these propositions be true.

8.2. Now let us consider a proof; we must show that the property stated in the theorem is true for the primitive propositions and that it remains true when the rules of reasoning are applied, and to show this in such a way that by repeating the proofs below a known number of times, we can be sure that the conclusion of the proof possesses the desired property.[14]

---

[13] ⟦This expansion is called the *common expansion* in the Introduction, p. 6 above, and in various footnotes throughout this volume.⟧

[14] In this section, except for 4, there are to be no real variables in the propositions aside from those explicitly indicated, except possibly the variables $a_1, ..., a_n$ in the expansions.

As we have said, in what follows we deal with the second method (6.2).

1. The property obviously holds for identities of the first kind containing arbitrary propositions, from the rule of substitution of Chap. 1, 3.1.

2. Suppose that the property is true for $\Phi(xy_1y_2...y_p)$; then it is still true for $(x).\Phi(xy_1y_2...y_p)$, as can be seen from the remark of 8.12.

3. Suppose that the property is true for $\Phi(yyz_1...z_n)$, and let $\varphi(xyz_1...z_n)$ be the expansion of $\Phi(xyz_1...z_n)$. We can see immediately that the expansion of $\Phi(yyz_1...z_n)$ is $\varphi(yyz_1...z_n)$. Then the remark of 8.12 shows that the property is true for $(\exists x).\Phi(xyz_1...z_n)$.

4. The property remains true when the rules of passage are applied. In fact,

(a) The expansions of $(\exists x).\Phi(x). \vee p$ and $(\exists x).\Phi(x) \vee p$ are equivalent; for if the expansions of $\Phi(x)$ and p are $\varphi(x)$ and ω, then the two expansions are

$$\varphi(a_1) \vee \varphi(a_2) \vee \cdots \vee \varphi(a_n) \vee \omega$$

and

$$\varphi(a_1) \vee \omega . \vee \varphi(a_2) \vee \omega . \vee \cdots \vee \varphi(a_n) \vee \omega,$$

which are equivalent.

(b) The expansions of $(\exists x).\Phi(x) . \& p$ and $(\exists x).\Phi(x) \& p$ are equivalent; for, using the same notation, these are

$$\varphi(a_1) \vee \varphi(a_2) \vee \cdots \vee \varphi(a_n) . \& \omega$$

and

$$\varphi(a_1) \& \omega . \vee . \varphi(a_2) \& \omega . \vee \cdots \vee . \varphi(a_n) \& \omega,$$

which are equivalent by the distributivity theorem (Chap. 1, 5.34)

5. If the property is true for $\Phi(y_1y_2...y_n) \vee \Phi(y_1y_2...y_n)$, then it is also for $\Phi(y_1y_2...y_n)$, as can be seen from the remark of 8.12.

6. If the property is true for $\Phi(y_1y_2...y_n)$ and for $\Phi(y_1y_2...y_n) \supset \Psi(y_1y_2...y_n)$, then it is true for $\Psi(y_1y_2...y_n)$. In fact, let $\varphi(y_1y_2...y_n)$ and $\psi(y_1y_2...y_n)$ be the expansions of $\Phi(y_1y_2...y_n)$ and $\Psi(y_1y_2...y_n)$. From the fact that the propositions $\varphi(y_1y_2...y_n)$ and $\varphi(y_1y_2...y_n) \supset \psi(y_1y_2...y_n)$ become true when the y_i are replaced by the a_i in any way whatsoever, we can deduce the same property holds for $\Psi(y_1y_2...y_n)$ [rather, for $\psi(y_1y_2...y_n)$].

8.3. REMARK 1. When a proposition satisfies the condition stated in the theorem, we say that it is true in a *domain of n elements*,[15] and the corresponding necessary criterion for the truth of a proposition is called the *criterion of the domain of order n*.

We note that if a proposition is true in a domain of n elements, then it is true in every domain of a lesser number of elements. (To see this, it suffices to make a sufficient number of the a_i identical to each other.)

The domains considered here are said to be 'finite' (as opposed to the infinite domains of Chap. 5).

8.31. We can see that the expansion of a proposition p without apparent variables is a propositional function of the first kind of the propositions $\Phi(a_{i_1} a_{i_2} \dots a_{i_r})$ obtained from the atomic propositions by replacing the variables by the a_i in any manner whatsoever. If logical values are given to these propositions, then logical values for the expansion of p can be deduced. We say that this is the logical value of p corresponding to these logical values. We can see that with this nomenclature the logical value of a true proposition is always 'true', from the theorems of 8.1 and Chap. 1, 5.21.

8.4. REMARK 2. We can see that in order to obtain the criterion of order 1 it suffices to omit all quantifiers and replace all the variables by the same letter. The result must be an identity if the original proposition is true.

A consequence of this is that the theory developed so far is consistent (for if P and $\sim P$ were both true, then their expansions in a domain of one individual, p and $\sim p$, would both be true. This is impossible, from Chap. 1, § 4).

8.5. REMARK 3. A proposition true in all finite domains is not necessarily true, as the following example shows:

$$\sim :: (xyz):. \Phi(xy) \ \& \ \Phi(yz) . \supset \ \Phi(xz) :\& \sim \Phi(xx)$$
$$:.\& . (y)(\exists x). \Phi(xy).$$

This proposition is true in every finite domain, as can easily be seen. However, it is not true.[16]

---

[15] [[Herbrand's use of 'true' in 'true in a finite domain' must, of course, be distinguished from his use of 'true' to mean 'provable'.]]

[16] In fact, if we use the notation of arithmetic and replace $\Phi(xy)$ by $x > y$, the result is a theorem false, that is, refutable, in arithmetic. It will result further on from the consistency of arithmetic that the proposition cannot be an identity.

9. APPLICATIONS

We are going to study a few classical cases in which the criteria of domains furnish sufficient conditions for truth.

9.1. THEOREM. *For the proposition*

$$(x_1 \ldots x_n)(\exists y_1 \ldots y_p) . \Phi(x_1 \ldots x_n y_1 \ldots y_p)$$

to be true, it is necessary and sufficient that it be true in a domain of n elements $a_1, a_2, \ldots, a_n$.[17]

Obviously, it is necessary.

It is also sufficient; for, in this case the disjunction of the $\Phi(a_1 \ldots a_n y_1 \ldots y_p)$, with the y's replaced by the a's in all possible ways, is true. Indeed, each of the terms of the disjunction implies $(\exists y_1 \ldots y_p) \, \Phi(a_1 \ldots a_n y_1 \ldots y_p)$. From the identity of the first kind

$$\vdash : . A_1 \supset P .\&. A_2 \supset P .\&. \cdots \&. A_r \supset P .\&. A_1$$
$$\vee A_2 \vee \cdots \vee A_r : \supset P$$

we can deduce

$$\vdash : (\exists y_1 \ldots y_p) . \Phi(a_1 \ldots a_n y_1 \ldots y_p) .$$

And from this we can deduce the desired proposition, by means of the first rule of generalization.

NOTE. We might have $p=0$ or $n=0$; in the latter case it suffices to verify the proposition in a domain of one individual, as can easily be seen.

9.2. Consider a *proposition P in which all the atomic propositional functions have only one argument.* We shall put this proposition into a canonical form.[18]

Let $\Phi_1(x), \Phi_2(x), \ldots, \Phi_n(x)$ be the atomic propositional functions. Consider the 2^n products that can be formed with these propositional functions either preceded or not by the $\sim$ sign. For example, if $n=2$, these products are

$$\Phi_1(x) \,\&\, \Phi_2(x) \qquad \Phi_1(x) \,\&\, \sim\Phi_2(x)$$
$$\sim\Phi_1(x) \,\&\, \Phi_2(x) \qquad \sim\Phi_1(x) \,\&\, \sim\Phi_2(x).$$

---

[17] See *Bernays and Schönfinkel 1928*.

[18] The result of this section has been found independently by a number of authors. See *Behmann 1922, Löwenheim 1915*, and finally *Hilbert and Ackermann 1928*, p. 77. We give, however, a proof which we believe to be new.

Let $q = 2^n$, and call these products $A_1(x), A_2(x), ..., A_q(x)$. We have

$$\vdash \sim . A_i(x) \ \& \ A_j(x) \quad \text{if} \quad i \neq j \ ;$$
$$\vdash \sim A_i(x) . \equiv . A_1(x) \ \lor \ A_2(x) \ \lor \ \cdots \ \lor \ A_{i-1}(x) \ \lor \ A_{i+1}(x)$$
$$\lor \ \cdots \ \lor \ A_q(x),$$

where the disjunction on the right side contains all the $A(x)$ except $A_i(x)$. (These are both identities of the first kind, and can be verified immediately.)

Let p_i be the proposition $(\exists x) \, A_i(x)$. We shall show that a proposition equivalent to P and of the following form can be found: a propositional function of the first kind of the p_i and the $A_i(x_\alpha)$ (where the x_α are real variables), in which all the $A_i(x_\alpha)$ occur positively.

This is proved by recursion on the construction of the proposition in the second method (6.2).

1. If it is true for P and for Q, it is also for $P \lor Q$;

2. If it is true for P, then it is true for $\sim P$. It suffices to note that the occurrences of the $A_i(x)$ become negative, but $A_i(x)$ can be replaced by

$$\sim . A_1(x) \ \lor \ \cdots \ \lor \ A_{i-1}(x) \ \lor \ A_{i+1}(x) \ \lor \ \cdots \ \lor \ A_q(x),$$

from 4.2.

3. If it is true for $\Phi(x)$, then it is true for $(\exists x) . \Phi(x)$. In fact, put $\Phi(x)$ into disjunctive normal form; it then has the form $\Omega_1(x) \lor \Omega_2(x) \lor \ldots \lor \Omega_p(x)$; each of these terms $\Omega_i(x)$ of the disjunction is a product of propositions p_i, $\sim p_i$, and $A_i(x_\alpha)$. (From Chap. 1, 5.11, there are in fact no occurrences of $\sim A_i(x_\alpha)$.)

Since $\sim . A_i(x) \ \& \ A_j(x)$ is true if $i \neq j$, we can see that we can assume that each x_α appears once and only once in the $A_i(x_\alpha)$ appearing in any one of these products. From the fact that

$$(\exists x) . \Omega_1(x) \ \lor \ \Omega_2(x) \ \lor \ \cdots \ \lor \ \Omega_p(x)$$

is identical to

$$(\exists x) . \Omega_1(x) \ \lor \ (\exists x) . \Omega_2(x) . \lor \ \cdots \ \lor . (\exists x) . \Omega_p(x),$$

as can be seen without any difficulty, the desired result can easily be deduced.

4. It remains to be seen that the $\Phi_i(x)$ can be expressed as a function of the $A_i(x)$. Indeed, we can prove immediately, by means of the theorem of Chap. 1, 5.21, that $\Phi_i(x)$ is equivalent to the sum of the $A_j(x)$ that

contain the term $\Phi_i(x)$ (and not its negation; there are 2^{n-1} such $A_j(x)$).

To establish whether a proposition $\Phi(x_1 \ldots x_n)$ (without any other real variables), which contains only atomic propositions of one argument, is true, we consider $(x_1 x_2 \ldots x_n).\Phi(x_1 x_2 \ldots x_n)$ (which amounts to the same thing; see 4.7).

From the above, this is equivalent to a propositional function $A(p_1, p_2, \ldots, p_q)$ of the p_i; we shall show that *it is necessary and sufficient that this function be an identity of the first kind.*

The condition is obviously sufficient, from the theorem of § 4. That it is necessary results from the following considerations. If $A(p_1, p_2, \ldots, p_q)$ were not an identity, then there would be a system of logical values for the p_i which would give it the logical value 'false' (Chap. 1, 5.2). In this case we let, for the sake of argument, $p_1, p_2, \ldots, p_r$ $(r \leqslant q)$ be those of the p_i which have the logical value 'true' in this system.[19] Consider a domain of r individuals $a_1, a_2, \ldots, a_r$. We wish to give the following logical values to the $A_i(a_j)$: true if $i=j$, false otherwise. From this we can easily derive the logical values which must be given to the $\Phi_i(a_j)$;[20] with these logical values we can see that $p_1, p_2, \ldots, p_r$ have the logical value 'true' in the domain, the other p_i have the value 'false', as then does $A(p_1, p_2, \ldots, p_q)$ as well. As we saw, this is impossible (see 8.21) if $\Phi(x_1 \ldots x_n)$ is to be true.

This proof shows that we can also state our criterion as follows (8.3): *For a proposition containing n atomic propositional functions of one argument to be true, it is necessary and sufficient that it be true in a domain of 2^n elements.*

9.3. Aside from the two cases mentioned above, the only case for which it is known that a criterion of domains is necessary and sufficient for the truth of a proposition is the case of propositions of the form $(y_1 y_2 \ldots y_n)$ $(\exists x)(z_1 z_2 \ldots z_p).A(y_1 y_2 \ldots y_n x z_1 z_2 \ldots z_p)$ (without any other variables). This case was treated by Ackermann (*1928*), and we shall speak of it again in Chap. 5, p. 177 below. The particular case of propositions $(\exists x)(y).A(xy)$ had already been treated by Bernays and Schönfinkel (*1928*).

---

[19] [[Herbrand here ignores the case $r=0$, but fills in this lacuna in *1931*, footnote 45, p. 246 below.]]

[20] It suffices to give $\Phi_i(a_j)$ the same logical value as the sum of the $A_m(a_j)$ containing in their products $\Phi_i(a_j)$ and not $\sim \Phi_i(a_j)$.

NOTE A

(footnote 6, p. 78 above)

For illustrative purposes, let all the occurrences of p in $F(p)$ be positive. Then it is not always the case that $\vdash p \supset q .\supset. F(p) \supset F(q)$, if p or q contains real variables which become apparent in $F(p)$ or $F(q)$. For example, $p \supset \Phi(x) .\supset. (x) p \supset (x) \Phi(x)$ is not an identity. The error in Herbrand's proof arises from a misapplication of the first rule of generalization in step 4; if the real variable x appears in p or q, we cannot deduce $\vdash p \supset q .\supset. (x) F(p) \supset (x) F(q)$ from $\vdash p \supset q .\supset: (x) F(p) .\supset F(q)$. Herbrand also errs in step 2 by assuming that identities of the first kind are provable even when their atomic propositions are replaced by nonelementary propositions. However, a correction is easily made by using the result of 4.1; this involves no circularity, since the proof of 4.1 does not rely on 3.3.

We shall prove by induction the amended version of the theorem:

Let $F(p)$ be a propositional function of the proposition p in which all of p's occurrences have the same sign. If the occurrences of p in $F(p)$ are positive, then from $\vdash p \supset q$ we can deduce $\vdash F(p) \supset F(q)$; if they are negative, then from $\vdash p \supset q$ we can deduce $\vdash F(q) \supset F(p)$.

1. The theorem is obviously true when $F(p)$ is an atomic proposition.

2. Suppose that from $\vdash p \supset q$ we can derive $\vdash F(p) \supset F(q)$ and $\vdash G(p) \supset G(q)$. From the identity $A \supset B .\supset:. C \supset D :\supset: A \lor C .\supset. B \lor D$, which satisfies the condition of 4.1, with A replaced by $F(p)$, B by $F(q)$, C by $G(p)$ and D by $G(q)$, by applying the rule of implication twice we obtain $\vdash F(p) \lor G(p) .\supset. F(q) \lor G(q)$.

3. Similarly, using $A \supset B .\supset. \sim B \supset \sim A$, we conclude that if from $\vdash p \supset q$ we can deduce $\vdash F(p) \supset F(q)$, then from $\vdash p \supset q$ we can also deduce $\vdash \sim F(q) \supset \sim F(p)$.

4. Suppose that from $\vdash p \supset q$ we can deduce $\vdash F(p) \supset F(q)$. Since from the latter we can deduce successively $\vdash (x) F(x) .\supset F(q)$ and $\vdash (x) F(p) .\supset. (x) F(q)$, by using the rules of generalization and passage, hence from $\vdash p \supset q$ we can deduce $\vdash (x) F(p) .\supset. (x) F(q)$. A similar proof suffices for $(\exists x) F(p)$.

The procedure of applying generalization rules so as to insure that step 4 works is the crucial step in each of Herbrand's proofs of the equivalence of various formulations of quantification theory (6.3ff.). See also footnote 11, p. 86 above.

NOTE B

(footnote 10, p. 87 above)

In order to show that if P is a tautology (that is, if P results from an identity of the first kind $A[p_1, p_2, ..., p_n]$ by replacing $p_1, p_2, ..., p_n$ by arbitrary propositions) then P is derivable, Herbrand reduces the problem of deriving the tautology

$$A[(\exists x)\,\Phi_1(x), ..., (\exists x)\,\Phi_1(x); (\exists x)\,\Phi_1(x), ..., (\exists x)\,\Phi_1(x); \Phi_2, ..., \Phi_n]$$

to that of deriving the tautologous disjunction of

$$A[\Phi_1(x_i), ..., \Phi_1(x_i); \Phi_1(x_{\alpha+1}), ..., \Phi_1(x_{\alpha+\beta}); \Phi_2, ..., \Phi_n],$$

where i goes from $\alpha+1$ to $\alpha+\beta$. (Call the former tautology R and the latter Q.) That is, Herbrand argues that from a derivation of Q we can construct a derivation of R. However, his proof is erroneous in two places. First, in proving that Q is indeed a tautology, he systematically reverses negative and positive occurrences of the atomic propositions. Second, the proof cannot proceed by induction on the number of quantifiers in the tautology that is to be shown provable: Q may contain more quantifiers than R, since Q is a β-fold disjunction each disjunct of which contains $\alpha+\beta$ fewer quantifiers than R.

The first error is easily corrected. Given that $B(c; c, ..., c, r)$ is an identity of the first kind, we must prove that

$$B(a_{\alpha+1}; a_{\alpha+1}, ..., a_{\alpha+\beta}, r) \vee ... \vee B(a_{\alpha+\beta}; a_{\alpha+1}, ..., a_{\alpha+\beta}, r) \qquad (1)$$

is one also, where in $B(c; a_{\alpha+1}, ..., a_{\alpha+\beta}, r)$ all occurrences of c are positive and all occurrences of the a_i are negative. In a suitable conjunctive normal form of $B(c; a_{\alpha+1}, ..., a_{\alpha+\beta}, r)$ every conjunct is a disjunction of propositions of the forms $\sim a_i$, c, r and $\sim r$. Hence for $B(c; c, ..., c, r)$ to be an identity, it is necessary and sufficient that each conjunct of the normal form of $B(c; a_{\alpha+1}, ..., a_{\beta+1}, r)$ which does not contain both r and $\sim r$ contain both c and $\sim a_i$ for some i. Any assignment of logical values to the propositions $a_{\alpha+1}, ..., a_{\alpha+\beta}, r$ either assigns 'false' to all the a_i, so that each conjunct has the logical value 'true', that is, all disjuncts of (1) have the logical value 'true', or else assigns 'true' to at least one a_i, so that all conjuncts of $B(a_i; a_{\alpha+1}, ..., a_{\alpha+\beta}, r)$ are 'true'. Hence proposition (1) comes out 'true' under all assignments of logical values to its atomic propositions, so that it is an identity of the first kind.

To correct the second error, we shall index finite sets of propositions in such a way that induction will apply to Herbrand's procedure. Given a collection $\{\Phi_1, ..., \Phi_m\}$ of propositions, where each Φ_i contains q_i quantifiers, we define the Index of this collection as the q-tuple $\langle a_q, a_{q-1}, ..., a_1 \rangle$, where $q = \max(q_i)$ and a_i is the number of distinct subscripts $j \leq m$ such that $q_j = i$. For example, the Index of $\{(x)\,(\exists y)\,(\exists z)$

(w) $Fxyzw$, $(\exists x)$ (y) Gxy, $(\exists w)$ $(\exists v)$ $Fwwvv\}$ is the 4-tuple $\langle 1, 0, 2, 0 \rangle$. We order the finite tuples as follows: $\langle a'_{q'}, ..., a'_1 \rangle$ is less than $\langle a_q, ..., a_1 \rangle$ if either $q' < q$ or else $q' = q$ and there is a $j \leqslant q$ such that $a'_j < a_j$ and for all k, $j < k \leqslant q$, $a'_k = a_k$. (This is the ordinary lexicographical ordering; note that it is a well-ordering of all finite tuples.)

The Index of the collection $\{\Phi_1(x_{\alpha+1}), ..., \Phi_1(x_{\alpha+\beta}), \Phi_2, ..., \Phi_n\}$ is less than the Index of the collection $\{(\exists x)\, \Phi_1(x), \Phi_2, ..., \Phi_n\}$; for we obtain the former collection from the latter collection by replacing one proposition with, say, k quantifiers (namely, $(\exists x)\, \Phi_1(x)$) by β propositions each with $k-1$ quantifiers (namely, $\Phi_1(x_{\alpha+1}), ...,$ $\Phi_2(x_{\alpha+\beta})$). Hence Herbrand's proof shows that the problem of proving a tautology P is reducible to that of proving another tautology P', where the finite collection of propositions that replace the letters of an identity of the first kind to give rise to P' has a lesser Index than the finite collection of propositions giving rise to P. Since this ordering is a well-ordering, we eventually reduce the problem of proving the original proposition R to that of proving a proposition $A''(\Psi_1, ..., \Psi_m)$, where $A''(p_1, ..., p_m)$ is an identity of the first kind and the Index of $\{\Psi_1, ..., \Psi_m\}$ is a 0-tuple, that is, $\Psi_1, ...,$ Ψ_m are elementary propositions.

This sort of induction does not at first blush satisfy Herbrand's requirement that the number of steps needed, starting from R, be bounded (above, p. 50). However, an arithmetical computation can be carried out beforehand that gives a bound on the number of propositions we must deal with at any stage of the reduction procedure (this bound depends on the number of occurrences of each Φ_i appearing in R and on the number of quantifiers in each Φ_i). This furnishes a bound on the number of steps in the procedure.

This proof shows that all tautologies can be derived from quantifier-free tautologies using just the rules of generalization and passage, and the extended rule of simplification: from

$$\vdash.\Phi(x_1 x_1 x_2 ... x_n) \vee \Phi(x_2 x_1 x_2 ... x_n) \vee ... \vee \Phi(x_n x_1 x_2 ... x_n)$$

deduce

$$\vdash.(\exists y)\, \Phi(y x_1 x_2 ... x_n).$$

For the derivation of R from Q uses only these rules, so if Q can be derived from a quantifier-free tautology in this way, so can R. Hence, Herbrand has shown that all tautologies are *normal identities* in the sense of *1928*, p. 30 above (see the last paragraph of the Note to *1928*, p. 34 above). Furthermore, the above proof can also be used to show that all tautologies have a special form of property A; see Note D, p. 189 below.

CHAPTER 3

MATHEMATICAL THEORIES

1. THE GENERAL NOTION OF A MATHEMATICAL THEORY

1.1. So far we have studied the logical rules for obtaining true propositions; in order to obtain mathematical theories it suffices, in principle, to consider certain determinate propositions to be true. Any proposition is then considered true if it can be deduced from these propositions by the rules of reasoning. But this is only the simplest case; we shall indicate a rather general schema for theories which can, it seems (see the Introduction) give rise to most known mathematical (or logical) theories.

In what follows, we shall call a *letter* not only letters of the alphabet, but also any other sign which we have agreed to consider as such. Thus, as in the preceding chapter, letters such as x_1 and x_2 with different indices will be considered different.

We shall henceforth call by definition any system of signs which satisfies the description we give a *theory*.

1.11. 1. As before, lower case letters designate variables; but it is necessary to consider these to be of several sorts. There can even be an indefinite number of sorts of letters (see 1.2 below). The letters of different sorts are distinguished by the form of the signs which represent them, which, for example, can be written with subscripts. Each sort of letter is called, following Russell's terminology, a 'type' of variable.

1.12. 2. There can be a certain number (or even an indefinite number) of different letters (which can be distinguished by subscripts when there are an indefinite number) whose use is the same as the use of variables except that they cannot appear in quantifiers. Each of these letters is considered to be of a definite type. These letters are called *constants*; we say that they are the *primitive constants*.

1.13. 3. There is a certain number (or even an indefinite number) of different signs which are called *descriptive functions*. With regard to these, it is necessary to introduce the notion of *individuals* of a determinate type. A descriptive function is always to be accompanied by a definite number of individuals, called its *arguments*, of definite types, in a definite order;

and it is itself considered to be of a definite type. The combinations of signs which are called individuals are defined as follows:

(a) The primitive constants and the variables of a determinate type are individuals of that type.

(b) A descriptive function of a determinate type, accompanied by individuals in the required manner, is itself an individual of this type.

In short, we see that the individuals are formed by iteration of the descriptive functions, starting with the constants and the variables.

The functions we have just discussed are called *elementary descriptive functions*; similarly, in general, any individual represented by a collection of signs containing the variables $x_1, x_2, ..., x_n$ is said to be a descriptive function (or simply a function) of these variables, its *arguments*.

A descriptive function of primitive constants is said to be a *constant*. A constant can always be considered to be a descriptive function of no arguments, which we shall do from now on.

In ordinary mathematics, the different types correspond to different sorts of objects imagined, and the descriptive functions to ordinary functions of one or several variables. (In general, an individual y is a function of the individuals $x_1, x_2, ..., x_n$ if to every system $x_1, x_2, ..., x_n$ there corresponds one and only one individual y.)

1.14. 4. There is a certain number of different signs (or even an indefinite number), each of which can appear only when accompanied by a certain number of individuals of definite types in a definite order, and is said to be an *atomic propositional function* of these individuals. In proofs, these are considered to be propositions.

As in Chap. 2, all other propositions are constructed starting with these. The real variables of a proposition are called its 'arguments', and the proposition a 'propositional function' of these variables.

The atomic propositional functions translate the fundamental relations that can exist between the objects of the theory under consideration. Those having only one argument translate the fundamental properties that these objects can have.

1.15. 5. There is a certain number (or an indefinite number) of propositions which are considered true. These are called *hypotheses* or *axioms* or *primitive propositions* of the theory. Among them appear the primitive propositions described at the beginning of Chap. 2 (the identities of the first kind containing elementary propositions); these are always omitted ⟦in the specification of a theory⟧.

1.16. 6. There can also be special rules of inference in the theory. We shall see an example of this at the beginning of Chap. 4. But this is an exceptional case; if no formal indication is made, we shall suppose that there are none of these.

1.17. A proposition will be said to be *true* in this theory, or to be a *theorem* of this theory, if it can be deduced from the hypotheses by means of the rules of reasoning of Chap. 2, completed as indicated in 1.4, and the rules of which we have just spoken.

We still indicate that a proposition is true (in a definite theory) by writing the sign ⊢ in front of it.

1.2. Let us note right away that when we speak of an indefinite number of signs or hypotheses, we mean that we have a definite law which always permits us to write new signs or hypotheses. In any definite proof we always use only a determinate number of these; but it is essential to note that this number depends on the proof envisaged. Any definite proposition always contains only a definite number of different signs.

1.3. We shall see below several examples of mathematical theories; for example, arithmetic, in which there is only one type, one fundamental descriptive function $a+1$, one atomic propositional function $a=b$, and one primitive constant 0; and the theory of Russell and Whitehead, in which there is an infinity of types. We note that in general a theory has an indefinite number of hypotheses, often of the following form: for every definite propositional function $\Phi(x_1 x_2 \ldots x_n)$, the proposition $A[\Phi(x_1 x_2 \ldots x_n)]$ is true, where $A[p]$ is a propositional function (Chap. 2, 1.41) of p.

The simplest example of a mathematical theory is the one in which there are neither constants nor descriptive functions nor hypotheses, an indefinite number of ⟦atomic⟧ propositional functions, and only one type. This is the theory studied in Chap. 2.

1.4. Let us now suppose that we are considering the mathematical theory derived from this last one by the addition of an indeterminate number of descriptive functions and constants. We also suppose, for more generality, that there is an indefinite number of types. The statement of the second rule of generalization must then be changed slightly (this is the above-mentioned modification of the rules of reasoning which must be made for all theories containing descriptive functions); it becomes the following:

If $\Phi(f, x_1, x_2, ..., x_n)$ is true, where f is either a real variable, or a descriptive function whose arguments are real variables, or a constant, then $(\exists y).\Phi(yx_1x_2...x_n)$ is true.

We still say, by extension, that a proposition true in the theory under consideration is a *propositional identity*.

This extension of the theory of Chap. 2 is the theory we shall use from now on.[1] The essential new feature of this theory is the introduction not of different types, but rather of descriptive functions. Henceforth, the atomic propositions will be of the form $\Phi(f_1f_2...f_n)$, where $f_1, f_2, ..., f_n$ are individuals, not necessarily variables. We shall see, moreover, in Chap. 5 that the decision problem for this new theory reduces to the same problem as that for the theory of Chap. 2. This means that we can avoid, if we like, the use of descriptive functions. But they are necessary in order to translate ordinary mathematical theories into signs.

1.41. It is easy to see that in addition to the former rule of substitution (Chap. 2, 5.1) we now have another:

In a propositional identity, an elementary descriptive function may be replaced by a descriptive function of the same type and with the same arguments as the original one.

All other results of the first six sections of Chap. 2 still hold. Of course, the second rule of generalization of the second method of § 6 must be modified as indicated above.

1.42. The theory of domains developed in § 8 can be applied almost without change in this new case. It suffices to proceed as follows:

1. With each type we associate a certain number of variables of this type, which we call elements of the domain of this type.

2. We associate in any way we like an element of the domain of the same type as f with each individual that is an elementary descriptive function $f(a_{i_1}, a_{i_2}, ..., a_{i_q})$ whose arguments are elements of the domain.

3. Then we modify the rule defining the expansion of $(\exists x).\Phi(x)$ on the basis of the expansion of $\Phi(x)$ as follows: If the latter expansion is

---

[1] [[In the notes below, we shall denote this theory by 'Q_H'.]]

$\varphi(x)$, then the former one is $\varphi(a_1) \vee \varphi(a_2) \vee \ldots \vee \varphi(a_p)$, where a_1, $a_2, \ldots, a_p$ are the elements of the domain of the type of x.

4. When the expansion of a proposition without real variables has thus been obtained, we use the correspondence described in clause 2 to arrive at a proposition without descriptive functions, by replacing the $f(a_{i_1}, a_{i_2}, \ldots, a_{i_q})$ by the corresponding elements of the domain. The proposition thus obtained is the final expansion.

With this modification, all the results of the theory continue to hold (in particular, we can deduce from it the consistency of the theory considered in 1.4).

The criteria of domains obviously permit us to prove the consistency of any theory whose axioms are true in a finite domain (for example, the theory of fields).[2]

2. ELEMENTARY STUDY OF MATHEMATICAL THEORIES

2.1. DEF. 1. A theory is said to be *consistent* if there is no proposition p such that p and $\sim p$ are both true in it.

We note that in an inconsistent theory every proposition q is true; for if p and $\sim p$ are true, so are p and $p \supset q$ (which is nothing but $\sim p \vee q$); hence q is true.

DEF. 2. A theory is said to be *completely determined* [*à complète déter-*

---

[2] [[We shall also call the expansion of a proposition P over a finite domain as defined by clauses 1–4 above a *common expansion* of P, just as we did the original notion of Chap. 2, § 8. In this last paragraph, Herbrand has shifted the meaning of 'P is true in a finite domain'; he now uses it to mean that the common expansion of P over the domain is truth-functionally satisfiable, for some choice of values for the descriptive functions. The consistency of a theory any conjunction of whose axioms has a satisfiable common expansion is easily proved as follows: suppose some finite conjunction of hypotheses H of this theory is such that $H \supset . p \& \sim p$ is an identity. Then $H^* \supset . p^* \& \sim p^*$ is a truth-functional identity, where H^* is the common expansion of H over a suitable domain, and p^* is the common expansion of p over the same domain. But this is impossible, for H^* is truth-functionally satisfiable by hypothesis, so there is an assignment of logical values to $H^* \supset . p^* \& \sim p^*$ under which this proposition has the logical value 'false'.]]

mination] if for every proposition *p* without real variables, either *p* or ~*p* is true.[3]

DEF. 3. We say a theory is *decidable* [*résoluble*] if there is a method allowing us to recognize whether or not a proposition is true in the theory, and if it is to furnish a proof of the proposition.

Hence, we can consider a consistent theory that is completely determined and decidable to be known perfectly, and the study of it from the mathematical viewpoint to have been completed. We shall see an example of such a theory further on [Chap. 4, § 7, p. 125 below].

2.2. We can prove without much difficulty that a mathematical theory can be modified by introducing new constants, types, or functions without there being in the new theory any true proposition that is not true in the original theory. However, these modifications can be useful in order to obtain series of true theorems, by taking the following remark into account: if some atomic propositional functions or fundamental descriptive functions do not appear in the hypotheses of a theory, then the rules of substitution (Chap. 2, 5.1; Chap. 3, 1.4) are applicable to these functions.

2.3. It is essential to distinguish theories in which there is a finite and determinate number of hypotheses from those which have an indefinite number of them. Here is an example of the latter case which furnishes us with the simplest example of a 'set theory': there are two types, that of the elements and that of the classes, and one atomic propositional function $x \in \alpha$ of variables x (of the type of the elements) and α (of the type of the classes). The hypotheses are all propositions obtained from

$$(\exists \alpha)(x) . x \in \alpha \equiv \Phi(x)$$

by replacing $\Phi(x)$ by any arbitrary propositional function of x. This

---

[3] In ordinary terminology, this is a theory for which the principle of the *excluded middle* is true. We shall not repeat here what we said in the Introduction [[p. 51 above]] regarding the distinction between the mathematical use of terms (which, for the excluded middle, is always legitimate) and their metamathematical use (which here corresponds to a property of theories in no wise essential and moreover undoubtedly rarely holds). [[In more recent terminology, if the condition of Def. 2 is satisfied by a theory *T*, then *T* is said to be 'syntactically complete' or just 'complete'.]]

theory can easily be shown consistent, for its hypotheses are true in a finite domain (Chap. 3, 1.42).[4] In an analogous manner we can 'axiomatize' the theory employed by Russell and Whitehead in *Principia Mathematica* (we then have an indefinite number of types), and can just as well show its consistency, even when hypotheses such as the multiplicative axioms for each type (which correspond to the classical axiom of choice) are added.[5]

It must be noted that in a theory that has an indefinite number of hypotheses, only a finite and determinate number of these hypotheses is used in the proof of a given theorem; we do not, however, know beforehand which ones. These theories thus present special difficulties. It is remarkable, moreover, that every set theory permitting us to furnish a foundation for classical mathematical analysis has an infinity of hypotheses; only von Neumann's recent axiomatization (*1925*, *1928*) is an exception.

2.4. Henceforth we shall suppose implicitly that the hypotheses contain no real variables. This condition can always be satisfied by making use of the first rule of generalization (Chap. 2, 4.7).

Now let us consider a theory that has only a finite number of hypotheses. These can be replaced by their logical product, in such a way that there is now only one hypothesis (Chap. 1, 3.43). Furthermore, as we have just said, we can suppose that the hypotheses no longer contain any real variables. Let H be the proposition thus obtained. We shall show the

THEOREM. *A necessary and sufficient condition for the truth of a proposition* P ⟦*in this theory*⟧ *is that*

$$H \supset P$$

be a propositional identity (in the sense of 1.4).

This is proved by recursion on the proof of P.

1. The stated property remains true, obviously, for applications of the rules of passage.

---

[4] ⟦Here again, Herbrand is using 'true in a finite domain' to mean "has a truth-functionally satisfiable common expansion over some finite domain"; see footnote 2, p. 105 above.⟧

[5] ⟦Of course, the consistency of this theory cannot be shown when the axiom of infinity is added.⟧

2. It remains true for the rules of generalization, for from $\vdash H \supset \Phi(x)$ we can deduce $\vdash : H \supset . (x) \, \Phi(x)$, and from $\vdash . H \supset \Phi(yf)$ we can deduce $\vdash : H \supset . (\exists x) \, \Phi(yx)$, using the rules of generalization and passage, where f is any individual.

3. It remains true for the rules of simplification and implication, because of the identities of the first kind

$$H \supset . P \vee P :\supset . H \supset P$$
$$\vdash H \supset P .\&: H \supset . P \supset Q .:\supset . H \supset Q .$$

4. It is obviously true for the elementary identities of the first kind, because of the identity

$$\vdash : P \supset . H \supset P ,$$

and for the hypothesis itself, since

$$\vdash . H \supset H .$$

2.41. REMARK. 1. This theorem also leads to a result for theories with an infinity of hypotheses. In a proof of a given theorem P, only certain definite hypotheses are used. Assume these to be without real variables, and let H be their logical product. The same argument shows $H \supset P$ to be a propositional identity.

2.42. 2. This theorem reduces the study of any theory with a finite number of hypotheses to that of the theory considered in 1.4.

2.43. 3. From this theorem we can deduce that if a new hypothesis H without real variables is added to a theory, then a necessary and sufficient condition for the truth of a proposition P in the new theory is the truth of $H \supset P$ in the original one.

(For if H' is the product of the hypotheses of the original theory necessary to prove P, then $H \& H' .\supset P$ is an identity, from 2.4. This is equivalent to $H' \supset . H \supset P$, from which our remark can easily be deduced.

3. INCOMPLETE DESCRIPTIONS

3.1. Let us consider a mathematical theory with no special rule of inference. Let $A(x)$ be a propositional function of x which can contain constants but no real variables other than x. Assume the following propositions are true:

$$\vdash : (\exists x) A(x) \tag{1}$$

$$\vdash . A(a) \tag{2}$$

for all fundamental constants a of the same type as the argument of A (if there are any constants, (1) is deducible from (2)), and

$$\vdash . A(y_1) \& A(y_2) \& \cdots \& A(y_n) . \supset . A(f(y_1, y_2, \ldots, y_n)) \tag{3}$$

for all fundamental descriptive functions f of the same type as the argument of A.

It can easily be seen that (2) is true for every constant, and (3) for every descriptive function.

We shall then say that $A(x)$ is an incomplete description of x. The description $A(x)$ determines a relativization [[réduite]] (Chap. 2, § 8)[6] associated with every proposition, by the following rules: the relativization of an atomic proposition is the proposition itself. If the relativization of $\Phi(xy_1y_2\ldots y_n)$ is $\varphi(xy_1y_2\ldots y_n)$, then that of $(\exists x).\Phi(xy_1y_2\ldots y_n)$ is $(\exists x).A(x) \& \varphi(xy_1y_2\ldots y_n)$ [[where x is of the same type as the argument of A]]. Furthermore, as always, if the relativization of P is p then that of $\sim P$ is $\sim p$; and if the relativizations of P and Q are p and q, then that of $P \lor Q$ is $p \lor q$.

We assume furthermore that the relativizations of the hypotheses (assumed to be without real variables) are true.

3.2. THEOREM 1. *Under these conditions, if $\Phi(y_1y_2\ldots y_n)$ is true, then the relativization of $(y_1\ldots y_n).\Phi(y_1y_2\ldots y_n)$ is true.*

This theorem amounts to saying that we can restrict the individuals of the type of x to those for which $A(x)$ is true. We note the analogy with the criteria of domains (Chap. 2, 8.1).

We omit the proof of the theorem; it is carried out without any difficulty by recursion on the proof of $\Phi(y_1y_2\ldots y_n)$, in the method of Chap. 2, 6.2.

3.21. We can easily see that this can be generalized slightly by the use

---

[6] [[Herbrand uses the word 'réduite' here; except for this section, this word is throughout this volume translated 'expansion'. Here, however, in keeping with more standard terminology used for the proposition Herbrand defines, it is rendered 'relativization'.]]

of several incomplete descriptions $A(x)$, the argument of each being of a different type, so that the descriptions are imposed on individuals of different types.

3.3. THEOREM 2. *A necessary and sufficient condition for* $\Phi(y_1 y_2 \ldots y_n)$ *to become true when* $(x) A(x)$ *is added to the hypotheses is that the relativization of* $(y_1 y_2 \ldots y_n).\Phi(y_1 y_2 \ldots y_n)$ *be true.*[7]

1. This condition is sufficient, for the hypothesis $(x) A(x)$ entails the equivalence of $(\exists x).A(x) \,\&\, \Phi(x)$ and $(\exists x)\,\Phi(x)$, from which the equivalence of a proposition and its relativization can be deduced, by recursion on the construction of the proposition.

2. Let us show that it is necessary. If $\Phi(y_1 y_2 \ldots y_n)$ is true when $(x).A(x)$ is added to the hypotheses, the remark of 2.43 shows that

$$(y_1 y_2 \ldots y_n)\!:\!(x).A(x)\,.\supset.\,\Phi(y_1 y_2 \ldots y_n)$$

is true with the original hypotheses.

Hence its relativization is true. But the relativization of $(x).A(x)$ is a true proposition, from which it can be deduced that the relativization of $(y_1 y_2 \ldots y_n).\Phi(y_1 y_2 \ldots y_n)$ is true.

3.31. COROLLARY. Under the conditions stated at the beginning of 3.1, we can see that if a theory is consistent, it remains so when the hypothesis

$$\vdash :(x).A(x)$$

is added, for the relativization of a proposition of the form $p \,\&\, \sim p$ without real variables is false [[that is, not provable in the old theory]].

3.4. The theory developed above allows us to reduce theories containing different types to theories containing only one type.

Let us suppose, for the sake of argument, that there is a determinate number n of types in the theory (the same procedure would work if there were an indefinite number). We number the types from 1 to n, and in-

---

[7] [[As Herbrand notes in footnote 1 to *1931c* (p. 284 below), this theorem is false if $A(x)$ contains restricted variables; for then the argument in clause 2 fails, since the relativization of $(x).A(x)$ is not necessarily provable (see also Note C, p. 132 below). Note that the notion of incomplete description which Herbrand explains here is related to that of 'inner model' used by von Neumann (*1929*) and Gödel (*1940*) for consistency results in set theory.]]

troduce n propositional functions $\Phi_1(x)$, $\Phi_2(x)$,..., $\Phi_n(x)$, where $\Phi_i(x)$ has one argument of the ith type.

Let us consider a theory obtained from the original one by

1. Replacing the hypotheses (assumed to be without real variables) by their relativizations, which are obtained using the incomplete descriptions (3.21) $\Phi_1(x)$ for the first type, $\Phi_2(x)$ for the second,..., $\Phi_n(x)$ for the nth;

2. Adding the propositions of forms (1), (2), and (3) of 3.1 corresponding to each of the incomplete descriptions $\Phi_1(x)$, $\Phi_2(x)$,..., $\Phi_n(x)$ to the hypotheses;

3. Assuming that there is now only one type.

We shall henceforth designate by P^* the relativization of a proposition P which uses the descriptions $\Phi_1(x)$, $\Phi_2(x)$,..., $\Phi_n(x)$. We then have the theorem:

3.41. THEOREM. *A necessary and sufficient condition for the truth of a proposition P without free variables in the original theory is the truth of its relativization P^* in the new theory.*[8]

1. If P is true in the original theory, then there is a product H of hypotheses such that $H \supset P$ is an identity, from 2.4. All the conditions for the validity of Theorem 3.2 hold for the new theory; hence $H^* \supset P^*$, the relativization of $H \supset P$, is true in this theory. Hence P^* is also.

2. Suppose that P^* is true in the new theory. Then there is a certain product of hypotheses of this theory, containing relativizations of hypotheses of the original theory (and propositions of forms (1), (2), and (3) of 3.1), which we denote by M, such that $M \supset P^*$ is an identity.

We can see immediately that by replacing all the $\Phi_i(x)$ by identities (for example, of the form $p \vee \sim p$), a relativization A^* becomes equivalent to A (for $\Phi_i(x)$ & $\Omega(x)$ becomes equivalent to $\Omega(x)$, no matter what $\Omega(x)$ is).

This operation transforms M into a proposition equivalent either to a product of hypotheses of the original theory or to an identity (for hypotheses of forms (1), (2), and (3) of 3.1 become identities). Let N

---

[8] [[This theorem is true, but Herbrand's argument of clause 2 is not sufficient to prove it, for it is not obvious that if P^* is the relativization of P and is provable in one-sorted quantification theory, then P is provable in many-sorted quantification theory. See *Schmidt 1938* and *Wang 1952*.]]

be this proposition. From the rule of substitution (Chap. 2, 5.1), $N \supset P$ is an identity, and hence P is true in the original theory.

3.42. The above theorem provides a means of replacing the study of a theory which has several types by that of a theory which has only one type.

By taking into account the theorem of 2.4 and the result, to which we shall return in the last chapter, according to which we may always suppose that there are neither descriptive functions nor constants, we can see that the problem of recognizing if a given proposition is true in a theory having a finite number of hypotheses reduces to the *Entscheidungsproblem* as it was stated in Chap. 2, 2.1.

CHAPTER 4

ARITHMETIC

1. ARITHMETIC WITHOUT APPARENT VARIABLES

1.1. In what follows we shall consider theories which contain only one type of individual, called *numbers*. Among these there is one primitive constant, which is represented by 0. Furthermore, there is one elementary descriptive function of one argument, which we designate by $a+1$ (where a is the argument), and which is read 'a plus one'. There is one atomic propositional function of two arguments, $a=b$, which is read 'a equals b'.

We define:[1]

$$a \neq b. =. \sim .a = b \qquad Df.$$

1.11. Henceforth we shall call a 'numeral' any group of signs such as 0, $0+1$, $0+1+1$, etc.; we can define this by saying that 0 is a numeral, and if a represents a figure known to be a numeral, then so does $a+1$.

Throughout this chapter variables will be designated by x, y, z, t, s; on the other hand, the letters a, b, c, d will always be used for determinate numerals.

We note that it is essential to distinguish between numbers and numerals. A numeral is an individual of a determinate and given form: 0, for

---

[1] For this notation, see Chap. 1, 1.1.

example. It is, if you will, a simple figure, a cipher. As for a number, it can be any individual whatever; a letter x will henceforth be a number, but it is not a numeral. (It is clear that every numeral is a number.)[2]

1.12. If a is the numeral $0+1+1+\cdots+1$, where $+1$ is repeated n times, then $x+a$ denotes the descriptive function $x+1+1+\cdots+1$ where $+1$ is repeated n times; thus $0+a=a$.

We can also define $x+1$ by saying that $x+0$ represents x and $x+(a+1)$ represents $(x+a)+1$. We note that we can talk of the sum of two numerals; it is another numeral which the preceding definition immediately allows us to construct.

Further, we note that in the theory we study, all atomic propositions are of the form $a=b$, $x+a=b$, or $x+a=y+b$ (we repeat that x and y are definite variables, a and b definite numerals).

1.13. We say that two numerals are equal if they are identical, and that a numeral a is greater than a numeral b, or b is smaller than a, if a contains the sign $+1$ more times than does b.

If the numeral a is greater than or equal to the numeral b, we call $a-b$ the numeral obtained from a by removing as many $+1$ signs as b contains. We say that this new numeral is obtained by *subtracting* b from a.

1.14. We repeat: all these definitions are applicable only to determinate numerals, and indicate properties and operations which can actually be recognized and executed.

We shall henceforth need to use propositions containing indeterminate numerals (obviously, these are used in each particular case with determinate numerals only). We shall prove certain of their properties by inferring from the case in which one of these numerals equals a to the case in which it equals $a+1$, that is, by recursion. This is legitimate (see the Introduction), for every time we have a proposition containing determinate numerals, the argument leads, by a certain number of iterations, to the verification of the property under consideration.

1.2. Let us first consider a theory in which we employ no apparent variables. Hence, the only rules of reasoning are those stated in Chap. 1.

---

[2] [[Thus, a number is any numerical term, of the form x, $x+a$, or a, where x is a variable and a a numeral. A numeral is a term of the form $0+1+\ldots+1$.]]

This theory has the following hypotheses. First, the five hypotheses

(1) $x = x$
(2) $x = y . \supset . y = x$
(3) $x = y \ \& \ y = z . \supset . x = z$
(4) $x = y . \equiv . x + 1 = y + 1$
(5) $x + 1 \neq 0 \ ;$

and, in addition, all hypotheses of the form

(6) $x \neq x + a ,$

where a is an arbitrary, but determinate, numeral different from 0.

We add to these hypotheses all those obtained from them by replacing x, y, and z by determinate *numbers*, and a by a determinate *numeral*.

1.3. We shall designate this theory by Theory 1 (abbreviated Th. 1). We are going to deduce some of its consequences. In the following, a, b, and c designate arbitrary, but determinate, numerals.

1.31. If a and b are equal, then

$$\vdash . a = b .$$

1.32. If a and b are unequal, then

$$\vdash . a \neq b$$

(this results from the axioms (6)).

1.33 $\vdash : x + a = y + b . \equiv . x = y + (b - a)$

if b is greater than or equal to a. We are able to prove this in the following way. We have

$$\vdash : x = y + c . \equiv . x + 1 = y + c + 1$$

from axiom (4). Since (9) ⟦rather, (4)⟧ can be applied only when a and b are determinate numerals, a determinate number of steps leads to the result.

We prove the following propositions in a similar manner.

1.34 $\vdash . x + a = x + b . \equiv . a = b$

from the axioms (6) and 1.33.

1.35. $\vdash : y = x + a \ \& \ z = y + b . \supset . z = x + a + b$
1.36. $\vdash : y = x + a \ \& \ z = x + b . \supset . z = y + (b - a)$

if b is greater than or equal to a (these result from axioms (1), (2), and (3)).

These results will be used in investigating the canonical form of a proposition.

1.37. Finally, we note that we can always find a numeral different from any definite number of given numerals. (It suffices, for example, to add $+1$ to the largest of these numerals.)

All the investigations which follow will consist, at bottom, of studying true propositions, starting with the propositions obtained from them by replacing all variables by determinate numerals.

2. A CONSISTENCY THEOREM

2. We will prove the *consistency of this theory* (Chap. 3, 2.1). With every proposition P of this theory we associate another one by replacing each of the variables by 0; all the atomic propositions appearing in the new proposition are then of the form $a=b$, where a and b are numerals. We give this atomic proposition the logical value 'true' or 'false', according to whether the numerals a and b are identical or different. Then a determinate logical value is associated with the proposition P; we shall show that *if P is true, then this logical value is 'true'*.

On one hand, in fact, we can verify immediately, as in Chap. 1, § 3, that if the logical value 'true' corresponds to P and to $P \supset Q$, then it does also to Q. On the other hand, in order to verify that the logical value 'true' corresponds to every primitive proposition, it suffices to determine this logical value by taking successively all possible cases, according to whether the numerals obtained by replacing the variables in ⟦the terms substituted for⟧ x, y, and z by 0 are identical or not.

Since the logical value 'true' cannot be associated with both P and $\sim P$, they cannot both be true in the theory under consideration.

2.1. We note furthermore that for a proposition which does not contain variables, this criterion is sufficient: it suffices, in fact, to show that if a proposition P does not contain variables, then it is true or its negation is true when its logical value is 'true' or 'false', respectively.

We prove this by recursion on the construction of P.

For atomic propositions, this results from 1.31 and 1.32.

We can then see immediately that if it is true for P and for Q, then it is also for $\sim P$ and for $P \vee Q$.

Hence, from now on we can speak without ambiguity of the truth and falsity in the theory of a proposition without variables; for, every proposition that is not true has a true negation.

3. THE CANONICAL FORM OF A PROPOSITION

We shall indicate a procedure permitting us to recognize whether a proposition is true or not in this theory. For this it is necessary to put every proposition into a canonical form, that is, to find another proposition of canonical form which is equivalent to it.

Given a proposition, we begin by putting it into disjunctive normal form (Chap. 1, 5.1), and then we replace each term of the disjunction by a term which is equivalent to it. This is legitimate, from Chap. 1, 3.3. Each of these terms is a product of simple propositions (that is, of atomic propositions and negations of atomic propositions).

3.11. We shall constantly use the following fact: if P is true, $A \& P$ is equivalent to A and $A \vee P$ is true; if P is false, $A \vee P$ is equivalent to A and $A \& P$ is false.

3.12. Let us show first that a product of atomic propositions is equivalent to a proposition either

of the form $0 \neq 0$,

or of the form $0 = 0$,

or of the following form:

the variables in this new proposition are of three kinds, those of the first kind denoted by $x_1, x_2, ..., x_n$, those of the second kind by $y_1, y_2, ...,$ y_p, and those of the third kind by $z_1, z_2, ..., z_q$; it is a product of atomic propositions of the following forms:

Either $x_i = a_i$, each x_i occurring in one and only one such equation;

Or $z_i = y_j + b_i$, each z_i occurring in one and only one such equation (where the a_i and b_j are numerals). We note that the variables of certain kinds may be totally absent.

We shall prove this by recursion on the number of variables.[3]

When there is only one atomic proposition in the product, then it is of one of the following three forms:

---

[3] [[Herbrand's proof in fact proceeds by induction on the number of atomic propositions in the product.]]

(a) $x+a=b$, in which case it is either false, hence equivalent to $0 \neq 0$, or else equivalent to $x=b-a$ (from 1.33 and axiom (6));

(b) $x+a=x+b$, in which case it is either false, hence equivalent to $0 \neq 0$, or true, hence equivalent to $0=0$ (from 1.34, 1.31, and 1.32).

(c) $x+a=y+b$, in which case it is equivalent to $x=y+(b-a)$ if, for example, b is greater than a (from 1.33).

Now let us add a new atomic proposition to a product of the above-mentioned form. Either

(a) *It contains no variables.* Then we know whether it is true or false. In the first case, the new atomic proposition can be omitted, and in the second case the entire product can be replaced by $0 \neq 0$ (from 1.31, 1.32, and 3.11).

(b) *Or it is of the form $t+a=b$, where t is a variable.* Obviously, by replacing t by the value it takes in one of the other factors of the product, if it appears there (this is legitimate from 1.35), we can always replace this atomic proposition by another one equivalent to it, either reducing to case (a) above, or of the same form but such that t is a variable of the second kind. In this last case, if a is greater than or equal to b [rather, if a is greater than b], the product is equivalent to $0 \neq 0$. Otherwise, the atomic proposition is equivalent to $t=b-a$; then t is replaced by this numeral in the equations which contain t,[4] and the product takes the desired form (from 1.33, axiom 6, and 3.11).

(c) *Or it is of the form $t+a=t+b$.* If a is different from b, then the product is equivalent to $0 \neq 0$; otherwise, this new atomic proposition can be omitted (1.34, 1.31, 1.32, and 3.11).

(d) *Or it is of the form $t+a=s+b$.* Then, as in (b), we can suppose s and t to be of the second kind. We assume b to be greater than or equal to a; then the atomic proposition is equivalent to

$$t = s + (b - a) \qquad \text{(from 1.33)}.$$

---

[4] [[In clauses (b) and (d), t is to be replaced by $b-a$ and $s+(b-a)$, respectively, only in the equations of the original product; since the converses of 1.35 and 1.36 are not true, the occurrence of t in the new atomic proposition cannot be eliminated. That Herbrand's procedure preserves equivalence is insured by the following principle of substitution: if P is a proposition, and P' is obtained from P by substituting some number v for a variable u wherever it appears, then $\vdash : P \mathbin{\&} u = v . \equiv . P' \mathbin{\&} u = v$. This is proved by using 1.35, 1.36, and repeated applications of Chap. 1, 3.3 (p. 58 above.]]

By replacing t by this value in all the equations containing t,[4] we reduce the product to the desired form (from 1.35).

3.13. Now let us add inequalities to the product. An analogous discussion leads to the following canonical form of a product of simple propositions:

(a) Either $0=0$,

(b) or $0 \neq 0$,

(c) or a product of propositions $x_i = a_i$ for $i = 1, 2, ..., n$, $z_i = y_j + b_i$ for $i = 1, 2, ..., q$, where j depends on i (each x_i and each z_i can appear in one and only one equality),

$y_i \neq y_j + b_i$ (a pair i, j can give rise to several inequalities),

$y_i \neq d_i$ (the same y_i can appear in several of these inequalities).

By taking the remarks of 3.11 into account, we can derive from this the canonical form of a proposition, which is:

(a) Either $0=0$

(b) or $0 \neq 0$

(c) or a sum of products of the form we have just indicated.

Thus,

$$x = 0 \; \vee \, . \, x = 1 \; \& \; z_1 = y_1 + 1 \; \& \; z_2 = y_2 + 1 \; \& \; y_1 \neq y_2$$
$$\& \; y_1 \neq 1$$

is of canonical form.

Finally, we note that a proposition can be put into canonical form in several ways. In particular, if in a term of the disjunction there is a factor such as $z_i = y_j$, we can put z_i in place of y_j as a variable of the second kind, by replacing y_j by z_i in all the other factors.

4. A CRITERION OF TRUTH

4. Let us consider a proposition P; let Q be an equivalent proposition in canonical form. Either Q is $0=0$, in which case P is true; or else Q is $0 \neq 0$, in which case $\sim P$ is true. In the third case, we shall show that the variables of P can be replaced by numerals so that Q is true.

In fact, Q is a disjunction; let us consider one of its terms. It is this term that we shall make true. First, we equate the variables which are of the first kind (3.12) in this term to the numerals to which they are set equal in the term. Now let us consider the variables of the second kind

$y_1, y_2, ..., y_p$. First for y_1 we take a value such that all the inequalities $y_1 \neq a_i$ are true, where a_i is a number [rather, numeral]. Then we pick y_2 such that all the inequalities containing y_2 alone, or both y_2 and y_1, are true when y_1 is replaced by its value; this is possible from 1.37. In this way we pick numerals for the y_i step-by-step according to the following law: having chosen $y_1, y_2, ..., y_i$, we pick y_{i+1} in such a way that all the inequalities containing either y_{i+1} alone or both y_{i+1} and y_j (where j is less than $i+1$) are true.

Finally, we choose the variables of the third kind in such a way that the equalities which relate them to those of the second kind are true.

It is then obvious that when all variables are replaced in the indicated manner, Q becomes true (according to the criterion of 2.1).

4.1. We thus come to the conclusion that either $\sim P$ can be proved or else the variables of P can be replaced in such a way that P becomes true. By replacing P by $\sim P$ [in this statement], *we have thus indicated a procedure permitting us, given a proposition, either to prove that it is true or else to replace its variables by numerals that make it false.*

In the second case, because of the consistency of our theory, the proposition cannot be true;[5] hence this criterion permits us to recognize whether a proposition is true.

4.11. We could also say, in summary, that a proposition is true when we know that every system of numerals put in place of its variables makes it true.

4.12. In particular, let us consider the proposition $P \equiv Q$. The above method then allows us either to prove the equivalence of P and Q or else to replace the variables in them by numerals which make one proposition true and the other false.

5. INTRODUCTION OF APPARENT VARIABLES

5. We now consider another mathematical theory, in which apparent

---

[5] [[If P is provable in Th. 1, so is every proposition obtained from P by replacing its variables by numerals (this is proved by induction on the proof of P). Hence, if P is provable and P can be made false by a suitable such replacement, we then have a formal contradiction in Th. 1.]]

variables can be used, and which has the following hypotheses:

(1) $x = x$
(2) $x = y . \supset . y = x$
(3) $x = y \ \& \ y = z . \supset . x = z$
(4) $x = y . \equiv . x + 1 = y + 1$
(5) $x + 1 \neq 0$
(6) $x \neq x + a$ (for every numeral $a \ [\![a \neq 0]\!]$).

We call this theory Theory 2 (abbreviated Th. 2).

We note that it is quite obvious, now that apparent variables are used, that all the hypotheses of the previous theory are true in the new one (because of the identity $\vdash : (x) . \Phi(x) . \supset . \Phi(y)$).[6]

Hence this theory differs from the previous one only in the introduction of apparent variables.

The consistency of this theory and of the one which we shall consider further on was proved for the first time by von Neumann, who used a very complicated method (*1927*). A previous attempt by Ackermann (*1924*) was criticized by von Neumann, who showed the errors and lacunae in it. Finally, Hilbert (*1927*) and Bernays (*1927*) indicated the outlines of another method, but without completing the proof. In the following we shall explain a new method that, aside from its relative simplicity, also enables us to prove more than just consistency.

With every proposition of Th. 2 we shall associate certain propositions of Th. 1, which we call its *expansions* [*réduites*], and which have the property of all being equivalent to each other in Th. 1. We say that a proposition is an expansion of P if it can be derived from P by the procedure we shall indicate, or if it is equivalent in Th. 1 to a proposition derived from P in this way.

5.1. These expansions are defined by recursion on the construction of P, in the second method of Chap. 2, 6.2. At the same time we shall show their equivalence, where the second rule of generalization is modified as stated in Chap. 3, 1.4.

---

[6] [[Th. 2 has as axioms not all the substitution instances of (1)–(6), but the propositions $x = x$, etc., themselves, where x is a variable. From an axiom, we can deduce its universal closure by the first rule of generalization, and then, using the above identity, any instance of the axiom. Hence all axioms of Th. 1 are provable in Th. 2.]]

(a) An expansion of an atomic proposition is the atomic proposition itself.

(b) If an expansion of P is p, then an expansion of $\sim P$ is $\sim p$.

(c) If expansions of P and Q are p and q, respectively, then an expansion of $P \vee Q$ is $p \vee q$.

We observe that in each of these operations we obtain for $\sim P$ and for $P \vee Q$ only expansions which are equivalent to each other, if this was the case for all the expansions of P and Q.

5.11. We must now define an expansion of $(\exists x).\Phi(xy_1y_2...y_n)$ on the basis of an expansion of $\Phi(xy_1y_2...y_n)$.

For this, consider an expansion of the latter proposition put into [canonical] disjunctive normal form. To obtain the expansion of the former proposition, we shall replace each term of the disjunction of this normal form by another term. Hence let us consider a term of this disjunction, and within this term the simple propositions containing x. We will operate on this term in a way that corresponds to the elimination of x from a system of equalities and inequalities in ordinary algebra.

(a) If x is of the first or third kind, we omit the simple propositions in which it occurs. If, after this operation has been carried out everywhere, no more simple propositions remain, we replace the term under consideration by $0=0$. We note that this operation amounts to replacing x by the value to which it is equal in the term under consideration.

(b) If x is of the second kind:

(α) Either there is an equality such as $x=y$ [rather, $y=x$] in the term under consideration, in which case this equality is eliminated and x is replaced everywhere by y. Actually, we saw that in this case we could suppose that x was not of the second kind.

(β) Or there are no equalities containing x; in this case the inequalities containing x are omitted and, after this is done, if no more simple propositions remain, the term is replaced by $0=0$.

(γ) Or all the equalities containing x are of the form $y=x+a$, where a is a numeral different from 0, in which case we consider one of these equalities in which a is smallest. Let this be $y=x+a$. Then this equality is omitted from the product, and equalities of the form $z=x+b$ are replaced by $z=y+(b-a)$, and inequalities of the forms $x\neq b$ and $z+b\neq x+c$ by $y\neq a+b$ and $z+a+b\neq y+c$, respectively. After this, all inequalities $y \neq 0$, $y \neq 1$, etc., up to $y \neq a - 1$, are added to the product.

The above definitions allow us to associate expansions to every proposition. To show that these expansions are all equivalent to each other, it remains for us to show that once we know this for all the expansions of $\Phi(x y_1 y_2 \dots y_n)$, then the same holds for all the expansions which the preceding definition allows us to associate with $(\exists x) \, \Phi(x y_1 y_2 \dots y_n)$. (We assume that x, y_1, y_2, ..., y_n are the only real variables.)

5.2. This results from the following properties. Let $\varphi(x y_1 y_2 \dots y_n)$ be an expansion of $\Phi(x y_1 y_2 \dots y_n)$, and $\psi(y_1 y_2 \dots y_n)$ an expansion of $(\exists x)$. $\Phi(x y_1 y_2 \dots y_n)$ which is derived from $\varphi(x y_1 y_2 \dots y_n)$ by means of the preceding definition.

1. *If a system of numerals* b, $a_1, a_2, \dots, a_n$, *put in the place of* x, y_1, $y_2, \dots, y_n$ *makes* $\varphi(x y_1 y_2 \dots y_n)$ *true,*[7] *then the system* $a_1, \dots, a_n$ *makes* $\psi(y_1 y_2 \dots y_n)$ *true.*

2. *We can furnish a procedure which allows us, given a system of numerals* $a_1, a_2, \dots, a_n$ *that makes* $\psi(y_1 y_2 \dots y_n)$ *true, to find a numeral* b *such that the system of numerals* b, $a_1, a_2, \dots, a_n$ *makes* $\varphi(x y_1 y_2 \dots y_n)$ *true.*

Indeed, let us assume that b, $a_1, \dots, a_n$ makes $\varphi(x y_1 y_2 \dots y_n)$ true. This system thus makes true one of the terms of the disjunction which forms $\varphi(x y_1 \dots y_n)$ (for if it gave the logical value "false" to all terms of the disjunction, then the whole disjunction would be false; see 2.1). We can immediately see that it $[\![a_1, a_2, \dots, a_n]\!]$ makes the corresponding term of $\psi(y_1 y_2 \dots y_n)$ true. (To verify this, we consider separately each of cases (a), (b_α), (b_β), and (b_γ).)

Conversely, if $a_1, a_2, \dots, a_n$ makes $\psi(y_1 y_2 \dots y_n)$ true, it makes true a term of the disjunction which forms $\psi(y_1 y_2 \dots y_n)$. In each of the cases (a), (b_α), (b_β) the numeral b can easily be determined by either the equalities or the inequalities. In case (b_γ), it is necessary to subtract a numeral a from one of the numerals $a_1, a_2, \dots, a_n$ in order to find b; this is possible because the inequalities $x \neq 0$, $x \neq 1$, ..., $x \neq a - 1$ appear in this term.

Now let us suppose that from two equivalent expansions φ_1 and φ_2 of $\Phi(x y_1 y_2 \dots y_n)$, we have derived two expansions ψ_1 and ψ_2 of $(\exists x)$. $\Phi(x y_1 y_2 \dots y_n)$. If they were not equivalent we could find values $a_1, a_2, \dots,$

---

[7] For brevity, we shall then say that "the system b, $a_1, a_2, \dots, a_n$ makes $\varphi(x y_1 y_2 \dots y_n)$ true".

a_n for $y_1, y_2, \ldots, y_n$ which would make one of them true (say ψ_1) and the other one false (from 4.12). From this we could derive a system b, a_1, $a_2, \ldots, a_n$ making φ_1 true, hence φ_2 true. Then $a_1, a_2, \ldots, a_n$ would make ψ_2 true. Hence, we have arrived at a contradiction in Th. 1 (impossible, from § 2).

We have thus succeeded in associating expansions with every proposition. These expansions contain no apparent variables and are all equivalent to each other.

5.31. REMARK 1. We define the expansions of $(x).\Phi(xy_1y_2\ldots y_n)$ to be the same as those of $\sim(\exists x).\sim\Phi(xy_1y_2\ldots y_n)$ (from Chap. 2, 6.2).

If a system of numerals $a_1, a_2, \ldots, a_n$ put in the place of $y_1, y_2, \ldots, y_n$ makes this expansion false, then we can find a b such that the system b, $a_1, a_2, \ldots, a_n$ put in the place of $x, y_1, y_2, \ldots, y_n$ makes the expansions of $\Phi(xy_1y_2\ldots y_n)$ false.

For, the system $a_1, \ldots, a_n$ makes the expansions of $(\exists x).\sim\Phi(xy_1\ldots y_n)$ true; hence we can find a b such that the system b, $a_1, \ldots, a_n$ makes the expansions of $\sim\Phi(xy_1\ldots y_n)$ true, and hence the expansions of $\Phi(xy_1\ldots y_n)$ false.

5.32. REMARK 2. *If an expansion of $\Phi(xyz_1\ldots z_n)$ is $\varphi(xyz_1\ldots z_n)$, then an expansion of $\Phi(x, x+a, z_1\ldots z_n)$ is $\varphi(x, x+a, z_1\ldots z_n)$.*

We show this by recursion on the construction of Φ.

If it is true for Φ and for Ψ, then obviously it is true for $\sim\Phi$ and for $\Phi \vee \Psi$.

We show that if it is true for $\Phi(xyz_1\ldots z_n)$, whose expansion is $\varphi(xyz_1\ldots z_n)$, then it is still true for $(\exists z_1).\Phi(xyz_1\ldots z_n)$, whose expansion is $\psi(xyz_2\ldots z_n)$. If this were not the case, then $(\exists z_1).\Phi(x, x+a, z_1z_2\ldots z_n)$ would have an expansion $\omega(xz_2\ldots z_n)$ not equivalent to $\psi(x, x+a, z_2\ldots z_n)$. Hence there would be a system of numerals making one true and the other false. Let us suppose, for example, that ψ is thus made true; then we could find another numeral for z_1 making, with the preceding numerals, $\varphi(x, x+a, z_1\ldots z_n)$ true; but this is an expansion of $\Phi(x, x+a, z_1\ldots z_n)$ by hypothesis. Hence the original system of numerals must make $\omega(xz_2\ldots z_n)$ true, which yields a contradiction.

We can argue in the same way in the other case.

5.33. REMARK 3. We can verify in an analogous manner that *if an expansion of $\Phi(xy_1y_2\ldots y_n)$ is $\varphi(xy_1y_2\ldots y_n)$, then an expansion of $\Phi(ay_1y_2\ldots y_n)$ is $\varphi(ay_1y_2\ldots y_n)$ (where a is a numeral).*

6. A NECESSARY CONDITION FOR TRUTH

6. We shall now prove the

THEOREM. *If a theorem is true in Th. 2, then its expansions are true in Th. 1.*

It suffices to show that one of its expansions is true. We prove this by recursion.

(a) The expansions of the primitive propositions are these propositions themselves; and they are true in Th. 1.

(b) Let $\varphi(xy_1...y_n)$ be an expansion of $\Phi(xy_1...y_n)$, and $\psi(y_1...y_n)$ an expansion of $(x).\Phi(xy_1...y_n)$. Assume the former is true in Th. 1; we shall show that the latter is true. If it were not true, then there would be numerals $a_1, a_2, ..., a_n$ which, put in the place of the y_i, would make ψ false. Hence, we could find a numeral b such that the expansions of $\Phi(xy_1...y_n)$ would become false when $x, y_1, ..., y_n$ were replaced by $b, a_1, ..., a_n$. This is impossible from § 2.

(c) In order to apply the second rule of generalization in the form of Chap. 3, 1.4, we note that the only individuals of the theory under consideration are of the form a or $y+a$, where a is a numeral. Let t denote this individual.

Assume the expansions of $\Phi(tyz_1z_2...z_n)$ are true; we show that an expansion of $(\exists x).\Phi(xyz_1z_2...z_n)$ is true. Let $\varphi(xyz_1...z_n)$ be an expansion of $\Phi(xyz_1...z_n)$, from which the expansion of $(\exists x).\Phi(xyz_1...z_n)$ is derived.

Now, $\varphi(tyz_1...z_n)$, which is (from 5.32 and 5.33) the expansion of $\Phi(tyz_1...z_n)$, is true. Hence every system of numerals put in place of $y, z_1, ..., z_n$ makes the expansion of $(\exists x).\Phi(xyz_1...z_n)$ true, from (5.2); hence this expansion is true, from 4.11.

(d) We can see immediately that the expansions of identities of the first kind are true, from Chap. 1, 3.1, and that the expansions remain true when the rule of simplification or implication is used.

We have thus proved the theorem under consideration.[8]

6.1. From this we can easily derive the

THEOREM. *Th. 2 is consistent.*

---

[8] [[Herbrand omits the rules of passage, but it is not difficult to show that if P' is derived from P by an application of a rule of passage, then the expansions of P and P' are equivalent.]]

The expansion of $0 \neq 0$ is in fact this proposition itself, and it is false in Th. 1 (see Chap. 3, 2.1).

In the same way, we can see that *any proposition whose expansion is true in Th. 1 can be added to the hypotheses of Th. 2* [without the theory's becoming inconsistent].

7. A CRITERION OF TRUTH

We have thus found a necessary criterion for the truth of a proposition in Th. 2. Let us add the proposition

$$x = 0 . \vee . (\exists y) . x = y + 1 \tag{1}$$

to the axioms of this theory. Basically, this proposition means that we can always subtract 1 from any number different from 0. The expansion of $(\exists y).x = y + 1$ is $x \neq 0$; hence the expansion of the new axiom is true, and the theory remains consistent. Let us call this theory Theory 3 (abbreviated Th. 3).

Th. 3 differs from Th. 2. In fact, if in Th. 2 we replace the descriptive function $x + 1$ by $x + 1 + 1$, then we can see that every theorem of Th. 2 remains true in Th. 3 (for the axioms remain); but our new axiom becomes false (as can be seen by replacing x by $0 + 1$ in it).[9]

We shall show that *the criterion found above is sufficient in Th. 3.*

7.1. We note first that propositions such as

$$x = 0 . \vee . x = 1 . \vee . (\exists y) . x = y + 1 + 1$$
$$x = 0 . \vee . x = 1 . \vee . x = 1 + 1 . \vee . (\exists y) . x = y + 1 + 1 + 1$$

and, in general,

$$x = 0 . \vee . x = 1 . \vee . \cdots . \vee . x = a - 1 . \vee . (\exists y) . x = y + a$$

(where a is a numeral) are true in the new theory. $\tag{2}$

We prove this by recursion on the numeral a. Let H be the product $x \neq 0 \ \& \ x \neq 1 \ \& \ \ldots \ \& \ x \neq a - 1$, and assume that

$$\vdash : H . \supset . (\exists y) . x = y + a \tag{3}$$

[9] [[That is, Th. 2 is satisfied when the variables are interpreted as ranging over the natural numbers and the formal operation $+1$ is interpreted as the function $+2$; whereas Th. 3 is not satisfied by this interpretation, since there is no natural number y such that $1 = y + 2$.]]

has been proved (this is the same as (2)). But we have

$$\vdash : x \neq a \;\&\; x = y + a \,.\, \supset \,.\, y \neq 0$$

(which is the same as

$$\vdash : y = 0 \;\&\; x = y + a \,.\, \supset \,.\, x = a,$$

which results from 1.35); from which, by taking (1) and an identity of the first kind into account, we obtain

$$\vdash : x \neq a \;\&\; x = y + a \,.\, \supset \,.\, (\exists z) \,.\, y = z + 1 \;\&\; x = y + a \,;$$

and from this,

$$\vdash : x \neq a \;\&\; x = y + a \,.\, \supset \,.\, (\exists z) \,.\, x = z + a + 1,$$

as can easily be deduced from 1.35 and Chap. 2, 3.2.[10]
Hence,

$$\vdash : x \neq a \,.\&\,.\, (\exists y) \,.\, x = y + a :\supset\,.\, (\exists z) \,.\, x = z + a + 1 \qquad (4)$$

from the first rule of generalization. (3) and (4) then yield

$$\vdash : H \;\&\; x \neq a \,.\, \supset \,.\, (\exists z) \,.\, x = z + a + 1$$

in virtue of an identity of the first kind; and this is the desired result.

7.2. To prove our assertion, it suffices to prove the following theorem.

THEOREM. *In the new theory, every proposition is equivalent to all its expansions.*

This is proved by recursion on the construction of the proposition.

If the theorem is true for P and for Q, then it obviously is also for $\sim P$ and $P \vee Q$.

Let us assume it true for $\Phi(xy_1y_2\ldots y_n)$ and prove it for $(\exists x).\Phi(xy_1y_2\ldots y_n)$. Let $\varphi(xy_1\ldots y_n)$ be an expansion of $\Phi(xy_1\ldots y_n)$, assumed to be equivalent to Φ. From this we can deduce $(\exists x).\varphi(xy_1\ldots y_n). \equiv .(\exists x).\Phi(xy_1\ldots y_n)$ (Chap. 2, 4.2); hence the expansions of $(\exists x).\varphi(xy_1y_2\ldots y_n)$ and of $(\exists x).\Phi(xy_1y_2\ldots y_n)$ are the same.

To derive the expansion of $(\exists x).\Phi(xy_1\ldots y_n)$ we follow the construction

---

[10] [[We need only the amended version of Chap. 2, 3.2 (see footnote 6, p. 78 above).]]

of § 3; we put φ into disjunctive normal form. Because of the easily-proven identity

$$\vdash:(\exists x).A_1x \lor A_2x \lor \cdots \lor A_nx. \equiv .(\exists x)A_1x$$
$$\lor (\exists x)A_2x \lor \cdots \lor (\exists x) A_nx,$$

it suffices to show that for any product $Pxy_1...y_n$ of the canonical form of 3.13 the new product derived from it by the operations of 5.11 is equivalent to $(\exists x).Pxy_1...y_n$.

We decompose the product P into two others, of which one is the product of the simple propositions containing x; hence P becomes $Qxy_1...y_n$ & $Ry_1...y_n$. Then $(\exists x).Pxy_1...y_n$ becomes equivalent to $(\exists x).$ $Qxy_1...y_n .\& Ry_1...y_n$.

We again consider the different cases of 5.11:

(a) if x is of the first kind, Q is of the form $x=a$. If x is of the third kind, Q is of the form $x=y+a$. The desired result then follows from

$$\vdash:(\exists x).x = z$$

(which results from $\vdash.z=z$, the first axiom of § 5, by the second rule of generalization).

(b) If x is of the second kind, in cases (α) and (β) of 5.11 the result is obvious. Case (γ) remains: here, after the transformations which keep P equivalent to itself and in which Q takes the form $y=x+a$, where a is different from 0, we replace Q by

$$y \neq 0 \& y \neq 1 \& \cdots \& y \neq a - 1$$

to obtain the expansion.

We must show

$$\vdash:(\exists x).y = x + a. \equiv .y \neq 0 \& y \neq 1 \& \cdots \& y \neq a - 1.$$

But this results from formula (2) of 7.1 and from

$$\vdash.x + a \neq 0, \qquad \vdash.x + a \neq 1,..., \qquad \vdash.x + a \neq a - 1$$

which are proved immediately from $x+1 \neq 0$, which is the fourth axiom of § 5.

7.2. Hence, these arguments show us that we have in Th. 3 a necessary and sufficient criterion for the truth of a proposition. Given a proposition without real variables, there corresponds to it an expansion without any variables, hence one which is true or whose negation is true, from 2.1. Hence, in summary (using the definitions of Chap. 3, 2.2):

Th. 3 is consistent, completely determined, and decidable.

Our method also yields a supplementary result: if

$$\vdash:(\exists x).\Phi(xy_1y_2\ldots y_n)$$

and if $\varphi(xy_1\ldots y_n)$ is the expansion of $\Phi(xy_1\ldots y_n)$, then from $y_1, y_2, \ldots, y_n$ we can calculate the x's which make $\Phi(xy_1\ldots y_n)$ true. It suffices to review the construction of the expansion of $(\exists x).\Phi(xy_1\ldots y_n)$ to see that, as a system of numerals replacing $y_1, y_2, \ldots, y_n$ makes true one or another of the products of simple propositions whose disjunction constitutes the expansion of $(\exists x).\Phi(xy_1\ldots y_n)$, and consequently this expansion is always true, we can determine the numerals which, if they replace x, make $\varphi(xy_1y_2\ldots y_n)$ true. (We do this by operations of the following form: either taking x equal to a given numeral, or to one of the numerals replacing the y_i, or to one of these numerals increased or decreased by a given numeral; or else taking x different from several of these expressions.)

Hence, in summary, in Th. 3 we can construct the numbers whose existence we can prove.

8. THE AXIOM OF MATHEMATICAL INDUCTION

8.1. We can now study the propositions obtained from

$$\Phi(0).\&.(x).\Phi(x) \supset \Phi(x+1) :\supset \Phi(y)$$

by replacing $\Phi(x)$ by any definite propositional function (possibly containing variables other than x). The collection of these propositions constitutes what is ordinarily called 'the axiom of mathematical induction'.

We note that calling this an axiom conflicts with our terminology; for proposition (1) symbolizes an infinity of axioms.

These propositions are true [[in Th. 3]]. In fact, let $\varphi(x)$ be an expansion of $\Phi(x)$. If proposition (1) were not true, then there would be numerals making its expansion false. We replace the variables of $\varphi(x)$ other than x by these numerals; $\varphi(x)$ becomes $\varphi'(x)$. Let a be the numeral which must replace y; then we can see that $\varphi'(a)$ would be false, $\varphi'(0)$ true, and the expansions of $(x).\varphi'(x) \supset \varphi'(x+1)$ would be true. (From the remark of 5.3, instead of forming the expansion of $(x).\Phi(x) \supset \Phi(x+1)$ and then replacing the other variables by determinate numerals, we can obtain the same result by replacing these variables at once by these numerals [[and then forming the expansion]].) Hence for any numeral b, as can easily be deduced from 5.2 (1), $\varphi'(b) \supset \varphi'(b+1)$ is true; in particular,

$$\varphi'(0) \supset \varphi'(1)$$
$$\varphi'(1) \supset \varphi'(2)$$
$$\vdots$$
$$\varphi'(a-1) \supset \varphi'(a)$$

are true. But $\varphi'(0)$ is true and $\varphi'(a)$ is false, which yields a contradiction.

8.2. Thus, we see that the axiom of mathematical induction is a consequence of the preceding ones. But conversely, from it we can deduce the following propositions:

1. $\qquad \vdash .x \neq x + a$.

Indeed, we have $\vdash .0 \neq 0 + a$ (from 1.32), and

$$\vdash :x \neq x + a . \supset . x + 1 \neq x + a + 1$$

for, from axiom (4) (§ 5)

$$\vdash :x = x + a . \equiv . x + 1 = x + a + 1 .$$

If $\Phi(x)$ is replaced by $x \neq x+a$, the axiom of mathematical induction yields the desired result.

2. $\qquad \vdash :x = 0 . \vee . (\exists y).x = y + 1$

For, $\qquad \vdash .0 = 0 . \vee . (\exists y).x = y + 1$

and $\qquad \vdash :.x = 0 . \vee . (\exists y).x = y + 1 :\supset: x = 0$
$$. \vee . (\exists y) x + 1 = y + 1 .$$

(This results from only $\vdash .(\exists y).x+1=y+1$, which is a consequence of $x+1=x+1$ and the second rule of generalization.)[11]

---

[11] [[This should be $\vdash :0 = 0.\vee.(\exists y).0 = y+1$ and $\vdash :.x = 0 .\vee. (\exists y).x = y+1 :\supset:$ $x + 1 = 0 .\vee. (\exists y).x + 1 = y+1$; for from these and a suitable induction axiom we can conclude $\vdash :x = 0 .\vee. (\exists y)x = y+1.$]]

8.3. We thus see that Th. 3 can be based on the following axioms:

$$x = x$$
$$x = y . \supset . y = x$$
$$x = y \,\&\, y = z . \supset . x = z$$
$$x + 1 = y + 1 . \equiv . x = y$$
$$x + 1 \neq 0$$

and the axioms derivable from

$$\Phi(0) .\&. (x) . \Phi(x) \supset \Phi(x+1) : \supset . \Phi(y)$$

by replacing $\Phi(x)$ by any propositional function.

These are somewhat like Peano's axioms for arithmetic.

We note that we could have based Th. 1 on the axioms derivable from the first five (of 1.2) by substitution and on the rule

If $\vdash \Phi(0)$ and $\vdash .(x).\Phi(x) \supset \Phi(x+1)$, then $\vdash .\Phi(y)$.

The proofs would remain the same, but then we would not have put into evidence the remarkable fact that in Th. 3 (and, as can easily be seen, in Th. 1), the 'axiom of mathematical induction' is a consequence of a certain number of its particular cases.

8.4. Von Neumann, in the article cited above (*1927*) proved that when the consistency of the first five of the above axioms has been proved, the consistency of the axioms derived from (1) can be deduced immediately. The method he used is at bottom the following:

In any definite proof, proposition (1) is used for only a finite number of functions $\Phi(x)$. Let these be $\Phi_1(x), \Phi_2(x), ..., \Phi_n(x)$. We can verify immediately that the logical product of the propositions $(y):.\Phi_i(0) .\&. (x).\Phi_i(x) \supset \Phi_i(x+1) :\supset \Phi_i(y)$ satisfies the conditions of the theorem of Chap. 3, 3.3, upon seeing that

$$\vdash :. \Phi_i(0) .\&. (x). \Phi_i(x) \supset \Phi_i(x + 1) : \supset . \Phi_i(0)$$
$$\vdash :: \Phi_i(0) .\&. (x). \Phi_i(x) \supset \Phi_i(x + 1) : \supset . \Phi_i(y) .: \supset :. \Phi_i(0)$$
$$.\&. (x). \Phi_i(x) \supset \Phi_i(x + 1) : \supset . \Phi_i(y + 1)$$

(these are identities which can easily be proved).[12]

8.5. To arrive at a theory equivalent to classical arithmetic, it is yet necessary to introduce definitions by recursion. To do this, we allow

[12] [[See Note C, p. 132 below.]]

ourselves to adjoin to the theory a certain number of times new descriptive functions of one or several arguments. Each time we do this with axioms of the following form: let $f(x, y_1, y_2, ..., y_n)$ be the descriptive function introduced; suppose that in the theory to which $f(x, y_1, y_2, ..., y_n)$ is added we have

$$\vdash: . (\exists z)(x): x = z . \equiv . \Phi(xy_1 ... y_n)$$
$$\vdash: . (\exists z)(x): x = z . \equiv . \Psi(x'xy_1 ... y_n),$$

with definite propositional functions Φ and Ψ. Then we add the axioms

$$\vdash . \Phi[f(0, y_1, y_2, ..., y_n), y_1, y_2, ..., y_n]$$
$$\vdash . \Psi[f(x, y_1, ..., y_n), f(x+1, y_1, y_2, ..., y_n), y_1, y_2, ..., y_n]$$
$$\vdash . x = x' \ \& \ y_1 = y_1' \ \& \ y_2 = y_2' \ \& \ ... \ \& \ y_n = y_n'$$
$$. \supset . f(x, y_1, y_2, ..., y_n) = f(x', y_1', ..., y_n').$$

New axioms are introduced for each of these extensions; these result from the axiom of mathematical induction when propositional functions $\Phi(x)$ containing the new descriptive functions are used.

The consistency of this new extension has not yet been proved. (Hilbert has indicated that he possesses a proof of it, but he has never published it.) We shall prove it in the following chapter only under certain conditions which we shall indicate there [[6.8, p. 182]].

8.6. The method used in this chapter is applicable to other cases. It always furnishes the decidability of the theory under consideration, as well as its consistency (Chap. 3, 2.1). It seems to us that its principle can be applied in all theories for which we have a method of recognizing the truth of propositions (the fact must then be noted that this method yields the decidability of a theory only under the condition that the theory is consistent). The fact that we have dealt with hypotheses without apparent variables is secondary (we can always suppose that this is the case; see Chap. 5 [[6.7]]). On the other hand, the use of definite individuals, here the numerals, to carry out the proofs is essential; but one could always construct similar individuals in any mathematical theory, if necessary, by introducing constants and using descriptive functions.

We have verified that this method permits us to prove the consistency of a theory slightly more general than that considered in this chapter, with two propositional functions $x = y$ and $x < y$, and two descriptive functions $x + 1$ and $x - 1$, with the axioms which are easily imagined to lead to a theory translating the arithmetic of positive and negative integers. It seems probable to us that this would permit us equally to arrive at the consistency of the theory of real fields and of 'real closed' fields;[13] but the methods of the next chapter lead us to that goal more easily.

NOTE C

(footnote 12, p. 130 above)

Let T be the theory whose axioms are the universal closures of the five axioms of 8.3. Herbrand wishes to use the notion of incomplete description (Chap. 3, 3.3, p. 108 above) to prove that if T is consistent, then so is the theory obtained from T by adding any finite conjunction of induction axioms $\Phi(0)$ &. (x) . $\Phi(x) \supset \Phi(x+1) :\supset \Phi(y)$. Indeed, if $A(y)$ is such a conjunction, it is an incomplete description of y; for $A(0)$ and $A(y) \supset A(y+1)$ are provable in T, so for any constant c, $A(c)$ is provable in T. Furthermore, the relativizations to $A(y)$ (in the sense of Chap. 3, 3.1) of the axioms of T are provable in T, as can easily be seen. However, to prove the desired relative consistency theorem, Herbrand needs Theorem 3.3 of Chap. 3, which, as was noted in footnote 7, p. 110 above, is false if $A(y)$ contains restricted variables (as it does here). For example, let $A(y)$ be $\Phi(0)$ &. (x). $\Phi(x) \supset \Phi(x+1) :\supset \Phi(y)$, where $\Phi(x)$ is $x=0 .\vee. (\exists z)$. $x = z + 1$. Then T is satisfied by interpreting variables as ranging over natural numbers, and interpreting the formal operation $+1$ as $+2$, yet the relativization of $(y) A(y)$ to $A(y)$ is false under this interpretation.

The procedure of *von Neumann 1927* that Herbrand cites is not, however, fallacious. We shall sketch it briefly, using a notation quite different from von Neumann's. Von Neumann's basic theory includes, in addition to the axioms of 8.3, the axiom schema of what Herbrand calls the "simplest set theory" (p. 106 above), that is, a comprehension axiom schema

$$(\exists \alpha) (x) (x \in \alpha \equiv \Phi(x)),$$

where Φ may be replaced by any proposition not containing α. Let $A(y)$ be the second order proposition

$$(\alpha) :. 0 \in \alpha .\&. (x). x \in \alpha \supset (x+1) \in \alpha :\supset. y \in \alpha.$$

Take $A(y)$ as an incomplete description, and define the relativization of a proposition to $A(y)$ as Herbrand does (p. 109 above) with the following addition: if the relativization of $\Phi(\alpha)$ is $\varphi(\alpha)$, and α is a variable of the second type, then the relativization of

---

[13] 'Reell abgeschlossen'; cf. *Artin and Schreier 1926*. [[The method of 'elimination of quantifiers' was extended to real closed fields by Tarski; see his *1948* and *1951*, p. 54.]]

$(\exists \alpha) \, \Phi(\alpha)$ is $(\exists \alpha) \, \varphi(\alpha)$. Now the relativization of $(y).A(y)$ to $A(y)$ is

$$(y)::.A(y) \supset :: (\alpha):.0 \in \alpha \,.\&: (x):A(x) \supset . \, x \in \alpha \supset (x+1) \in \alpha :\supset. \, y \in \alpha,$$

which, since $A(0)$ and $A(y) \supset A(y+1)$ are provable, is equivalent to

$$(y)::A(y) \supset (\alpha):.A(0) \,\& \, 0 \in \alpha \,.\&: (x):A(x) \,\& \, x \in \alpha \,.\supset. \, A(x+1)$$
$$\&\,(x+1) \in \alpha :\supset. \, A(y) \,\& \, y \in \alpha.$$

This last proposition is easily proved, using the comprehension axiom.

Thus, this allows a relative consistency proof, for the relativization to $A(y)$ of any comprehension axiom is provable in the original theory, so Herbrand's Theorem 3.3 of Chap. 3 does hold. Von Neumann, however, does not explicitly formulate this procedure as a consistency proof; after constructing $A(y)$ he says merely that it furnishes us with "a complete number concept, which possesses not only all properties of Z [[the natural numbers as defined by the five axioms of T]], but also the property of mathematical induction, which Z lacks" (*von Neumann 1927*, p. 39). It is interesting to note that von Neumann later used the relativization technique to prove the consistency of the axiom of foundation with the axioms of Zermelo-Fraenkel set theory (*1929*).

CHAPTER 5

THE PROPERTIES OF TRUE PROPOSITIONS

1. THOROUGH STUDY OF THE RULES OF PASSAGE

1. Throughout the present chapter we shall work with the theory of Chap. 3, 1.4, which we obtained from the theory of Chap. 2 by adding descriptive functions.[1] As we pointed out in Chap. 3, nearly all the results of Chap. 2 continue to hold for this extended theory. For the sake of

---

[1] [[Throughout Chap. 5, Herbrand flouts the rules stated in Chaps. 1 and 2 for the formation of propositions, in particular regarding the use of dots. Hence, in the interest of clarity, the translators have modified the symbolism in this chapter somewhat: arguments of a propositional function are now always separated by commas (thus, we write $\Phi(x_1,...,x_n)$ instead of $\Phi(x_1...x_n)$) and parentheses and brackets are used instead of dots for the punctuation of propositions. (Readers who wish to read this chapter without having read Chaps. 2 and 3 should see p. 44 above for a short exposition of the notation, and should note in particular that when Herbrand says a proposition is true, he means it is provable in his formulation of quantification theory.)]]

simplicity we assume – and this will not change anything essential – that we have variables of one type only.

In the present section we shall study the various forms that a proposition can take when the rules of passage are applied to it. Not all the results that we shall obtain will be used in the rest of the present chapter, but in deriving them we shall have an opportunity to introduce notions that we shall need in § 2.

We recall the theorem of Chap. 2, 3.101, which states that by applying the rules of passage we can find, for any given proposition P, a certain proposition ⟦in prenex form⟧ equivalent to P and said to be *tied* to P. We refer the reader to the same place for the definition of *proposition in prenex form*.

To avoid ambiguities we shall assume throughout the present chapter that no two quantifiers contain the same letter.

1.1. A sequence of quantifiers will be called a *type*.[2] Two types will be said to be *similar* if they differ only in the variables that they contain; thus

$$+ x_1, - x_2, + x_3$$

and

$$+ y_1, - y_2, + y_3$$

are similar types.

1.11. The *type of a proposition P* will be the type formed by the quantifiers that occur at the beginning of the prenex proposition tied to P.

We shall now investigate in more detail ⟦than in Chap. 2⟧ what are the types of those prenex propositions obtained from a given proposition P by means of the rules of passage.[3] These types will be called the *types attached* ⟦*attachés*⟧ to P.

To say that $\pm x_1, \pm x_2, ..., \pm x_n$ is a type attached to a proposition P is, as we see, to say that we can, by means of the rules of passage, first put P into the form $(\pm x_1) P_1(x_1)$, then put $P_1(x_2)$ into the form $(\pm x_2) P_2(x_2)$, and so forth; this amounts to saying that we can pull the quantifiers

$$(\pm x_1), (\pm x_2), ..., (\pm x_n)$$

out of the proposition one after another.

---

[2] ⟦The word 'type' here is used in a totally different sense from in the first paragraph of this chapter and in 6.6, where it means a sort in a many-sorted theory (Chap. 3, 1.11).⟧

[3] ⟦This question is answered in 1.5.⟧

1.12. Let us recall the following remark (proved in Chap. 2, 3.12):

LEMMA 1. *There exist types attached to the proposition* $\Phi[(\pm x) A(x)]$ *that have* $(\pm x)$ *as their leftmost quantifier; here* $\Phi(p)$ *is a propositional function of the first kind in p and may, moreover, contain atomic propositions other than p.*

1.2. Now, using [[just]] the rules of passage, we shall decrease the scope of x as much as we can. To decrease this scope step by step, we make use of the following two consequences of the rules of passage:

(1) If the scope of x is $\sim\Phi(x)$, we can decrease this scope so that it becomes $\Phi(x)$;

(2) If the scope of x is $\Phi(x) \vee p$ or $p \vee \Phi(x)$, we can decrease this scope so that it becomes $\Phi(x)$, provided p does not contain x.

Thus we shall finally bring the proposition into a form in which the scope of x will be an atomic proposition, or a proposition of the form $\Phi(x) \vee \Psi(x)$, where $\Phi(x)$ and $\Psi(x)$ actually contain x, [[or a proposition of the form $(\pm y) \Phi(y)$]].

We now start from a given proposition P; we consider the rightmost quantifier and, using (1) and (2), reduce its scope as much as possible. We thus obtain its *minimal scope*. Once this is done, we perform the same operation on the second quantifier, counted from the right; we proceed thus until the scope of the leftmost quantifier has been minimized. The proposition has then taken what we shall call its *canonical form*, which is characterized by the fact that the scopes of all its variables are minimal [[with respect to the rules of passage]].

For example, the canonical form of

$$(x)(\exists y)(z)\{[\Phi(x) \& \Psi(x, y)] \vee \Phi(z)\},$$

is

$$(x)[\Phi(x) \& (\exists y) \Psi(x, y)] \vee (z) \Phi(z);$$

the minimal scope of z is $\Phi(z)$, that of y is $\Psi(x, y)$, and that of x is

$$\Phi(x) \& (\exists y) \Psi(x, y). [4]$$

Merely by considering each rule of passage we see that, if a proposition results from another by the rules of passage, the two propositions have the same canonical form.

[4] [[In this example it must be assumed that $\Phi(x)$ and $\Psi(x)$ are such that no further application of (1) and (2) is possible; moreover, contrary to Herbrand's system, here & is taken as primitive.]]

1.3. It is quite obvious that, if we consider the scopes of two different variables, either these scopes are disjoint or one scope is included in the other. A variable x will be *dominant* in a proposition P if ⟦in the canonical form of P⟧ the scope of x is not included in the scope of any other variable.

For example, x and z are dominant in the proposition given above.

LEMMA 2. *If $x_1, x_2, ..., x_n$ are the dominant variables of a given proposition and $\Phi_1(x_1), \Phi_2(x_2), ..., \Phi_n(x_n)$ are their respective minimal scopes, the proposition, once in canonical form, can be written $A[(\pm x_1) \Phi_1(x_1), (\pm x_2) \Phi_2(x_2), ..., (\pm x_n) \Phi_n(x_n)]$, where $A(p_1, p_2, ..., p_n)$ is a propositional function of the first kind.*

We observe, incidentally, that if this lemma is true we can give a similar form to the $\Phi_i(x_i)$, and so on.

The lemma follows immediately from the fact that, except for the scopes of the dominant variables ⟦and their quantifiers⟧, a proposition in canonical form contains no signs other than $\sim$ and $\vee$. Since, as we just saw, the scopes of the x_i do not overlap, the proposition is a propositional function of these scopes ⟦together with their quantifiers⟧, hence cannot, relative to these scopes, be a propositional function of the second kind.

1.4. We can now define what we shall call the *scheme* ⟦*schème*⟧ of a proposition. It will be an array, formed of signed letters ⟦that is, each letter is preceded by the sign $+$ or $-$⟧ and braces, that will be defined by recursion on the number of apparent variables of the proposition.

First, the scheme of an elementary proposition is taken to be empty.

Then, the scheme of a ⟦nonelementary⟧ proposition P – which, as we just saw, can be put into the ⟦canonical⟧ form

$$A[(\pm x_1) \Phi_1(x_1), (\pm x_2) \Phi_2(x_2), ..., (\pm x_n) \Phi_n(x_n)],$$

where x_i is the dominant variable of $\Phi_i(x_i)$ – is to be obtained from the schemes of the propositions $\Phi_1(x_1), \Phi_2(x_2), ..., \Phi_n(x_n)$ thus: if the schemes of these propositions are respectively the arrays $S_1, S_2, ..., S_n$, the scheme of P will be

$$\pm x_1 \{S_1$$
$$\pm x_2 \{S_2$$
$$\cdots\cdots\cdots$$
$$\pm x_n \{S_n.$$

In this list the vertical ordering is of no consequence. The vari-

ables $x_1, x_2, ..., x_n$ will be called the *dominant variables of the scheme.*
For example, the scheme of the proposition already considered in 1.2 is

$$+ x \{- y$$
$$+ z.$$

That of

$$(\exists x)[(y)\, \Phi(x, y) \lor (z)\, \Phi(x, z)] \lor (x')(y')\, \Phi(x', y')$$

⟦if this proposition is assumed to be in canonical form⟧ is

$$- x \begin{cases} + y \\ + z \end{cases}$$
$$+ x' \{+ y'.$$

We shall agree to omit the brace when it separates two successive
variables on the same line, as in the first scheme, which we now write

$$+ x \quad - y$$
$$+ z.$$

Hence we see that the scheme of a proposition is an array formed of
signed letters; the letters are the apparent variables of the proposition,
the sign that goes with each of them tells us whether it is general or
restricted,[5] and each letter may be followed by a ⟦signed⟧ letter or by a
brace joining several ⟦signed⟧ letters. ⟦Even if no proposition is given,⟧
such an array will, in what follows, still be called a *scheme.*[6]

A *line* of a scheme will be a sequence of signed letters of the scheme
such that ⟦the first letter of the sequence is a dominant variable of the
scheme and⟧ each letter ⟦in the sequence after the first⟧ occurs in the

[5] ⟦⟦The convention that Herbrand makes here clearly conflicts with the one that he
made previously (Chap. 2, 1.5), namely, that '$(+x)$' stands for '(x)', and '$(-x)$' for
'$(\exists x)$'. Herbrand observes his new convention in §§ 1 and 2 of Chap. 5, then occasionally
reverts to his previous convention in subsequent sections.⟧⟧

[6] It is convenient to agree that in a scheme no two letters shall ever be identical.

⟦⟦When no proposition is given, Herbrand still calls the letters in the scheme that
are not behind any brace the *dominant* variables of the scheme; moreover, he refers
to the letters in the scheme that are preceded by '$+$' as the *general* variables of the
scheme and to those that are preceded by '$-$' as the *restricted* variables of the scheme.
This generalized notion of scheme becomes important in § 2.

In *1931*. p. 248 below, Herbrand points out that his notion of scheme is related to
Ackermann's 'Stammbaum' (*1928*, p. 646) and also to the notion of free group.⟧⟧

scheme immediately on the right of the letter that precedes it in the sequence or immediately on the right of the brace affixed to that letter. Hence every line of a scheme can be regarded as a type, and this type will be said to be the *type of the line* (see 1.1).

Thus the lines of the scheme of the proposition considered above are

$$-x \quad +y,$$
$$-x \quad +z,$$

and

$$+x' \quad +y'.$$

In particular, a type is a scheme that has a single line.

1.41. We see immediately that, according to Lemma 2 and the definition of the scheme [[of a proposition]], a variable y comes after a variable x in a line of the scheme [[of a proposition P]] if and only if [[in P]] the minimal scope of y is included in the minimal scope of x.

We shall say that in a proposition P a variable x *dominates* a variable y if and only if the minimal scope of y is included in the minimal scope of x. We shall also say that in a proposition P a variable x is *superior to* a variable y if the scope of y is included in the scope of x (hence x dominates y if and only if, when the proposition P is in canonical form (1.2), x is superior to y).

We readily see that, if x dominates y, y cannot be superior to x.

1.42. A type is said to be *deduced* from a scheme if the variables of the type are all the letters of the scheme and, whenever in some line of the scheme one letter precedes another, the first letter also precedes the second in the type. Thus, in the example considered above, we obtain a type deduced from the scheme by writing on one line the five signs $-x$, $+y$, $+z$, $+x'$, and $+y'$ in such a way that x' precedes y' and x precedes y and z (there are twenty such permutations).

Given any type deduced from the scheme [[of a proposition P]], we see that, if x dominates y [[in P]], then x precedes y in the type.

1.43. Before we proceed to the proof of the theorem that concludes the present section, let us observe that, given a proposition P and the proposition P' that we obtain from P by deleting the quantifier of a dominant variable, we obtain the scheme of P' by deleting the variable [[and the brace that immediately follows it, if any]] from the scheme of

P; this can be readily seen from the recursive definition of scheme and from Lemma 2.

1.5. THEOREM. *The types attached to a proposition are the types deduced from the scheme of that proposition.*

This theorem, which answers the question raised at the beginning of the present section, is proved as follows.

(1) *Any type deduced from the scheme is a type attached to the proposition.*

For, to obtain a type deduced from the scheme, we can proceed thus: we delete a dominant variable [[and the brace affixed to it, if any]] from the scheme [[and write the variable somewhere]]; from the new scheme so obtained we delete a variable that is dominant in this new scheme and write it to the right of the variable first considered; we continue in this manner until we have exhausted all the variables of the original scheme. It follows from Remark 1.43 and Lemma 1 (1.12) that we can exhaust in this fashion all the [[apparent]] variables of the proposition in question, hence that the variables that we have thus successively selected form a type attached to the proposition.

(2) *Any type attached to the proposition is a type deduced from the scheme.*

To see this it suffices to observe that, if x is superior to y in a proposition, y cannot dominate x and to remember the characteristic property (1.42) of a type deduced from the scheme.

2. PROPERTY A

2. In the present section we shall study the most general properties that are sufficient for a proposition to be true; in subsequent sections we shall see that these properties are also necessary.

For the sake of simplicity we assume, first, that *there are no descriptive functions in the propositions under investigation.*[7]

2.1. We begin by defining the notion of *normal identity.* Let P be a proposition with which, by means of the rules of passage, we have associated some prenex form,

$$(\pm x_1, \pm x_2, ..., \pm x_n) M (x_1, x_2, ..., x_n).$$

[7] [[The case in which the proposition contains descriptive functions is taken up in 2.4.]]

In the matrix M of this prenex form we replace each restricted variable either by a real variable of P (we can even assume that this real variable does not actually occur in P – in which case it will be said to be fictitious) or by a general variable that is superior (1.41) to the restricted variable in the prenex form (that is, a general variable whose quantifier, in the type of this prenex form, precedes that of the restricted variable considered). We shall say that the proposition P is a *normal identity* if [[for some prenex form P' of P]] at least one elementary proposition Π obtained [[from P']] in the manner just described is an identity of the first kind. We say also that such an identity is *associated with* P and that the type $\pm x_1, \pm x_2, ..., \pm x_n$ [[of P']] is a *normal* type.

For example,

$$(x)\, \Phi(x) \lor (\exists y) \sim \Phi(y)$$

is a normal identity; for we can turn it into

$$(x)(\exists y)[\Phi(x) \lor \sim \Phi(y)],$$

and, if y is replaced by x, the matrix becomes

$$\Phi(x) \lor \sim \Phi(x),$$

which is an identity.[8]

2.11. We see that to pass from a proposition P to an identity Π associated with P we must repeatedly perform the following operations [[on some prenex form of P]]:

(1) Delete a quantifier of a general variable, so that the variable becomes real;

(2) Delete a quantifier of a restricted variable and replace the restricted variable by a real variable, that is, pass from a proposition of the form $(\exists y)\, \Phi(x, y)$ to the proposition $\Phi(x, x)$.

In the example above we would first replace the [[prenex form of the]] proposition by

$$(\exists y)[\Phi(x) \lor \sim \Phi(y)]$$

and this in turn by

$$\Phi(x) \lor \sim \Phi(x).$$

We readily see that every normal identity is true: by the rules of gener-

---

[8] [[In the last formula the French text has 'y' for 'x', which is a misprint.]]

alization, in each of the two operations just described the first proposition is true provided the second proposition is true.[9]

We can always actually decide whether a proposition P is a normal identity: we take all the types attached to P and [[for each type]] consider all the propositions obtained when in the matrix of P each restricted variable y is replaced [[by some real variable or]] by some general variable that precedes y in the type; the criterion of Chap. 1, 5.21, then enables us to decide whether one of the propositions thus obtained is an identity. Thus we have to run through only a finite number of tests.

2.12. From a normal identity we obtain another normal identity (equivalent to the first, according to Chap. 2, 4.6) if, in a normal type, we permute two successive restricted quantifiers or two successive general quantifiers. We obtain other normal identities (implied by the first) if, in a normal type, we shift a restricted quantifier to the right or a general quantifier to the left.

2.13. We obtain an example of a class of normal identities when we put nonelementary propositions for the atomic propositions in those identities of the first kind in which each atomic proposition has at most one positive occurrence and at most one negative occurrence. To see this it suffices to look again at our proof in Chap. 2, § 4,[10] that the identities of the second kind thus obtained are true.

2.2. Henceforth we shall use the following notation: if $M(x_1, x_2, ..., x_n)$ is an elementary proposition (in general, the matrix of a proposition), a substitution on the x_i, that is, the replacement of $x_1, x_2, ..., x_n$ by other letters $y_1, y_2, ..., y_n$, will be denoted by a letter such as S, with or without subscripts, and the result of this substitution, namely $M(y_1, y_2, ..., y_n)$, by $M(S)$.

Let us now consider a scheme such that each of its lines is similar

---

[9] [[Thus, a proposition is a normal identity if and only if it is provable from a quantifier-free identity by the use of at most the two rules of generalization and the rules of passage.]]

[10] [[That is, the proof of Chap. 2, § 4 shows by induction that for every such identity of the second kind P, there is a type attached to P which is a normal type. Compare this proof with that of Chap. 5, 5.3, Lemma 3, p. 172 below. See also Note D, p. 188 below.]]

(1.1) to a type attached to some proposition P.[11] For each line of the scheme, let us take a similar type attached to P and correlate the kth letter of the line with the kth letter of the type. The replacement of the apparent variables of P by the corresponding letters of a line of the scheme defines a substitution; there are as many substitutions as there are lines. Let us denote these substitutions by $S_1, S_2, \ldots, S_m$; if M is the matrix of P and T is any type deduced from the scheme, the proposition

$$(T)[M(S_1) \vee M(S_2) \vee \cdots \vee M(S_m)]$$

is said to be a *proposition derived from P*. We readily see that this proposition does not [[essentially]] depend upon the particular type T selected (this, incidentally, is of no importance for what follows). The scheme is said to *generate* the derived proposition, and the proposition is said to be *derived from P* by the scheme.

For example, given the proposition

$$(\exists x)(y) M(x, y),$$

in which $M(x, y)$ is elementary, and the scheme

$$- x \begin{cases} + y \\ + z, \end{cases}$$

we obtain the derived proposition

$$(- x, + y, + z)[M(x, y) \vee M(x, z)].$$

We see quite easily that, to pass from a proposition P to a proposition derived from P, we must repeatedly perform the following operation: if $(\pm x_1, \ldots, \pm x_n) M(x_1, \ldots, x_n)$ is any prenex form of P, we go from a proposition Q of the form

$$(\pm x_1, \ldots, \pm x_r)[A(x_1, \ldots, x_r) \\ \vee (\pm x_{r+1}, \ldots, \pm x_n) M(x_1, \ldots, x_r, x_{r+1}, \ldots, x_n)]$$

---

[11] [[The scheme now being considered is not in general the scheme of P, nor need all the lines of this scheme be similar to one and the same type attached to P. See Note E, p. 190 below.]]

to a proposition Q' of the form

$$(\pm x_1, ..., \pm x_r)[A(x_1, ..., x_r)$$
$$\vee (\pm x_{r+1}, ..., \pm x_n) M(x_1, ..., x_r, x_{r+1}, ..., x_n)$$
$$\vee (\pm y_{r+1}, ..., \pm y_n) M(x_1, ..., x_r, y_{r+1}, ..., y_n)].$$

This operation enables us to pass from a proposition derived from P by a given scheme to a proposition derived from P by a new scheme that differs from the given scheme in having just one more line. Therefore, a proposition is equivalent to any proposition that is derived from it (because of the identity $(P \vee P) \equiv P$ and Chap. 2, 6.1).[12]

2.3. Let us now assume that we have found a proposition P' that is derived from P, is a normal identity, and – this further hypothesis is not essential – is such that one of the normal types (2.1) of P' is deduced (1.42) from the scheme generating P';[13] moreover, [[for that normal type]] let Π be some identity associated with P'. We shall then say that P *has property A*, that Π is *an identity associated with P*, that the scheme generating P' is *associated with P*,[14]

---

[12] [[See Notes D and E, pp. 188 and 190 below.]]

[13] [[The scheme Σ generating P' from P need not be the scheme of P'. Hence, it might not be possible to deduce from Σ all the types attached to P'; in particular, it might not be possible to deduce from Σ any normal type of P'. For example, let P be $(\exists x) (y) Fxy \supset (y') (\exists x') Fx'y'$, let P' be $(x) (\exists y) (y') (\exists x') (Fxy \supset Fx'y')$, and let Σ be

$$+x \quad -y \quad +y' \quad -x'.$$

Then

$$+y' \quad +x \quad -y \quad -x'$$

is a normal type of P', but neither this type nor any other normal type of P' can be deduced from Σ. See 1.42 above.]]

[14] [[In general, the lines of the scheme generating P' cannot all be disjoint; for consider the following proposition P:

$$(x) (y) (\exists z) \{[Fy \& (Gy \vee \sim Gz)] \vee [\sim Fy \& (Hx \vee \sim Hz)]\}.$$

P has property A, an associated scheme being

$$+x \quad +y \left\{ \begin{array}{l} -z \\ -z'. \end{array} \right.$$

But from P no normal identity can be generated by any scheme all of whose lines are disjoint.]]

and that the normal type of P' in question is *associated with* P.[15]

We see that every proposition having property A is an identity.[16] Furthermore, a normal identity has property A (the associated scheme is simply the normal type).

In the scheme ⟦associated with P⟧ let us put for each restricted variable the general or real variable by which we replaced it ⟦in P'⟧ in order to obtain Π. Then, as in 2.2, the lines of the ⟦resulting⟧ scheme determine substitutions, namely $T_1, T_2, ..., T_m$. If M is the matrix of P, we see that Π is nothing but $M(T_1) \vee M(T_2) \vee ... \vee M(T_m)$.

We observe that property A is not a property in the sense of the Introduction, for, given an arbitrary proposition P, we do not know how to decide whether P has property A. Hence, only if we can actually show that a proposition satisfies our definition shall we say that the proposition has property A. The same remark will apply to properties B and C, to be defined in the next section.

2.31. Thus, to show that a proposition has property A we must first construct an associated scheme, then deduce from it an associated type ⟦if possible, otherwise find a normal type for the derived proposition⟧, and finally specify those general ⟦and real⟧ variables by which we must replace the restricted ones in order to obtain an associated identity (this will yield what we shall call *associated equations* between restricted and general variables).

For example, let P be a proposition that can, by means of the rules of passage, take the ⟦prenex⟧ forms

$$(y)(\exists x)(z)(\exists t)\, M\,(x, y, z, t)$$

and

$$(z)(\exists t)(y)(\exists x)\, M\,(x, y, z, t).$$

---

[15] ⟦According to these definitions, a proposition P need not be in prenex form in order to have property A, but any normal identity P' generated from P by any associated scheme must be in prenex form. However, it is possible to generalize the notion of a generating scheme so that a normal identity associated with P need not be in prenex form. Such a generalization is important because of the falsity of Lemma 3.3. See below: Notes G, p. 193, and H, p. 199, and also footnote 60, p. 171.⟧

[16] ⟦See Note F, p. 192 below.⟧

Let us assume that

$$M\left(z'', y, z, y'\right) \vee M\left(y', y', z', z''\right) \vee M\left(y', y', z'', z''\right)$$

is an identity. Then P has property A, an associated scheme, as we can easily verify, being

$$+z \quad -t \quad +y \quad -x$$
$$+y' \quad -x' \begin{cases} +z' & -t' \\ +z'' & -t''. \end{cases}$$

An associated type is

$$+y', +z, -t, +y, -x', +z', +z'', -x, -t', -t'',$$

and the associated equations for that associated type are

$$t = y', x' = y', x = z'', t' = z'', \quad \text{and} \quad t'' = z''.$$

The proposition derived from P is

$$(+y', +z, -t, +y, -x', +z', +z'', -x, -t', -t'')$$
$$[M\left(x, y, z, t\right) \vee M\left(x', y', z', t'\right) \vee M\left(x', y', z'', t''\right)],$$

which is a normal identity.

2.32. REMARK 1. We can always replace an associated type by another differing only in that a given general variable has been shifted to the left (for this will not prevent us from retaining the same associated equations); this remark is the analogue of 2.12.

2.33. REMARK 2. If a proposition has property A, we can assume that immediately behind each brace in the associated scheme only restricted variables occur. For, if an isolated fragment of the scheme is

$$\pm x \begin{cases} +y \\ +y', \end{cases}$$

we can replace this fragment by

$$\pm x \quad +y.$$

This can always be done, because, according to Remark 1 (2.32), from any type associated with P we can obtain one in which y' follows y; hence we can, by deleting y' in the first type, obtain a type that is associated with P but is deduced from the second scheme, since this deletion amounts to replacing y' by y in the associated identity.[17]

2.34. REMARK 3. We have not obtained a uniform procedure that would enable us to decide whether any given proposition has property A, for in general we do not know how to find the associated scheme.

However, there is a class of propositions for which we have such a procedure, namely, the class of propositions such that the matrix of each is a disjunction of atomic propositions and of negations of atomic propositions. Using the same notation as above, in 2.2, let us assume that an identity associated with a given member P of this class is[18]

$$M(S_1) \vee \cdots \vee M(S_m).$$

It follows from Chap. 1, 5.22, that for two suitable subscripts, i and j, $M(S_i) \vee M(S_j)$ would also be an identity.[18] The two substitutions [[S_i and S_j]] would correspond to two lines of the scheme, and these lines together would form a new scheme. If the lines were $\pm x_1, ..., \pm x_\alpha$, $\pm y_1, ..., \pm y_\beta$ and $\pm x_1, ..., \pm x_\alpha, \pm z_1, ..., z_\beta$, the new scheme would be

$$\pm x_1 \cdots \pm x_a \begin{cases} \pm y_1 \cdots \pm y_\beta \\ \pm z_1 \cdots \pm z_\beta, \end{cases}$$

and clearly this scheme, too, would be associated with P.[19] But there are only finitely many such [[two-line]] schemes; hence by means of only a finite number of tests (this number can be computed quite easily as soon as the proposition P has been stated) we can decide whether P has property A.[20]

---

[17] [[Let us say that a scheme in which no general variable occurs immediately behind a brace is *reduced*. Then Remark 2 tells us that a proposition P has property A *only if* there is at least one reduced scheme that generates a normal identity from P. But, by the definition of property A, a proposition P has property A *if* there is at least one scheme generating a normal identity from P. Hence Herbrand has proved that in order to show that a proposition has property A we need consider only reduced schemes. See below: 4.3, 5.1, and footnote 57, p. 169.]]

[18] [[The French text has 'Σ' for 'S'; but this is an oversight.]]

[19] [[In the French text, the letters of the scheme are unsigned.]]

[20] [[In 6.3, Herbrand remarks that the class of propositions just considered constitutes a solvable case of the decision problem, because of the proof in § 5 below that a proposition is provable if and only if it has property A. See also Note L, p. 262 below.]]

To carry out this test efficiently one should remember that not all the lines of a scheme need be similar to one and the same type attached to the proposition P (see 5.1).

2.4. We shall now assume that the propositions being studied contain descriptive functions. We shall give the same definitions as above for the notions 'normal identity' and 'property A', the only modification being that in a normal identity we can now replace a restricted variable either by a superior general variable, or by an (actually occurring or fictitious) real variable, as before, *or* by a descriptive function whose arguments are such variables. An equation between a restricted variable and a descriptive function of superior general or real variables will still be called an associated equation (2.31).[21]

Let us try to test whether a proposition P [which may now contain descriptive functions] is a normal identity. To do this we have to decide whether the type (1.11) of at least one prenex form of P is normal. Hence let P' be any prenex form of P. In P' we shall replace each restricted variable by a superior general variable, by an (actually occurring or fictitious) real variable, or by a function of such variables; [for at least one replacement] the proposition Π thus obtained must [if the type of P' is normal] turn out to be an identity of the first kind. We consider all individuals (variables and descriptive functions) that in P' are arguments of propositional functions. In Π, because of the associated equations, some of these arguments become identical (hence any proposition that is obtained from P' by the consideration of other equations, but is such that the same arguments turn out to be identical, is also an identity of the first kind). Thus we must find those [associated] equations between arguments that turn P' into an identity of the first kind. There are only a finite and determinate number of equations between individuals. We obtain the associated equations by first equating restricted variables to

---

[21][[In a given occurrence of a descriptive function $f(z_1, z_2, ..., z_k)$ in a proposition P, each of the variables $z_1, z_2, ..., z_k$ may be real or apparent, and, if apparent, general or restricted. When, in trying to obtain a normal identity, we replace a restricted variable y by the descriptive function $f(x_1, x_2, ..., x_k)$, the variables $x_1, x_2, ..., x_k$ must be general variables that are superior to y in P or (possibly fictitious) real variables of P, no matter what the variables $z_1, z_2, ..., z_k$ are in the occurrences of $f(z_1, z_2, ..., z_k)$ in P.]]

general variables, to (actually occurring or fictitious) real variables, or to functions of such variables; then we have only to check whether these equations are associated equations.

Now, to find an appropriate set of associated equations is easy, if such a set exists; it suffices, for each system of equations between arguments, to proceed by recursion, using one of the following procedures, which simplify the system of equations to be satisfied.[22]

(1) If one of the equations to be satisfied equates a restricted variable x to an individual, either this individual contains x ⟦or some other restricted variable⟧, and then the equation cannot be satisfied, or else the individual does not contain x ⟦or any other restricted variable, or any general variable that is not superior to x⟧, and then the equation will be one of the associated equations that we are looking for; in the other equations to be satisfied we replace x by the individual;

(2) If one of the equations to be satisfied equates a general variable to an individual that is not a restricted variable, the equation cannot be satisfied;

(3) If one of the equations to be satisfied equates $f_1(\varphi_1, \varphi_2, ..., \varphi_n)$ to $f_2(\psi_1, \psi_2, ..., \psi_m)$, either the elementary functions f_1 and f_2 are different, and then the equation cannot be satisfied, or they are the same, and then we turn to those equations that equate the φ_i to the ψ_i.

Therefore, if we successively consider each prenex form of P, we shall be able, after a finite and determinate number of steps, to decide whether the proposition P is a normal identity.

Similarly, given a proposition P and any scheme, we can test whether a proposition P' derived from P by the scheme is a normal identity, hence whether the scheme permits us to show that P has property A.[23]

3. PROPERTIES B AND C

3.1. In what follows we shall consider certain collections of letters; these

---

[22] ⟦⟦That an equation 'is to be satisfied' means here that it is to be shown to be associated.⟧⟧

[23] ⟦⟦The last paragraph of Section 2 in the French text reads: "Au bout d'un nombre fini et déterminé d'opérations de ce genre, on arrivera à vérifier si une proposition est normale (ou donc si elle possède la propriété A pour un schème associé donné)". Herbrand's parenthesis was expanded into the last paragraph of the English text.⟧⟧

collections will be called *domains* [[*champs*]], and the letters the *elements* of the domains.

We shall also consider functions that will be either descriptive functions or new functions; the new functions will be called *index functions* (and will play a role analogous to that of the descriptive functions).[24] In general, we shall have a number of symbols,

$$f_i(x_1, x_2, ..., x_{n_i})^{.}, \quad i = 1, 2, ..., m^{.},$$

which will be called the *elementary functions* (the x_i will be their arguments); from these we shall form further functions by the following procedure: if $\varphi_1, \varphi_2, ..., \varphi_n$ are functions and $f(x_1, x_2, ..., x_n)$ is an elementary function, $f(\varphi_1, \varphi_2, ..., \varphi_n)$ will also be a function.

We now define the *height of a function*. The height of an elementary function is 1; the height of a nonelementary function $f(\varphi_1, \varphi_2, ..., \varphi_n)$ will be greater by 1 than the maximum of the heights of the functions φ_i. We shall also say that the height of an element of a domain is 0.

By definition the *height of a proposition* will be the maximum of the heights of the descriptive functions occurring in it.

If with a system consisting of an elementary function $f(x_1, x_2, ..., x_n)$ and n letters $a_{i_1}, a_{i_2}, ..., a_{i_n}$ taken from a given domain (these letters being in a definite order) we correlate an element of the domain, this element will be called the *value* of the function for these values of the arguments, or the *value* of $f(a_{i_1}, a_{i_2}, ..., a_{i_n})$. We define the *value* of a nonelementary function, when this value exists, in terms of the values of the elementary functions as follows: if the functions $\varphi_1, \varphi_2, ..., \varphi_n$ take respectively the values $a_{i_1}, a_{i_2}, ..., a_{i_n}$ when values are assigned to their arguments, then the value assigned to the function $f(\varphi_1, \varphi_2, ..., \varphi_n)$ is the value assigned to $f(a_{i_1}, a_{i_2}, ..., a_{i_n})$. We consider also functions of 0 argument; with each of them we correlate a fixed element of the domain, which will be its *value*. These functions are similar to constants (Chap. 3, 1.12).

A function that [[whenever the values of its arguments are taken in a given domain]] has its value in the domain is said to be *attached* to the domain.

---

[24] Observe the close relation between the index functions and Hilbert's logical functions (see *Hilbert 1927*). [[See Note J, p. 201 below.]]

3.11. In what follows we shall often have to *equate*[25] two elements of a domain. We now define this operation.

Let C be any domain consisting of the elements $a_1, a_2, \ldots, a_n$. To equate a_α to a_β in the domain C is to replace C by any domain Γ satisfying the following four conditions:

(1) Γ has the same attached functions as C;

(2) To each element of C there corresponds exactly one element of Γ and to each element of Γ there corresponds at least one element of C;

(3) Any two elements of C correspond to the same element of Γ if and only if they are the values of individuals obtained thus: we consider the individuals whose expressions, formed from the elementary functions attached to the domain, contain a_α or a_β, and in these expressions we replace a number of occurrences of a_α by a_β, or vice versa (thus, the elements a_α and a_β of C correspond to the same element b_i of Γ; if $f(x)$ is a function attached to the domain C, $f(a_\alpha)$ and $f(a_\beta)$ correspond to the same element b_j of Γ);

(4) If $f(x_1, x_2, \ldots, x_n)$ is a function attached to C [hence, by (1), to Γ], the *value* of $f(b_{i_1}, b_{i_2}, \ldots, b_{i_n})$ is taken to be the element of Γ that corresponds to $f(a_{j_1}, a_{j_2}, \ldots, a_{j_n})$, where the elements a_{j_s} of C correspond

---

[25] [[The notion of equating elements of a domain will be used repeatedly by Herbrand. Although the definition he now gives is rather unclear, the underlying idea is simple.

A domain C with its attached functions can be viewed as a slight generalization of an abstract algebra (generalization because an attached function need not be defined for all elements in C). Let R be any congruence relation on C. Then any two elements a_α and a_β of C will be said to be *equated* (under R) if and only if they are congruent under R. (Of course, a_α and a_β can be congruent only if they are accepted as arguments by the same functions.) But then the domain Γ introduced by Herbrand can be taken to be the quotient algebra C/R. Hence the homomorphism in stipulation (4) is the natural homomorphism of C onto Γ. Finally, as Herbrand says, by picking one representative from each of the congruence classes, we can embed Γ in C, and the natural homomorphism becomes an endomorphism on C. (When, however, Herbrand comes to apply his notion of equating, he usually does *not* begin with a specification of the congruence R on C; rather, he first specifies an endomorphism on C and then uses this endomorphism to determine R. See especially the arguments for (c) in 3.3, as well as footnotes 37, 39, and 43.)]]

to the elements b_{i_s} of Γ (clearly, this assignment specifies a unique value).

This definition allows us to take for the letter b_j any letter that is one of the corresponding elements of C, for example the letter with the least subscript. Then Γ becomes a part of C, and the values of the attached functions [[for arguments in Γ]] are the same in the two domains. Henceforth this is what we shall do.

3.2. From now on we shall consider a proposition P in which there may occur descriptive functions (and even variables of various types, if we so desire; the occurrence of such types would change nothing essential in what follows, but to simplify notation we shall always assume that there is only one type). We shall assume that P contains no real variable: if P does contain the real variables $x_1, x_2, ..., x_n$, we replace it by (x_1) $(x_2)...(x_n) P$; see Chap. 2, 4.7; in 3.221 we shall see that the order in which we take $x_1, x_2, ..., x_n$ is immaterial for the considerations that follow.

With each *general* variable y we correlate an index function whose arguments are the restricted variables that *dominate* y (1.41). In particular, to a real variable there corresponds a function of 0 argument (a 'constant').

3.21. We now consider a domain C_1 consisting of the letters $a_1, a_2, ...,$ a_{n_1}. In what follows we shall assume that this domain is fixed; later (3.51) we shall see that we can take any domain for C_1. A domain C_2 is then obtained thus: to each elementary function (index function or descriptive function) taken together with a given system of arguments chosen in C_1 we assign a letter that will be in C_2; this letter is to be the value of the function for the system of arguments, and the assignment is such that each letter of C_2 will be the value of just one function for just one system of arguments. Let $a_{n_1+1}, ..., a_{n_2}$ be the elements of C_2. In general, we construct C_k from $C_1, C_2, ..., C_{k-1}$ by assigning a letter of C_k to each elementary function taken together with a given system of arguments; these arguments are chosen in [[the union of]] $C_1, C_2, ...,$ and C_{k-1}, and at least one argument is taken in C_{k-1}; the assignment is so made that each element of C_k corresponds to just one function for just one system of arguments. The letter assigned is to be the value of the function for the system of arguments.

We thus construct $C_1, C_2, ..., C_{p+1}$; finally, if h is the height of the proposition P, we construct $C_{p+2}, ..., C_{p+h+1}$ (omitting from these latter domains, if we so desire, elements corresponding to the index functions; it is easily seen that this will not affect our argument).[26]

For each k let $a_{n_{k-1}+1}, ..., a_{n_k}$ be the elements of C_k. We shall call the number k the *order* of C_k. Moreover, we shall write N for n_p.[27] We note that C_k contains the values of all the functions of height $k-1$ when their arguments are taken in C_1.

We could construct similar domains by starting from any descriptive or index functions whatever, and not from [[just]] those supplied by the proposition P. The functions thus used will be said to *generate* the domains.

3.211. When we say that we *equate* (3.11) two elements in the domains $C_1, C_2, ..., C_p$, we mean that we equate them in the domain that is the union of these domains; using the convention made at the end of 3.11, we see that each domain C_i is replaced by a domain Γ_i that consists of elements of C_i.[28]

3.212. We shall say that we have a *system of logical values* in these domains whenever a logical value has been assigned to each atomic proposition that we obtain by replacing the arguments of the atomic propositions of P with elements of the domains. From such a system

---

[26] [[The subscripts 'p', '$p+1$', and '$p+h+1$' that Herbrand introduces here find their justification on p. 153 below. Note that p and q here range over natural numbers, in contrast to their other use as sentence letters.]]

[27] [[Several points to be made in footnotes below can be stated more easily if we now say that each element of C_k is also *of order k* and write G_p for the union $C_1 \cup C_2 \cup ... \cup C_p$. Thus $N = n_p$ is the cardinality of G_p. (This use of G_p should not be confused with Herbrand's use of D_p, introduced in 4.1; see footnote 54, p. 167.) Moreover, it will henceforth be assumed that all the elements of G_p are arranged in some sequence in which, for each $k \leqslant p$, no element of order k precedes any elements of order less than k.]]

[28] [[Apparently, Herbrand is here stipulating that only elements of the same order (that is, elements belonging to the same domain C_i) are to be equated in $G_p = C_1 \cup C_2 \cup ... \cup C_p$. (Let us say that such an equating is *order-preserving*.) But in all subsequent important applications of equating he flouts this stipulation (see footnotes 34 and 43, and Note G).]]

we can derive the logical value of any proposition that is free of both apparent variables and descriptive functions and contains as real variables only elements of the domains.

3.22. Any proposition included in a given proposition P, that is, any proposition of which P is a propositional function (the first proposition is always the scope of some logical sign), will be called a *part*, or a *subproposition*, of P. With each part of the proposition P we correlate a proposition, called an *expansion* [*réduite*] (Chap. 2, § 8),[29] according to the following rules:[30]

(1) The expansion of an atomic proposition is the proposition itself;

(2) If the expansion of A is a, that of $\sim A$ is $\sim a$;

(3) If [the expansion of A is a and] that of B is b, that of $A \vee B$ is $a \vee b$;

(4) In case x is a general variable, if the expansion of $\Phi(x)$ is $\varphi(x)$, the expansion of $(\pm x)\,\Phi(x)$ is $\varphi\,[f_x(y_1, y_2, ..., y_n)]$, where $f_x(y_1, y_2, ..., y_n)$ is the index function corresponding to x (hence $y_1, y_2, ..., y_n$ are real variables of $\Phi(x)$);

(5) In case x is a restricted variable, if the expansion of $\Phi(x)$ is $\varphi(x)$, the expansion of $(-x)\,\Phi(x)$ is

$$\varphi(a_1) \vee \varphi(a_2) \vee \cdots \vee \varphi(a_N),$$

and the expansion of $(+x)\,\Phi(x)$ is

$$\varphi(a_1) \,\&\, \varphi(a_2) \,\&\, \cdots \,\&\, \varphi(a_N).$$

These rules enable us to associate an expansion with any proposition assumed to contain no real variables. Let us now replace by their values all the functions that occur in the expansion, so that no function remains in the expansion. Obviously we can do this, by introducing elements of the domains $C_{p+1}, C_{p+2}, ..., C_{p+h+1}$. We thus obtain a proposition Π.

---

[29] [[The *expansion* (that is, the common expansion) correlated in § 8 of Chap. 2 with a proposition P must be sharply distinguished from the *expansion* now to be specified.]]

[30] [[For each $p \geqslant 1$ these rules specify the expansion of P with respect to the elements of G_p (see Rule 5, where N is the cardinality of G_p). To make this dependence on G_p explicit, we shall sometimes speak of *the expansion of P over G_p*.]]

If Π is an identity of the first kind, we shall say that P has *property B of order p.*[31]

Let us perform the same operations again, but now *let the index functions that replace the general variables have for their arguments not the ⟦restricted⟧ variables dominating these general variables but the ⟦restricted⟧ variables superior (1.41) to these general variables.* If the proposition Π thus obtained is an identity, we shall say that *P has property C of order p.*[32]

3.221. We see immediately that – as was noted in 3.2 – if we start from a proposition containing real variables, properties B and C are independent of the order in which we generalize these variables (hence do not depend upon which of these variables dominate a given variable). For the index functions of 0 argument that correspond to the real variables have their values in C_2; they play no role in the construction of the domains that come after C_2.

---

[31] [[Herbrand will also call the expression Π, which is free of both quantifiers and functions, an *expansion of P*. Note that Π contains elements of $C_{p+1} \cup ... \cup C_{p+h+1}$, $h \geqslant 0$, but the expansion of P determined just by Rules 1–5 contains elements only of $G_p = C_1 \cup ... \cup C_p$.

Note further that, if A is any subproposition of P, the expansion of A need not occur in the expansion of P. Indeed, if A lies within the scopes of $n > 0$ restricted quantifiers $\pm x_1,..., \pm x_n$ and if either at least one variable x_i, $i = 1,..., n$ occurs in A or at least one general quantifier occurs in A, the expansion of A does not occur in the expansion of P. Rather, with respect to each given system of values for $x_1,..., x_n$, a substitution instance of the expansion of A occurs in the expansion of P. However, for convenience we shall continue to speak in subsequent footnotes of each such substitution instance as the *expansion of A in the expansion of P* (for a given set of values $x_1,..., x_n$). If $n = 0$ and A occurs positively in P, then the expansion of A in the expansion of P *is* the expansion of A. (In addition, if A occurs negatively in P and contains any quantifiers, then the expansion of A in the expansion of P does not have even this relation to the expansion of A, for variables restricted in A are general in P, and *vice versa*.)]]

[32] [[In the present paragraph Herbrand has again, just as noted in the first paragraph of footnote 31, specified two expressions, both of which we will again call expansions of P. We shall need to distinguish the two expansions defined in the preceding paragraph from the two expansions just defined. So, in analogy with Herbrand's usage in 3.4 below, let us call each of the former a *first expansion of P over G_p*, and each of the latter a *second expansion of P over G_p*.]]

We see that property B and property C are identical if the proposition is in canonical form (1.2 and 1.41).

3.3. LEMMA. *For every p, if a proposition has property B, or property C, of order p, any proposition derived from it by the rules of passage has property B, or property C, of order p, provided the domain C_1 is the same in both cases.*[33]

We shall show that the properties are preserved when any rule of passage is applied.

(1) *Case of property B.*

For the rules of passage governing the sign $\sim$, the lemma immediately follows from Chap. 1, 3.42.

If we consider the rules of passage governing the sign $\vee$, we see immediately (by using Chap. 1, 5.34) that $(x)\,[\Phi(x) \vee p]$ and $(x)\,\Phi(x) \vee p$ always have equivalent expansions; similarly for $(\exists x)\,[\Phi(x) \vee p]$ and $(\exists x)\,\Phi(x) \vee p$.

(2) *Case of property C.*

For the rules of passage governing the sign $\sim$, the result follows from Chap. 1, 3.42.

Let us now consider the rules of passage governing the sign $\vee$.

(a) *Passage from $(\pm x)\,\Phi(x) \vee p$ to $(\pm x)\,[\Phi(x) \vee p]$, and inverse passage, in case x is a general variable.*

It is sufficient to observe that these two subpropositions have identical expansions.

(b) *Passage from $(\exists x)\,\Phi(x) \vee p$ to $(\exists x)\,[\Phi(x) \vee p]$, and inverse passage, in case x is a restricted variable* (hence the occurrence is positive).

In its first form P will be written P_1 and, in its second, P_2. In P_2 the index functions of the general variables of the subproposition p are functions of x. If y is a general variable of p and $x_1, x_2, ..., x_n$ are the restricted variables superior to x, let $f_y(x_1, x_2, ..., x_n, x)$ be the index

---

[33] [[This is the basic lemma of Herbrand's thesis (see, for example, his remarks in 6.2). But for certain cases of property C it is false (see Note G, p. 193 below). To be able to carry out Herbrand's argument in the remainder of the present chapter – in particular, the argument for his Fundamental Theorem – we must substantially emend this lemma (see Note G).]]

function of y in P_2 and let $f_y(x_1, x_2, ..., x_n)$ be the index function of y in P_1.[34]

The descriptive and index functions of P_1 will, from C_1, generate the domains $C_2^{(1)}$, $C_3^{(1)}$, ... The functions of P_2 differ from those of P_1 only in that, for each general variable y of p, $f_y(x_1, x_2, ..., x_n, x)$ has taken the place of $f_y(x_1, x_2, ..., x_n)$, and they will, from C_1, generate the domains $C_2^{(2)}$, $C_3^{(2)}$, ...

(1)[35] Let us observe that we can pass from the $C_i^{(2)}$ to the $C_i^{(1)}$ thus: for each general variable y of p and for[36] each given system of elements $x_1, x_2, ..., x_n$ [in the union] of the $C_i^{(2)}$, the values of $f_y(x_1, x_2, ..., x_n, x)$ for all x in the $C_i^{(2)}$ are all equated (3.211) to one of these values, namely $f_y(x_1, x_2, ..., x_n, a_i)$, where a_i is an arbitrary element of the $C_i^{(2)}$. The domains $C_i^{(1)}$ can then be regarded as part of the domains $C_i^{(2)}$.[37] So we see that we can pass from the expansion of P_2 to a proposition equivalent to the expansion of P_1 by doing the following: for[36] each given system of values of $x_1, x_2, ..., x_n$, we replace, in the expansion of P_2,

[34] [[The notations $f_y(x_1, x_2, ..., x_n, x)$ and $f_y(x_1, x_2, ..., x_n)$ exhibit just the restricted variables that are now at the center of Herbrand's attention. For, in general, the index functions of y will have as arguments also those $s \geq 0$ restricted variables $z_{y_1}, z_{y_2}, ..., z_{y_s}$ whose quantifiers occur in p and are superior to y.]]

[35] [[In this paragraph Herbrand considers the case of the passage from $(\exists x)[\Phi(x) \vee p]$ to $(\exists x)\Phi(x) \vee p$. Hence he proves that, if the expansion of P_2 over $G_p^{(2)}$ is an identity, so is the expansion of P_1 over $G_p^{(2)}$.]]

[36] [[Herbrand writes "for each given system of elements $x_1, x_2, ..., x_n, y$", but 'y' is extraneous.]]

[37] [[For $n > 0$ and $p > 2$ the element a_i cannot be completely arbitrary if $G_{p+1}^{(1)}$ is to be embedded in $G_{p+1}^{(2)}$. Let $x_1, x_2, ..., x_n, x$ be elements of $G_{p+1}^{(2)}$ that are all of order 1, but let a_i in $G_{p+1}^{(2)}$ be of order p. Then the element b in $G_{p+1}^{(2)}$ that is the value of $f_y(x_1, x_2, ..., x_n, x)$ is of order 2 and the element d in $G_{p+1}^{(2)}$ that is the value of $f_y(x_1, x_2, ..., x_n, a_i)$ is of order $p+1$. Hence the element in $G_{p+1}^{(2)}$ that is the value of $f_y(b, x_2, ..., x_n, x_1)$ is of order 3. But the value of $f_y(d, x_2, ..., x_n, x_1)$ is of order $p+2$, hence is not an element of $G_{p+1}^{(2)}$. Therefore $C_3^{(1)}$ cannot be embedded in $G_{p+1}^{(2)}$. Hence a_i must always be an order less than or equal to the maximum of the orders of $x_1, x_2, ..., x_n$. However, to satisfy this requirement we need only take a_i to be always a_1. (Interestingly enough, in the original French text "$f_y(x_1, ..., x_n, a_1)$" occurs; but in his list of errata Herbrand changed this formula to "$f_y(x_1, ..., x_n, a_i)$".) Note that even this emended equating is not order-preserving (see above: footnotes 25 and 28).]]

the values of $f_y(x_1, x_2, ..., x_n, x)$ obtained for all x by the one value among them that is in the domains $C_i^{(1)}$. Hence, if the expansion of P_2 is an identity, so is the expansion of P_1.

(2) If the expansion Π_2 of P_2 is not an identity, there exists, according to Chap. 1, 5.21, a system of logical values (3.212) falsifying Π_2; hence, as we shall now show, there exists a system of logical values falsifying the expansion Π_1 of P_1.[38]

To do this we replace the expansion Π_1 of P_1 by another expansion, obtained as follows. Let $a_1, a_2, ..., a_N$ be the elements of the domains $C_1^{(2)}, ..., C_p^{(2)}$; in these domains we define the value of $f_y(x_1, x_2, ..., x_n)$ to be the value of $f_y(x_1, x_2, ..., x_n, a_i)$ for some a_i, which we shall select shortly and which will depend upon $x_1, x_2, ..., x_n$. This definition will permit us to take subdomains of these domains as the domains $C_i^{(1)}$. The modification that we intend to introduce consists in using all N elements of ⟦the union of⟧ the $C_i^{(2)}$ to form the expansion of P_1, just as they are used to form that of P_2. In other words, of the five rules stated in 3.22 the fifth alone will undergo a modification, namely the following: the letters $a_1, a_2, ..., a_N$ will denote the elements of the domains $C_1^{(2)}$, $C_2^{(2)}, ..., C_p^{(2)}$, not those of the domains $C_1^{(1)}, C_2^{(1)}, ..., C_p^{(1)}$. The transformation described at the end of 3.22 ⟦that is, the replacement of functions by their values⟧ will, of course, be carried out in the $C_i^{(2)}$ and not in the $C_i^{(1)}$. We thus construct a new expansion Π_1' of P_1.[39]

---

[38] ⟦It is indeed true that, if the expansion of P_2 over $G_p^{(2)}$ is not an identity, neither is the expansion of P_1 over $G_p^{(2)}$, but the argument that Herbrand is about to give is faulty (see footnote 43).⟧

[39] ⟦Herbrand is doing two different things in this paragraph. First, to each ordered n-tuple $\langle a_{i_1}, ..., a_{i_n} \rangle$ of elements of $G_p^{(2)}$ he assigns a unique element a_i of $G_p^{(2)}$ so that for all a in $G_{(p)}^2$ the value in $G_{p+1}^{(2)}$ of $f_y(a_{i_1}, ..., a_{i_n}, a)$ is equated to the value of $f_y(a_{i_1}, ..., a_{i_n}, a_i)$. (This a_i is specified on p. 159, lines 8–19. Herbrand makes it depend upon both $a_{i_1}, ..., a_{i_n}$ and the particular system $\mathscr{S}$ of logical values that is assumed to falsify Π_2.) Herbrand concludes – falsely, as we shall see in footnote 43 – that, as a result of this equating, $G_p^{(1)}$ is embedded in $G_p^{(2)}$, and so he takes the expansion Π_1 of P_1 as being formed over this subset of $G_p^{(2)}$. That is, the value of $f_y(a_{i_1}, ..., a_{i_n}, a)$ in $G_p^{(2)}$ is defined by Herbrand to be $f_y(a_{i_1}, ..., a_{i_n}, a_i)$. (See footnote 25 above, p. 150.)

However, this is not the modification that Herbrand intends to introduce. Rather, as he says in the latter part of the paragraph, he constructs a new expansion Π_1' of P_1

If we observe that

$$[\varphi(a_{i_1}) \vee \varphi(a_{i_2}) \vee \cdots \vee \varphi(a_{i_m})] \supset [\varphi(a_1)$$
$$\vee \varphi(a_2) \vee \cdots \vee \varphi(a_N)]$$

and

$$[\varphi(a_1) \& \varphi(a_2) \& \cdots \& \varphi(a_N)] \supset [\varphi(a_{i_1})$$
$$\& \varphi(a_{i_2}) \& \cdots \& \varphi(a_{i_m})]$$

are identities and apply the theorem of Chap. 2, 3.2, we can conclude that $\Pi_1 \supset \Pi_1'$ is an identity. Hence, if Π_1' is not an identity, neither is Π_1.[40]

We now show that, if we have a system of logical values that falsifies Π_2, we can, by suitably choosing the value of each $f_y(x_1, x_2, \ldots, x_n)$, obtain a system of logical values that falsifies Π_1'.[41]

The expansions of the subpropositions $(\exists x)\, \Phi(x) \vee p$ and $(\exists x)[\Phi(x) \vee p]$ depend upon the ⟦restricted⟧ variables $x_1, x_2, \ldots, x_n$, which are superior to x. But we shall consider these expansions only for given values of these variables, namely, $a_{i_1}, a_{i_2}, \ldots, a_{i_n}$; then these expansions have only one occurrence in Π_2 and one in Π_1 ⟦rather, Π_1'⟧, as we can readily see.[42]

For these values, let $\pi(x)$ be the expansion ⟦in Π_2⟧ of p when p occurs in P_2 and let a_i be the ⟦still to be selected⟧ element such that, for each general variable y of p, the value of $f_y(a_{i_1}, a_{i_2}, \ldots, a_{i_n}, a_i)$ is the value of

(Continued note from page 157.)

over all of $G_p^{(2)}$, still assuming that the same a_i has been chosen. (Remember, an expansion can be formed over any union of domains.) He will then in the next few paragraphs show that $\Pi_1 \supset \Pi_1'$ is an identity and argue that Π_1' is false under $\mathscr{S}$.]]

[40] [[The inductive argument that Herbrand has just sketched in order to show that $\Pi_1 \supset \Pi_1'$ is an identity justifies the following more general result, which is used below in Note G, p. 193, and Note H, p. 199 below.

Let P be any proposition, Π an expansion of P over G, and Π' an expansion of P over G'. If G is a subset of G', then $\Pi \supset \Pi'$ is an identity. Thus, if P has property C of order p, it has property C of order q for each q greater than p. (Note that only the amended form of Theorem 3.2, Chap. 2, is necessary for the proof.) See 3.54 and footnote 49 below.]]

[41] [[Thus the specification of each a_i must satisfy the following two requirements: (1) $G_p^{(1)}$ is embeddable in $G_p^{(2)}$; (2) the extended expansion Π_1' of P_1 is false under a system of logical values if Π_2 is false under some system of logical values.]]

[42] [[See the second paragraph of footnote 31.]]

$f_y(a_{i_1}, a_{i_2}, ..., a_{i_n})$. We readily see that, when p occurs in P_1, its expansion $[\![$in $\Pi_1'$$]\!]$ is $\pi(a_i)$. Hence, when $(\exists x)\, \Phi(x) \vee p$ occurs in P_1, its expansion $[\![$in $\Pi_1'$$]\!]$ is

$$[\varphi(a_1) \vee \varphi(a_2) \vee \cdots \vee \varphi(a_N)] \vee \pi(a_i), \tag{1}$$

but, when $(\exists x)\, [\Phi(x) \vee p]$ occurs in P_2, its expansion $[\![$in $\Pi_2$$]\!]$ is

$$[\varphi(a_1) \vee \pi(a_1)] \vee [\varphi(a_2) \vee \pi(a_2)]$$
$$\vee \cdots \vee [\varphi(a_N) \vee \pi(a_N)]. \tag{2}$$

To proposition (2) the system $\mathscr{S}$ of logical values now under consideration $[\![$for $\Pi_2$$]\!]$ assigns either the logical value 'true' or the logical value 'false'.

1. If the logical value is 'true', then either at least one of the $\varphi(a_j)$ has the logical value 'true', and we set

$$f_y(a_{i_1}, a_{i_2}, ..., a_{i_n}) = f_y(a_{i_1}, a_{i_2}, ..., a_{i_n}, a_1),$$

or at least one of the $\pi(a_j)$, say $\pi(a_k)$, has the logical value 'true', and we set

$$f_y(a_{i_1}, a_{i_2}, ..., a_{i_n}) = f_y(a_{i_1}, a_{i_2}, ..., a_{i_n}, a_k).$$

2. If the logical value is 'false', we set

$$f_y(a_{i_1}, a_{i_2}, ..., a_{i_n}) = f_y(a_{i_1}, a_{i_2}, ..., a_{i_n}, a_1).$$

Thus we see that propositions (1) and (2) will have the same logical value.[43] So the method just described $[\![$of selecting $a_i$$]\!]$ does indeed give the same logical value to Π_2 and Π_1.

---

[43] $[\![$In his specification of a_i, Herbrand goes wrong. The difficulty is the same as the one described in footnote 37. If a_k is of too high an order, $G_p^{(1)}$ cannot be embedded in $G_p^{(2)}$. So let us once again modify Herbrand's argument and take a_i to be always a_1 (for all systems of logical values assigned to Π_2). But now we can no longer say, as Herbrand does, that, for each given set of elements $a_{i_1}, ..., a_{i_n}$, the expansion of $(\exists x)\, \Phi(x) \vee p$ in Π_1' has the same logical value under $\mathscr{S}$ as the corresponding expansion of $(\exists x)\, [\Phi(x) \vee p]$ in Π_2. However, we can say that, if any given expansion of $(\exists x)\, [\Phi(x) \vee p]$ in Π_2 is false under $\mathscr{S}$, the corresponding expansion of $(\exists x)\, \Phi(x) \vee p$ in Π_1' is also false under $\mathscr{S}$. But nothing more is required in order to prove that, if $\mathscr{S}$ falsifies Π_2, as we are assuming, then $\mathscr{S}$ falsifies Π_1'. For, by hypothesis, each expansion of $(\exists x)\, \Phi(x) \vee p$ occurs positively in Π_1 and each expansion of $(\exists x)\, [\Phi(x) \vee p]$ occurs positively in Π_2. Hence, if $\mathscr{S}$ verifies an expansion of $(\exists x)\, [\Phi(x) \vee p]$ in Π_2 and proposition (1) is the corresponding expansion of $(\exists x)\, \Phi(x) \vee p$ in Π_1', it does not matter for the falsity of Π_1' under $\mathscr{S}$ whether $\mathscr{S}$ verifies or falsifies proposition (1). So we need consider only those expansions of $(\exists x)\, [\Phi(x) \vee p]$ in Π_2 that are falsified by $\mathscr{S}$. (Compare the proof of Lemma I in Note G, p. 196 below.)$]\!]$

(c) *Passage from* $(x) \, \Phi(x) \vee p$ *to* $(x) \, [\Phi(x) \vee p]$, *and inverse passage, in a negative occurrence.*[44]

The argument is the same as in (b). Only the end is slightly modified. We have to consider

$$[\varphi(a_1) \, \& \, \varphi(a_2) \, \& \, \cdots \, \& \, \varphi(a_N)] \vee \pi(a_i) \tag{1}$$

and
$$[\varphi(a_1) \vee \pi(a_1)] \, \& \, [\varphi(a_2) \vee \pi(a_2)]$$
$$\& \, \cdots \, \& \, [\varphi(a_N) \vee \pi(a_N)]. \tag{2}$$

To proposition (2) the system of logical values under consideration [[for Π_2]] assigns either the logical value 'true' or the logical value 'false'.

1. If the logical value is 'true', either all the $\varphi(a_j)$ have the same logical value, and we put

$$f_y(a_{i_1}, a_{i_2}, ..., a_{i_n}) = f_y(a_{i_1}, a_{i_2}, ..., a_{i_n}, a_1),$$

or some $\pi(a_j)$, say $\pi(a_k)$, has the logical value 'true', and we put

$$f_y(a_{i_1}, a_{i_2}, ..., a_{i_n}) = f_y(a_{i_1}, a_{i_2}, ..., a_{i_n}, a_k).$$

2. If the logical value is 'false', some $\pi(a_j)$, say $\pi(a_k)$, has the logical value 'false', and we put

$$f_y(a_{i_1}, a_{i_2}, ..., a_{i_n}) = f_y(a_{i_1}, a_{i_2}, ..., a_{i_n}, a_k).$$

The end of the argument is then unchanged.

3.31. COROLLARY. Since properties B and C of order p are identical for a proposition in canonical form (3.221), *these two properties are always equivalent.*[45]

3.4. By considering the relation between the expansion of an arbitrary proposition P and the expansion of a prenex form of P, we can give property B a simple formulation.[46] We consider the domains C_i (of 3.21) that are generated by the elementary descriptive functions and by the index functions corresponding to the general variables of the proposition P, the arguments of each of these index functions being the [[restricted]] variables dominating the general variable with which the function is correlated. In the matrix of P we replace each restricted variable by an element arbitrarily chosen in [[the union of]] $C_1, C_2, ..., $ and C_p; then we

[44] [[See Note G, p. 193 below.]]

[45] [[See Note H, p. 199 below.]]

[46] [[In the French text the paragraph begins: "En mettant les propositions sous une forme normale, on peut mettre la propriété B sous une forme simple". The translators found it advisable to expand the text somewhat.]]

replace each general variable y by the value of the corresponding index function $f_y(a_{i_1}, a_{i_2}, ..., a_{i_n})$, the arguments $a_{i_1}, a_{i_2}, ..., a_{i_n}$ being the elements by which the restricted variables dominating y have been replaced; from the resulting proposition we eliminate each descriptive function by replacing it with its value. We now form the disjunction of all the elementary propositions that are thus obtained when we replace the restricted variables in all possible ways. To say that P has property B of order p amounts to saying that this disjunction is an identity; we can see this by simply going back to the definition of property B and applying it to a prenex form of P. This disjunction will henceforth be called *the first disjunction of order p associated with P*.

To show that P has property C we would now consider index functions that have superior ⟦restricted⟧ variables as arguments and we would construct the domains generated by the descriptive functions and these index functions. On P we would perform the same operations as above, but now we would replace each general variable y by the value of the corresponding index function $f_y(a_{i_1}, a_{i_2}, ..., a_{i_n})$, where the arguments $a_{i_1}, a_{i_2}, ..., a_{i_n}$ are the elements by which we replaced the restricted variables preceding y in the prefix (for these are the ⟦restricted⟧ variables superior to y in the prenex form). We thus obtain *the second disjunction of order p associated with P*, and this disjunction must be an identity if P is to have property C.[47]

---

[47] ⟦⟦Since we know (see Note H, p. 199 below) that for an arbitrary proposition P, even if P has property C of order p, no prenex form of P need have property C of order p, to obtain a correct definition of the second disjunction of order p associated with P we must replace the second sentence of this paragraph by the following sentence:

On P we would perform the same operations as above, but now we would replace each general variable y by the value of the corresponding index function $f_y(a_{i_1}, a_{i_2}, ...,$ $a_{i_n})$, where the arguments $a_{i_1}, a_{i_2}, ..., a_{i_n}$ are the elements by which we replaced the restricted variable *whose quantifiers have within their scopes the quantifier of y* (for these variables are the restricted variables superior to y).

But, when thus emended, the second disjunction of order p associated with P is what in Note G, p. 194 below and in the Introduction, p. 9 above, is called the standard expansion of P of order p. So, to avoid confusion in footnotes below, we shall preserve the term 'second disjunction of order p associated with P' for the nonemended notion. (Note, however, that if P is in prenex form, the (nonemended) second disjunction of order p associated with P is still the standard expansion of P of order p.)⟧⟧

3.5. We shall now make some very important remarks about properties B and C (the arguments are the mase for both).

3.51. (1) *The number of elements in the domain C_1 is immaterial* (hence we can in general take it equal to 1).

(a) We can increase the number. For let $C_1, C_2, ..., C_p, ...$ be any domains, and assume that C_1 has n elements, $a_1, a_2, ..., a_n$. Let $\Gamma_1, \Gamma_2, ...,$ $\Gamma_p, ...$ be some other domains generated by the same functions, and assume that Γ_1 has m elements, $a_1, a_2, ..., a_m$. Assume that $m < n$. The elements of Γ_i are denoted by the same letters as certain elements of C_i, so that a function $f(a_{i_1}, a_{i_2}, ..., a_{i_n})$ will have the same value on Γ_i as on C_i. Then the terms of the first associated disjunction of order p that corresponds to the domains Γ_i are some of the terms of the first associated disjunction of order p that corresponds to the domains C_i; hence, if the former is an identity, so is the latter, since $\vdash A \supset (A \vee B)$.

(b) We can decrease the number. Let us use the same notation. We can pass from C_i to Γ_i by equating (3.11; 3.211) $a_{m+1}, a_{m+2}, ..., a_n$ to, say, a_1. In the first associated disjunction of order p that corresponds to the domains C_i we replace $a_{m+1}, a_{m+2}, ..., a_n$ by a_1. We see immediately that the disjuncts thus obtained are disjuncts of the first associated disjunction of order p that corresponds to the domains Γ_i and are in fact all of these disjuncts. Hence, if the former disjunction is an identity, so is the latter, as we see by Remark 3.31 of Chap. 1.

3.52. (2) *Without modifying properties B and C, we can assume that the domains that we construct in order to show that a proposition has property B, or property C, are generated not only by the functions introduced above but also by other functions (called 'fictitious functions').* We can, in particular, introduce *fictitious* real variables, and this will lead to the introduction of fictitious *constants* (3.2).

Let $\varphi_i(x_1, x_2, ..., x_{n_i})$, with $i = 1, 2, ..., \alpha$, be the new functions that are introduced; let $\psi_j(x_1, x_2, ..., x_{m_j})$, with $j = 1, 2, ..., \beta$, be the original functions; let $C_1, C_2, ..., C_p, ...$ be the domains generated by the φ_i and the ψ_j. We equate all the elements that are values of the functions $\varphi_i(a_1^k, a_2^k, ..., a_{n_i}^k)$ to some element of C_1. We thus obtain the domains $C_1, \Gamma_2, \Gamma_3 ..., \Gamma_p$, generated by the functions ψ_j. By the argument used above in (b ⟦rather, a⟧) we see that, if the first associated disjunction of order p obtained by means of the former ⟦rather, latter⟧ domains is an identity, so is the disjunction obtained by means of the latter ⟦rather, former⟧ domains.

3.53. (3) *[For every p,]* *if both P and Q have property B [of order p]*, *then P & Q has property B [of order p]*.[48]

Let us construct the domains that correspond to the proposition $P \& Q$, namely $C_1, C_2, \ldots, C_p, \ldots$ In these domains the first disjunction of order p associated with P is of the form

$$P_1 \vee P_2 \vee \cdots \vee P_N,$$

where each P_i results from the matrix of P by the operations described in 3.4. According to 3.52, this first disjunction is an identity. Similarly, the disjunction associated with Q is of the form

$$Q_1 \vee Q_2 \vee \cdots \vee Q_M.$$

Now, clearly, the disjunction associated with $P \& Q$ contains all terms of the form $P_i \& Q_j$; according to Chap. 1, 5.34, it is an identity.

3.54. (4) *For every p, if a proposition P has property B, or property C, of order p, then P has property B, or property C, of order q for every q greater than p*.[49]

The domains considered are in one case $C_1, C_2, \ldots, C_p$ and in the other $C_1', C_2', \ldots, C_p', \ldots, C_q'$. Let us use the same letters for the elements of C_i', $1 \leq i \leq p$, as for those of C_i. Then the disjuncts of the first disjunction of order p associated with P are among those of the first disjunction of order q associated with P; hence, if the former disjunction is an identity, so is the latter (by virtue of the identity $\vdash A \supset (A \vee B)$).

3.6. Consider the following example of a proposition assumed to have property C of order 2:

$$(x)(\exists y)(z)\, P(x, y, z, f(y, z)),$$

where $f(y, z)$ is an elementary descriptive function; this proposition is of height 1.

Two index functions have to be introduced: φ_x, with no argument, for x and $\varphi_z(y)$ for z.

---

[48] [[Using the standard expansion of order p of P and that of Q, we can similarly prove: If both P and Q have property C of order p, then $P \& Q$ has property C of order p. (This is needed for the proof of Lemma 3 in 5.3 below.)]]

[49] [[To appreciate the simplicity gained by the use of the notion of standard expansion, compare the argument that Herbrand now gives for his result with the argument that is implicit in Herbrand's text on pp. 157–158 above (see footnote 40).]]

The domain C_1 will consist of a_1.

The domain C_2 will consist of a_2, which will be φ_x,

a_3, which will be $\varphi_z(a_1)$,

and a_4, which will be $f(a_1, a_1)$.

The domain C_3 will consist of

$a_5,\ a_6,\ a_7,$	which will be	$\varphi_z(a_2), \varphi_z(a_3), \varphi_z(a_4),$
$a_8,\ a_9,\ a_{10},$	which will be	$f(a_2, a_2), f(a_3, a_3), f(a_4, a_4),$
$a_{11}, a_{12}, a_{13},$	which will be	$f(a_1, a_2), f(a_1, a_3), f(a_1, a_4),$
$a_{14}, a_{15}, a_{16},$	which will be	$f(a_2, a_3), f(a_2, a_4), f(a_3, a_4),$
$a'_{11}, a'_{12}, a'_{13},$	which will be	$f(a_2, a_1), f(a_3, a_1), f(a_4, a_1),$
$a'_{14}, a'_{15}, a'_{16},$	which will be	$f(a_3, a_2), f(a_4, a_2), f(a_4, a_3).$

In C_4 we consider only a_{17}, which will be $f(a_3, a_6)$, a_{18}, which will be $f(a_4, a_7)$, and a_{19}, which will be $f(a_2, a_5)$.

For y we have to take successively $a_1, a_2, a_3,$ and a_4.

The disjunction of order 2 is

$$P(a_2, a_1, a_3, a_{12}) \lor P(a_2, a_2, a_5, a_{19})$$
$$\lor\ P(a_2, a_3, a_6, a_{17}) \lor P(a_2, a_4, a_7, a_{18}).$$

We see that $a_8, a_9, a_{10}, a_{11}, a_{13}, a_{14}, a_{15}, a_{16}$ [[and a'_{11}–a'_{16}]] play no role. If the rules of passage permit us to put the proposition into the form

$$(x)(z)(\exists y)\, P(x, y, z, f(y, z)),$$

then we have to equate $a_3, a_5, a_6,$ and a_7.

4. Infinite domains

We now introduce the fundamental notion of *infinite domain*.

4.1. Let C_1 be a domain consisting of the elements $a_1, a_2, ..., a_{n_1},$ and let us assume that we have a certain number of descriptive functions, index functions, and atomic propositional functions. We shall say that we have an *infinite domain* if we have a definite procedure for correlating with every number p: first, a domain C' that contains C_1; then, for the functions, a system of values (3.1) in C' that permits us to obtain in C' the value of any function of height not greater than p whenever the arguments are taken in C_1; and, finally, a system of logical values that are assigned to the atomic propositional functions whenever the variables of these functions are replaced by elements of C'. These functions, propositional functions, and logical values will be said to be *attached* to the infinite domain.

We shall sometimes consider also domains to which no propositional functions or logical values are attached; we shall always indicate explicitly when this is the case.

It is quite obvious that generally the number of elements of C' increases with p.

We shall say that C' is the *domain of order p* in the infinite domain; C_1 is the *domain of order 0*.

We observe that this definition differs from the definition that would seem the most natural only in that, as the number p increases, the new domain C' and the new values need not be regarded as forming an 'extension' [['prolongement']] of the previous ones. Clearly, if we know C' and the values for a given number p, then for each smaller number we know a domain and values that answer to the number; but only a 'principle of choice' could lead us to take a fixed system of values in an infinite domain.[50]

We now start from a proposition P of height h, with no real variables. With each restricted variable y of P we correlate an index function whose arguments are the general variables that *dominate* y. Let us consider an infinite domain for which the attached functions are these index functions and the elementary [[rather, descriptive]] functions of P, and the attached propositional functions are the atomic propositional functions occurring in P; let C_1 be the domain of order 0, D_p the domain of order p. [[We delete all quantifiers and]] in the matrix of P we replace each restricted variable of P by the corresponding index function. We thus obtain a proposition P'. Replacing its variables by some elements of D_p, we obtain another proposition, P''. We try to eliminate all the functions that occur in P'' by replacing them with their values. We thus obtain a proposition Π. (This is not always possible. But we carry out this replacement whenever we can, and we always can if p is greater than the height of the

---

[50] [[By a 'principle of choice' Herbrand means some form of the axiom of choice, and not an argument such as that in *Skolem 1922*. See the Introduction, p. 12 above, and also Note N, p. 268 below.]]

proposition P, for then it suffices to take elements of C_1 as arguments of the functions.)

We shall say that P is *true in the infinite domain* if for every number p we have a procedure enabling us to verify that each of the propositions ⟦obtained over D_p in the way Π was⟧ has 'true' as its logical value (derived from the logical values that its atomic propositions take in the domain).[51]

Let us start again from P; but now with each general variable y we correlate an index function whose arguments are the restricted variables that dominate y. We construct an infinite domain as above, using the new index functions instead of the old ones; in the matrix of P we now replace each general variable by the corresponding index function and perform the same operations as above; if all the propositions thus obtained have the logical value 'false', we shall say that P is *false in this infinite domain*.

It is absolutely necessary to adopt such definitions if we want to give a precise sense to the words 'true in an infinite domain', words that have frequently been used without sufficient explanation, and also if we want to justify a proposition proved by Löwenheim,[52] a proposition to which many refer without clearly seeing that Löwenheim's proof is totally inadequate for our purposes (see 6.4 ⟦rather, 6.2⟧) and that, indeed, the proposition has no precise sense until such a definition has been given.

4.11. We observe at once that, if P is true in an infinite domain, $\sim P$ is false in it and, if P is false in it, $\sim P$ is true in it.

4.2. To clarify the notion of infinite domain let us for the moment ignore the associated logical values; we can then classify the elements of D_p in the following manner: first we take the elements of C_1; then we take all the elements that are values of the functions of height 1 when the arguments of these functions are chosen in C_1; these elements form a domain Γ_2 (which may have elements in common with C_1);

---

[51] ⟦⟦Herbrand's use of 'true' in 'true in an infinite domain' must be sharply distinguished from his use of 'true' to mean 'provable in Q_H'. Moreover, his definition of 'true in an infinite domain' here differs from those in *1931* (p. 229 below) and *1931c* (p. 288 below) in that in the latter two places, each restricted variable x is replaced by a function whose arguments are the general variables *superior* to x (see also footnote 86, p. 183 below).⟧⟧

[52] *1915*; see also *Skolem 1920*.

then we take all the elements that are values of the functions of height 2 when the arguments of these functions are chosen in C_1; they form Γ_3; we thus form $\Gamma_1, \Gamma_2, \Gamma_3, ..., \Gamma_p, ...$ We shall have at least p terms; but, clearly, this sequence will terminate when some domain is entirely contained in the previous ones.[53]

Let us now look again at the domains considered in 3.21 for the proposition P; if we take C_1 as the first domain, we see that Γ_2 can be regarded as resulting from C_2 when some elements of C_2 are equated to some elements of C_1 or C_2 (see the conventions of 3.211); we see that in general Γ_k results from C_k when some elements of C_k are equated to some elements of $C_1, C_2, ..., C_{k-1}$, or C_k.

If we recall the theorem of Chap. 1, 5.21, we obtain the following two basic theorems:

4.21. (1) *A proposition P that is false in some* [*infinite*] *domain cannot* [*for any p*] *have property B* [*of order p*].

(2) *If* [*for every p*] *a proposition P does not have property B* [*of order p*], *we can construct an infinite domain in which P is false.*

The first theorem follows from the fact that for [the union of] C_1, $C_2, ...,$ and C_{p+h+1} we can immediately obtain from the infinite domain a system of logical values that gives the logical value 'false' to the first disjunction of order p associated with P (see 3.4). The second theorem follows from the fact that C_p determines precisely the domain of order p in the infinite domain that we are trying to find and that the logical values assigning the value 'false' to this disjunction (according to Chap. 1, 5.21) yield the attached logical values.[54]

To simplify we shall say (the meaning of the assertion being determined by Theorems (1) and (2) above):

The necessary and sufficient condition for a proposition not to have property B is that it be false in some infinite domain.[55]

---

[53] There may be elements of D_p that will not be contained in any of these domains; these elements will play no role in what follows.

[54] [[Thus, for each p, D_p can be taken to be

$$G_{p+h+1} = C_1 \cup C_2 \cup ... \cup C_{p+h+1}.]]$$

[55] [[Compare 6.2. The French expression translated here as "false in some infinite domain" is "fausse dans un champ infini". In other parts of this volume, the same expression is translated "false in an infinite domain".]]

4.3. The preceding considerations show that we need concern ourselves only with infinite domains of the following kind. Let C_1 be an arbitrary domain (consisting, for example, of one element). Let C_k be, for each $k > 1$, the domain obtained when, as in 3.21, with each function of height $k - 1$ that can be constructed from the elementary functions at our disposal and whose arguments are taken in C_1 we correlate one-to-one some element, which will be the value of the function. It then suffices, in defining the truth (or falsity) of a proposition of height h, to assume that the domain of order p in the infinite domain is given by the union of $C_1, C_2, ..., C_{p+h+1}$ (the attached functions being the descriptive functions and the index functions mentioned in 4.1) and by a system of logical values for the propositional functions having arguments in these domains. Such an infinite domain will be called a *reduced* domain. All the previous results still hold when the words 'infinite domain' are replaced by 'reduced domain'. For we can always assume that two different functions have different values: if two different functions have an element b as their common value, we replace b by two other elements, b_1 and b_2; the value of the first function will be b_1, that of the second b_2; and we stipulate that, for every atomic propositional function φ and for every system of arguments, the logical values of $\varphi(b_1, x_2, x_3, ..., x_n)$ and $\varphi(b_2, x_2, x_3, ..., x_n)$ will be the same as that of $\varphi(b, x_2, x_3, ..., x_n)$. We can similarly assume that any function takes different values for different arguments.

4.31. We can even start from several propositions; to define their truth we construct the domains C_k that correspond to their logical product (to define their falsity, those that correspond to their logical sum); we see immediately that, if each proposition is true in a reduced domain associated with their product (or false in a reduced domain associated with their sum), this product (or sum) is true (or false) in this domain, and conversely.

5. Fundamental theorem

5. Theorem. (1) *If for some number p a proposition P has property B of order p, the proposition P is true. Once we know any such p, we can construct a proof of P.*

(2) *If we have a true proposition P, together with a proof of P, we can,*

from this proof, derive a number p such that P has property B of order p.

We shall say: *The necessary and sufficient condition for a proposition P to be true is that for some p the proposition P have property B of order p.*

5.1. LEMMA 1. *A proposition P that ⟦for some p⟧ has property C ⟦of order p⟧ has property A.*

This will be proved when we have stated a scheme, a type, and a set of equations associated with the proposition P (see § 2).

Assume that P has property C of order p ⟦and is of height h⟧; let N be the number of elements in ⟦the union of all the domains up to and including⟧ C_p (same notation as in 3.21). Consider some prenex form of P without real variables, and take property C in the form of 3.4.[56] We shall construct a scheme associated with P (2.2) such that each restricted variable ⟦of the scheme⟧ is immediately behind a brace joining N rows;[57] we shall say that the restricted variable occurring in the ith row immediately on the right of the brace is *attached* to the element a_i. Hence, in an arbitrary line of the scheme, each restricted variable is attached to an element a_i, with $i \leq N$.

---

[56] ⟦Since, if P is not in prenex form, no prenex form of P need have property C of order p (see Note H, p. 199 below), to carry through the argument that Herbrand is about to give we must be able to calculate from the number p and the proposition P a number q such that some prenex form of P has property C of order q. Hence, in the light of 3.31′ of Note H the first two sentences in the present paragraph should be replaced by the following paragraph:

Let P contain j quantifiers and d descriptive functions, the maximum height of these functions being h, and assume that P has property C of order p. Let P′ be a prenex form of P without real variables. Then P′ has property C of order $q = \delta(j, d, p, n_1)$. Let N be the number of elements in G_q, and let us consider the second disjunction of order q associated with P′.

Moreover, throughout the remainder of Herbrand's proof of Lemma 1 in 5.1 read 'q' wherever the text has 'p'.⟧

[57] ⟦To Herbrand's definition of a scheme (1.4) we must add here the stipulation that the dominant variables of the scheme are joined by an initial brace. A row should not be confused with a line of the scheme. A row consists of just one signed letter immediately to the right of a brace.

Let us note that, if P contains r restricted quantifiers, the scheme now being constructed has N^r lines and is what in footnote 17 was called a reduced scheme.⟧

We shall now define a correspondence between the elements of all the domains [up to and including C_{q+h+1}] and the general variables of the scheme (and descriptive functions of such variables, if any).[58] We stipulate that each general variable y shall correspond to the element that is the value of $f_y(a_{i_1}, a_{i_2}, ..., a_{i_n})$, where f_y is the index function of y, and $a_{i_1}, a_{i_2}, ..., a_{i_n}$ are the elements attached to the restricted variables that occur on the same line as y but to its left. With the elements of C_1 we correlate fictitious (in the sense of 2.1) general variables. Finally, with each element of the domains [up to and including C_{q+h+1}] we correlate either a general variable, in accordance with the preceding rule, or a descriptive function of general variables, stipulating that for a *descriptive* function f, if $a_{i_1}, a_{i_2}, ..., a_{i_n}$ correspond to the general variables or to the functions $\varphi_1, \varphi_2, ..., \varphi_n$ of general variables,[58] the value of $f(a_{i_1}, a_{i_2}, ..., a_{i_n})$ in the domains corresponds to the function $f(\varphi_1, \varphi_2, ..., \varphi_n)$. We readily see that to each element of the domains there thus corresponds one and *only one* general variable or function of general variables.

Let the order of a line [in the scheme] be the greatest of the orders of the domains of any of the elements that correspond to the restricted variables of that line.

We obtain the associated type by selecting, one after another, all the variables occurring in the lines of order 1, then all those occurring in the lines of order 2, then all those occurring in the lines of order 3, and so on up to and including order p.

We obtain the associated equations by equating each restricted variable to the general variable, or the function of general variables, that corresponds to the element attached to the restricted variable. We see that a restricted variable is always equated to a general variable, or to a function of general variables, occurring in lines whose order is less than its own; hence these equations yield associated equations that are compatible with the type considered.

Now we only have to see that the disjunction thus obtained is an identity. But, clearly, this disjunction comes from the second disjunction of order p associated with P (3.4)[59] when each element of the domains is replaced by its corresponding general variable or function of general

[58] [[See footnote 21, p. 147 above.]]

[59] [[Rather, of order q associated with P' (see footnote 56).]]

variables (each line of the scheme corresponds to a disjunct of this identity).[60]

COROLLARY. *A proposition that* [[*for some number p*]] *has property B* [[*of order p*]] *is true.*

For we have seen that

(1) Property B is equivalent to property C (3.31)[45] and

(2) A proposition that has property A is true (2.3).[16]

This proves the first part of the theorem.

5.2. To prove the second part of the theorem we proceed by recursion on the proof of the proposition.

(1) [[For every p,]] if $P \vee P$ has property B [[of order p]], then P has property B [[of order p]]. This is seen at once from the definition [[of property B]] given in 3.22.

(2) [[For every p,]] if $\Phi(x)$ has property B [[of order p]], then $(x) \Phi(x)$ has property B [[of order p]]. For, as we saw in 3.2, in order to construct the expansions of $\Phi(x)$ and $(x) \Phi(x)$, we must first replace each of these propositions by the same proposition $(y_1, y_2, ..., y_n, x) \Phi(x)$, where y_1, $y_2, ..., y_n$ are the real variables of $(x) \Phi(x)$.

LEMMA 2. *Property C is preserved when the second rule of generalization (in the form given in Chap. 3, 1.4) is used.*[61]

[[This second rule of generalization is:]] If t is an individual that depends upon [[possibly fictitious]] real variables, we can go from $\vdash \Phi(t)$ to $\vdash (\exists x) \Phi(x)$.

---

[60] [[Thus, under the correspondence between elements of G_{q+h+1} and members of the associated scheme, the standard expansion of the prenex proposition P' (see footnotes 47 and 56) yields the identity associated with P, and hence shows that P has property A. But, then, a far more informative way of correcting Herbrand's argument for Lemma 1 than that given in footnote 56 would be to use the generalized notion of generating scheme mentioned in footnote 15, p. 144 above. For we would not need to consider a second disjunction of order q associated with P (that is, the standard expansion of P' of order q); rather, we would be able to set up a correspondence between the elements of G_{p+h+1} and members of the new scheme such that the standard expansion of P of order p would yield an identity associated with P.]]

[61] [[In general, the order does not remain invariant. If t is of height $k \geqslant 2$ and $\Phi(t)$ has property C of order p, then $(\exists x) \Phi(x)$ has property C of some order less than or equal to $p + k - 1$.]]

Let us take property C in the form given in 3.4.[62]

We know (3.221) that to the real variables there will correspond some fixed elements of C_2; so the element that will correspond to t will be in C_k for some $k \geq 2$; let us call this element a_i. Suppose that the first proposition has property C of order p. For the second proposition we consider the second associated disjunction (see 3.4) of order $p+k-1$, and in this disjunction we consider only the disjuncts in which x is replaced by a_i. We see immediately that their disjunction constitutes a second disjunction of order p associated with the proposition $\Phi(t)$, the first domain being C_1; hence it is a propositional identity; but then so is the original disjunction.

5.3. LEMMA 3. *For every p, if the propositions P and P $\supset$ Q have property C of order p, then Q has property C of order p.*[63]

According to 3.53, $P \& (P \supset Q)$ has property C of order p. We put P and Q into prenex form; they are then written

$$(\pm y_1, \pm y_2, ..., \pm y_r) M (y_1, y_2, ..., y_r, x_1, x_2, ..., x_n)$$

and

$$(\pm z_1, \pm z_2, ..., \pm z_s) N (z_1, z_2, ..., z_s, x_1, x_2, ..., x_n),$$

respectively, if we exhibit all the real variables (some may be fictitious (3.52) in P or in Q). The conjunction $P \& (P \supset Q)$ can be written, when transformed according to the rules of passage,

$$(- y_1^{\alpha_1}, + y_1^{1-\alpha_1}, - y_2^{\alpha_2}, + y_2^{1-\alpha_2}, ..., - y_r^{\alpha_r}, + y_r^{1-\alpha_r},$$
$$\pm z_1, \pm z_2, ..., \pm z_s) \{M (y_1^0, y_2^0, ..., y_r^0, x_1, x_2, ..., x_n)$$
$$\& [M (y_1^1, y_2^1, ..., y_r^1, x_1, x_2, ..., x_n)$$
$$\supset N (z_1, z_2, ..., z_s, x_1, x_2, ..., x_n)]\}.$$

In this proposition a_i is 0 or 1 according as y_i is restricted or general in P; moreover, for each pair of variables y_i^0 and y_i^1 we have a pair of successive quantifiers, of which the first is restricted and the second general (since whenever y_1^0 is restricted, y_1^1 is general, and conversely, according to Chap. 2, 3.102). For the proposition in question we take property C in the form given in 3.4. We therefore have domains $C_1, C_2, ..., C_k, ...,$

---

[62] [[Throughout the proof of Lemma 2 we should use the standard expansion of a proposition instead of the second disjunction of order p associated with the proposition; see footnote 47.]]

[63] [[See Note I, p. 200 below.]]

C_{p+h+1} generated by the descriptive and index functions of the proposition. We transform them into domains $C_1', C_2', ..., C_k', ..., C_{p+h+1}'$ as follows. First, C_1' is C_1. Then, for each $k > 1$, C_k' is obtained from C_k thus: let f_t be the index function of the [[general]] variable t; for each value of $y_i^{\alpha_i}$, we consider the elements of C_k that are values of $f_{y_i}^{1-\alpha_i}(y_1^{\alpha_1}, y_2^{\alpha_2}, ..., y_i^{\alpha_i})$ for all possible values of $y_1^{\alpha_1}, y_2^{\alpha_2}, ..., y_{i-1}^{\alpha_{i-1}}$, and [[in $C_1 \cup C_2 \cup ... \cup C_k$]] we equate all these elements to the value of $y_i^{\alpha_i}$; moreover, for each system of values of $z_{u_1}, z_{u_2}, ..., z_{u_j}$, we consider the elements of C_k that are values of $f_{z_j}(y_1^{\alpha_1}, y_2^{\alpha_2}, ..., y_r^{\alpha_r}, z_{u_1}, z_{u_2}, ..., z_{u_j})$ for all possible values of $y_1^{\alpha_1}, y_2^{\alpha_2}, ..., y_r^{\alpha_r}$ and [[in $C_1 \cup C_2 \cup ... \cup C_k$]] we equate all these elements to one of them.

Clearly, these new domains are the very domains that are generated from C_1 by the descriptive and index functions of Q. And we see, once the equating just presented is taken into account, that the second disjunction of order p associated with $P \& (P \supset Q)$ [[over the original domains]] becomes the identity

(I) $$[P_1 \& (P_1 \supset Q_1)] \vee [P_2 \& (P_2 \supset Q_2)]$$
$$\vee \cdots \vee [P_\gamma \& (P_\gamma \supset Q_\gamma)],$$

where P_i and Q_i, $1 \leq i \leq \gamma$, are the propositions obtained when the operations described in 3.4 are carried out over these new domains on the matrices of P and Q. Moreover,

(II) $$Q_1 \vee Q_2 \vee \cdots \vee Q_\gamma$$

differs from the [[second]] disjunction of order p associated with Q only in that certain disjuncts are repeated several times.[64]

Now, Theorem 5.21 of Chap. 1 shows that the truth of the disjunction (I) implies that of the disjunction (II), since, for each given system of logical values, there is an i such that the logical value 'true' is assigned to $P_i \& (P_i \supset Q_i)$, hence to $P_i \supset Q_i$, hence to Q_i, and hence to the disjunction (II).

[64] [[Throughout this last paragraph the prenex forms of P, Q, and $P \& (P \supset Q)$ should be understood when Herbrand speaks simply of P, Q, and $P \& (P \supset Q)$; see Note I. However, Herbrand's argument could be slightly modified so that Q need not be in prenex form.]]

If P should contain descriptive functions not occurring in Q, we would use Remark 3.52.

5.31. We now recall that

(1) Identities of the first kind, that is, with no apparent variables, have property B,

(2) Property B and property C are equivalent (3.31),[45] and

(3) For every p, if a proposition P has property B of order p, then P has property B of order q for every q greater than p (3.54).

Therefore, Lemma 2, Lemma 3,[63] the lemma of 3.3,[44] and the remarks of 5.2 prove the second part of the Fundamental Theorem.

REMARKS. (1) Properties A, B, and C are therefore equivalent[65] and can be said to be necessary and sufficient for the truth of a proposition. The preceding theorem then shows that the proof of any true proposition can be reduced to a canonical form, namely, one in which the proposition is obtained from its associated identity (2.3) (which is the [[second]] disjunction of order p associated with the proposition).[66]

(2) We could easily show that, if in the proof of a proposition P the second rule of generalization is used n times, for individuals of heights $h_1, h_2, ..., h_n$, then P has property B of an order at most equal to $h_1 + h_2 + ... + h_n + n$.[67]

(3) If there should be more than one type in the proposition under study, we would have to distinguish, in each domain, elements of different types (the value of a function, in particular, is of the type of that function) and replace a variable only by elements of the same type. But, aside from these points, nothing would be changed in the previous considerations. (An index function is taken to be of the same type as the variable to which it is attached.)[68]

---

[65] [[See Note H and footnote 56.]]

[66] [[In this canonical form for a proof of P, some prenex form P' of P is first proved, and then P is obtained by use of the rules of passage. Hence the associated identity (2.3) of P is indeed a second disjunction associated with P, for it is the standard expansion of P' (see footnotes 47 and 56). Compare Remark 4 in 6.4 below.]]

[67] [[This is false because of the falsity of Lemma 3.3 and Lemma 3 in 5.3.]]

[68] [[Here Herbrand extends his Fundamental Theorem to many-sorted logics (Chap. 3, 1.11). See also 6.6, p. 179 below and *1931*, p. 227 below.]]

6. Consequences

A. *Consequences Concerning the Decision Problem*

6.1. COROLLARY 1. We have seen[69] that the rule of implication is not necessary for the proof of a proposition having property A, provided we replace the rule of simplification by the following

GENERALIZED RULE OF SIMPLIFICATION. *If in a true proposition the subproposition $P \lor P$ is replaced by P, we obtain another true proposition.*

Now, from our theorem and Lemma 1 in 5.1 it follows that *every true proposition has property A.* Hence the only rules of reasoning that are needed are the rules of passage, the two rules of generalization and the generalized rule of simplification. The rule of implication drops out.

Because of the difficulties that the rule of implication might create in certain ⟦metamathematical⟧ demonstrations that proceed by recursion on ⟦formal⟧ proofs, we consider this result most important. It shows, moreover, that the rule of implication, whose origin, after all, is in the classical syllogism, is not necessary in building logic. (The rule remains necessary, however, in mathematical theories, which contain hypotheses.)

6.2. The theorems stated in § 5 and in 4.21 permit us to set forth the following results:

THEOREM 1. *If P is an identity, $\sim P$ is not true in any infinite domain*;

THEOREM 2. *If P is not an identity, we can construct an infinite domain in which $\sim P$ is true.*

Similar results have already been stated by Löwenheim (*1915*),[70] but his proofs, it seems to us, are totally insufficient for our purposes. First, he gives an intuitive meaning to the notion 'true in an infinite domain', hence his proof of Theorem 2 does not attain the rigor that we deem desirable (indeed the ⟦required⟧ proof is contained in the considerations of § 4 and of 5.1). Then – and this is the gravest reproach – because of the intuitive meaning that he gives to this notion, he seems to regard

---

[69] ⟦See 2.2, 2.3, and Note F, p. 192 below.⟧

[70] ⟦See the Introduction, p. 13 above.⟧

Theorem 1 as obvious. This is absolutely impermissible; such an attitude would lead us, for example, to regard the consistency of arithmetic as obvious. On the contrary, it is precisely the proof of this theorem (of which the lemma of 3.3 is a part) that presented us with the greatest difficulties.

We could say that Löwenheim's proof was sufficient in mathematics; but, in the present work, we had to make it 'metamathematical' (see Introduction) so that it would be of some use to us.

6.3. The two theorems that we just stated provide us with a method for investigating the decision problem. By means of this method we have succeeded in obtaining new solutions for all the particular cases already solved and even in somewhat extending these cases.[71] Moreover, we can now deal with a case that is essentially different from those already known, namely, the case of *a proposition whose matrix is a disjunction of atomic propositions and negations of atomic propositions* (the atomic propositions may contain descriptive functions). A proposition is an identity if and only if it has property A; in the present case, whether a proposition has property A can readily be decided by the use of 2.34 and 2.4.

6.4. REMARK 1. We see without difficulty that a proposition true in some finite domain (Chap. 2, 8.3) is also true in some infinite domain (here there is a bound, namely, the number of elements in the finite domain, on the number of elements in each domain D_n in the infinite domain); hence the theorem of Chap. 2, § 8, immediately follows from Theorem 1.[72]

REMARK 2. The notion 'satisfiability' ('Erfüllbarkeit') that Ackermann used in *1928* does not seem to us to be defined in a sufficiently complete manner, for we have not been given a precise stipulation that would

---

[71] For example, to the case of a disjunction of propositions of the form

$$(x_1 x_2 \ldots x_n) \, (\exists y) \, (z_1 z_2 \ldots z_p) \, A(x_1, x_2, \ldots, x_n, y, z_1, z_2, \ldots, z_p).$$

[[See *1931*, p. 249 below.]]

[72] [[As in Chap. 3, 1.42, Herbrand is once again using 'true in a finite domain' to mean that the common expansion of the proposition is truth-functionally satisfiable (see footnote 2 of Chap. 3, p. 105 above). See Note K, p. 259 below.]]

permit us to state that a proposition is 'satisfiable'.[73] Theorem 1 immediately allows us to remove this objection. Now, let P be a proposition of the form

$$(x_1, x_2, ..., x_n)(\exists z)(y_1, y_2, ..., y_p)$$
$$A(x_1, x_2, ..., x_n, z, y_1, y_2, ..., y_p).$$

If P is not an identity, we can construct an infinite domain in which $\sim P$ is true; clearly, merely by repeating Ackermann's argument, we see that there is also a finite domain, consisting of a known number of elements, in which $\sim P$ is true.[72] On the other hand, if P is an identity, $\sim P$ cannot be true in such a finite domain (according to Chap. 2, 8.1); we therefore have a criterion that enables us to decide whether P is an identity or not.

Moreover, it is possible, and simpler, to show by a similar argument that, if a proposition P of the form considered has property C, it has this property with an order that we can determine in advance; and this provides a criterion equivalent to the previous one.[74]

REMARK 3. We see the following: if to our rules of reasoning, listed at the beginning of Chap. 2, we were to adjoin other rules that could

---

[73] [[Herbrand is here contrasting Ackermann's intuitive (that is, set-theoretic) notion 'satisfiable' with his own metamathematical (that is, finitistic) notion 'true in an infinite domain', which by Theorems 1 and 2 of 6.2 is equivalent to the notion 'irrefutable in Q_H'. Herbrand is *not* demanding that a decision procedure for satisfiability be given. Indeed, he is objecting to Ackermann's use of 'satisfiability' with respect to a class K of propositions for which he knows that Ackermann (*1928*) has shown that:

For each proposition P in K, there is effectively obtainable a number n such that $\sim P$ is satisfiable if and only if the common expansion of $\sim P$ over a domain of cardinality n is truth-functionally satisfiable.

Rather, Herbrand is demanding that the notion 'satisfiability' not be used in metamathematics. (Of course, Herbrand permits 'truth-functional satisfiability'.) Hence, in this first paragraph of Remark 2, Herbrand exploits Ackermann's argument to prove that:

For each proposition P in K, there is effectively obtainable a number n such that P is provable in Q_H if and only if the common expansion of $\sim P$ over a domain of cardinality n is not truth-functionally satisfiable.]]

[74] [[See Herbrand's treatment of solvable cases of the decision problem, *1931*, pp. 246ff. below.]]

not be derived from them, then we would be led to regard as true ⟦that is, provable⟧ some propositions that are in fact false in some infinite domain. We must acknowledge that such a consequence would be difficult to accept. This fact corresponds to what the Germans call the *Vollständig-keit* of our system of rules. (If we could *prove* that these additional rules lead us to regard as true a proposition P that, without them, would not be so, then, as we can readily see, the inconsistency of classical mathematics would follow, because we could construct a denumerable set over which P would be false.) [75]

REMARK 4. We can view the theorem of § 5 as giving us a canonical form for every mathematical proof; for, if we know the order p with which a proposition has property B, we can, according to 5.1, specify the proof of this proposition. [66] More generally, we can say that, if a theorem P is true ⟦that is, provable⟧ in a theory on the basis of hypotheses (containing no apparent variables ⟦rather, containing no real variables⟧) whose logical product is H, the proof of P can be obtained in the following manner (according to 6.2 and Chap. 3, 2.4): *we try to construct an infinite domain in which $H \supset P$ is false, and after a certain number of operations we see that the construction is impossible.* [76] Thus we can say that, if the proposition is indeed a theorem, we can always give a proof of it that does not use any artifice, the role of artifices being only to make proofs shorter. [77]

B. *Consequences Concerning the Investigation of Mathematical Theories*

6.5. The theorems obtained in the previous sections have many applications; they provide a general method for the investigation of mathematical theories. We shall briefly point out some of these applications, laying stress on the most important of them, the consistency of ordinary arithmetic.

---

[75] ⟦See Note N, p. 265 below.⟧

[76] ⟦See the 'no-counterexample' proof techniques of Beth (*1955*) and Hintikka (*1955*); see also Skolem *1928* and *1929*, § 5. Kreisel (*1958*, p. 36) pointed out that Beth's constructive argument for modus ponens elimination (*1956*, pp. 38–40; see also *1959*, pp. 278–280) contains an error. But it should be noted that no argument that proceeds, as does Beth's, just by recursion on the construction of the 'eliminable formula' can succeed.⟧

[77] ⟦See *Gentzen 1934*, p. 177; in particular, consider Gentzen's "Er macht keine Umwege".⟧

(1) *If all the hypotheses of a theory are true in some infinite domain (4.31), the theory is consistent* (Chap. 3, 2.1).[78]

For, if a theory is inconsistent, we see immediately that we can find hypotheses $H_1, H_2, ..., H_n$, which can always be assumed to contain no apparent variables [[rather, no real variables]], such that $\sim (H_1 \& H_2 \& ... \& H_n)$ is an identity, hence has property B. But, according to 4.11, this is impossible, since $H_1 \& H_2 \& ... \& H_n$, by 4.31, is true in some infinite domain, and so $\sim (H_1 \& H_2 \& ... \& H_n)$ is false [[in this infinite domain]].

(2) *If a theory is consistent and has only a finite number of hypotheses,*[79] *we can construct an infinite domain in which these hypotheses are true.*[80]

It suffices, as we see immediately by virtue of 4.3, to make the logical product of these hypotheses true in a reduced domain (4.3).

We shall now briefly present some immediate consequences [[of (1) and (2)]]. But first we note that, if a theory contains constants, that is, descriptive functions of 0 argument, we shall have to represent these constants in the infinite domains by certain elements that we include in the domain of order 1.

6.6. The theorems stated in 6.5 can be used to show that no proposition [[written in the notation of but]] unprovable in a given theory becomes provable when certain changes are made in the theory.[81]

---

[78] [[This is one of the most important consequences of Herbrand's Fundamental Theorem and supplies much of the motivation for it; indeed, the present statement (1) greatly simplifies the Hilbert-Ackermann-von Neumann approach to proving the consistency of theories (see 6.8 below, *Ackermann 1924, Hilbert 1925* and *1927, Bernays 1927, von Neumann 1927*), also Bernay's discussion of this point (*1934a; 1936,* remark 1, pp. 115–116; *Hilbert and Bernays 1939,* pp. 38 and 48) as well as *Kleene 1952,* pp. 475–476, and the Introduction, p. 14 above.]]

[79] It is easy but unnecessary to remove the latter restriction.

[80] This proposition is the 'metamathematical' form of the proposition known as the 'Skolem paradox'; for one should observe that metamathematical arguments about infinite domains, when translated into mathematical arguments, become arguments about denumerable sets. [[See the Introduction, pp. 13 and 16 above, as well as Herbrand's remarks in *1930a,* p. 214 below, and *1931,* footnote 65, p. 256 below.]]

[81] [[Compare 6.6 with §§ 5–6 in *Skolem 1929* and with *Herbrand 1931,* pp. 232–235 below. Also, compare the last paragraph of 6.6 with *Craig 1957* and *1960.*]]

Let us assume, for example, that we have a theory with a certain number of types; for each type we can introduce the propositional function $x = y$, of arguments x and y, to be read 'x is equal to y', in which x and y will be of the type considered (hence we shall have different propositional functions, represented by arrays of signs that differ only in the type of the variables).

We add the following hypotheses, hereafter denoted by (1):

$$x = x, \ (x = y) \supset (y = x), \ \text{and} \ [(x = y) \ \& \ (y = z)] \supset (x = z)$$

for each type,

$$[(x_1 = y_1) \ \& \ (x_2 = y_2) \ \& \ \cdots \ \& \ (x_n = y_n)]$$
$$\supset [\Phi(x_1, x_2, ..., x_n) \supset \Phi(y_1, y_2, ..., y_n)]$$

for each atomic propositional function $\Phi(x_1, x_2, ..., x_n)$ and

$$[(x_1 = y_1) \ \& \ (x_2 = y_2) \ \& \ \cdots \ \& \ (x_n = y_n)]$$
$$\supset [f(x_1, x_2, ..., x_n) = f(y_1, y_2, ..., y_n)]$$

for each elementary descriptive function $f(x_1, x_2, ..., x_n)$.

Clearly, the last two formulas of (1) can be proved in the extended theory for every propositional function and every descriptive function.

Let us further assume that the hypotheses (1), together with the original ones, bring about the truth ⟦that is, the provability in the theory⟧ of a certain proposition P, which does not contain the new propositional function and was not true ⟦that is, provable in the theory⟧ before the introduction of this new propositional function. Let $H_1, H_2, ..., H_n$ be the hypotheses of the original theory that are necessary for the proof of P; then the hypotheses $H_1, H_2, ..., H_n$, and $\sim P$, which were conjointly consistent, become inconsistent when taken together with the hypotheses (1). Now, we can construct an infinite domain in which $H_1, H_2, ..., H_n$, and $\sim P$ are true; moreover, to make the hypotheses (1) true in this infinite domain we merely have to agree that $a_i = a_j$ (where a_i and a_j are elements of the domain) has the logical value 'true' just if the letters a_i and a_j are the same. But, since the hypotheses $H_1, H_2, ..., H_n$, $\sim P$, and (1) are true in some infinite domain, they cannot be conjointly inconsistent.

Therefore, *if a proposition is not true* ⟦*that is, provable*⟧ *before equality has been introduced, it cannot be so afterward.*

We could show by the same method that it is also possible to introduce into a theory the notion 'couple', $\langle x, y \rangle$, along with the axiom

$$(\langle x, y \rangle = \langle x', y' \rangle) \equiv [(x = x') \,\&\, (y = y')]$$

(provided that a couple is not of the type of its arguments). This would show the consistency of the theory of rational numbers.[82]

Let us now go back to the case in which equality was introduced and see how we can obtain a proof of a proposition P, not containing equality, in a theory without equality [once we have a proof of P in the extension of the theory obtained by adjunction of equality]. Let us assume that the proposition

$$(H_1 \,\&\, H_2 \,\&\, \cdots \,\&\, H_n \,\&\, H) \supset P,$$

where H is the product of those hypotheses (1) that we are using, has property B of order p. If we look at the proof of the results obtained in 4.21 and 4.3, we can conclude that

$$(H_1 \,\&\, H_2 \,\&\, \cdots \,\&\, H_n) \supset P$$

has property B of order p; from this last fact we can obtain a proof of P.

6.7. According to Löwenheim (*1915*), the decision problem would be solved for the general case if it were solved for the case in which each [atomic] propositional function has only two arguments; the proof, which rested on his insufficiently established results, is now completely justified.[83] We can even go further and:

(a) Prove that we can restrict ourselves to the case in which there is no longer any constant or descriptive function. For this we use, primarily, Russell and Whitehead's theory of descriptions. It would suffice first to introduce equality as in 6.6, and then to replace each descriptive function $f(x_1, x_2, ..., x_n)$ by a propositional function $\Phi(y, x_1, x_2, ..., x_n)$, which is to be taken as $y = f(x_1, x_2, ..., x_n)$, and add the hypotheses $(\exists z)\,(y)$ $[\Phi(y, x_1, x_2, ..., x_n) \supset (y = z)]$.

(b) Prove that we can restrict ourselves to the case in which either there is only one propositional function of three arguments [rather, one ternary

---

[82] And of Euclidean geometry, in Hilbert's axiomatization, without the completeness axiom. [[See *Hilbert and Bernays 1939*, pp. 33–48, especially pp. 38–48.]]

[83] [[See *1931*, pp. 235–243 below, for Herbrand's proof of this result and also for his proofs of the results announced here in (*a*) and (*b*).]]

predicate letter]] or there are no more than three propositional functions of two arguments [[rather, three binary predicate letters]].

(c) Prove easily that we can dispense with apparent variables if, following Hilbert, we introduce the 'logical function' (each proposition will give rise to such a function, with the real variables as arguments, and to a corresponding axiom; see *Hilbert 1927*). In particular, we can always assume that the hypotheses of a theory contain only real variables.[84]

6.8. *Consistency of arithmetic*. The results of 6.5 enable us to solve the problem of the consistency of arithmetic much more completely [[that is, for more extensive subsystems]] than we did in Chap. 4.

Let us recall that in arithmetic there is one atomic propositional function, $x = y$, one primitive descriptive function, $x + 1$, and one primitive constant, 0; we can, moreover, introduce new descriptive functions, which are defined by recursion (Chap. 4, 8.5).[85]

Let the domain A be the unbounded sequence of letters $a_0, a_1, a_2, \ldots,$ $a_n, \ldots$; we stipulate that a_0 shall be the constant 0. With these letters we shall form the domains that we need; we stipulate that $a_i = a_j$ shall have the logical value 'true' just if the subscripts i and j are identical.

Let $f(x_1, x_2, \ldots, x_n)$ be a (descriptive or index) function; we shall say that we know its value in the domain A if we have a procedure that enables us to assign a value to $f(a_{i_1}, a_{i_2}, \ldots, a_{i_n})$ for each system of arguments taken in the domain.

A proposition P will be said to be *true in the domain A* if, after correlating with each restricted variable x of P an index function whose arguments are the general variables superior to x and the real variables, we can so assign values in the domain A to these functions that the proposition obtained when the restricted variables of P are replaced by their index functions has the logical value (calculated as in 4.1) 'true', no matter which elements of the domain A are put for the general [[and real]] variables.

---

[84] [[See footnote 24, p. 149 above, and Note J, p. 201 below.]]

[85] [[In the next five paragraphs of the text Herbrand gives a new and very simple proof, based on Theorem 1 of 6.5, of the consistency of Theory 3 (p. 125 above); this proof, however, does not show the decidability of Theorem 3, as did the more complex argument of Chap. 4.]]

Clearly, if several propositions are true in the domain A, then A yields an infinite domain in which these propositions are true.[86]

Now, if we stipulate that the value of $a_i + 1$ is a_{i+1}, we can immediately see that all the axioms of § 5 of Chap. 4 are true in the domain A; moreover, the domain A yields an infinite domain once we agree that for each p the domain $[\![D_p]\!]$ of order p in this infinite domain consists of $a_0, a_1, ..., a_p$. Hence these axioms are consistent.

But now we can go further.[87]

I. *Introduction of recursive definitions.* Proceeding in a more general way than in Chap. 4, 8.5, we shall assume that to the theory considered[88] we can adjoin new descriptive functions and new hypotheses in the following manner: we assume that the modifications introduced above $[\![$in 6.6$]\!]$ have already led to a theory T whose hypotheses are true in the domain A; we introduce a new descriptive function $f(y, x_1, ..., x_n)$, of arguments $y, x_1, ..., x_n$, and add hypotheses of the form

$$\Phi[f(0, x_1, ..., x_n)], \tag{1}$$

$$\Psi[f(y, x_1, ..., x_n), f(y + 1, x_1, ..., x_n)], \tag{2}$$

$$[(y = y') \ \& \ (x_1 = x_1') \ \& \ \cdots \ \& \ (x_n = x_n')]$$
$$\supset [f(y, x_1, ..., x_n) = f(y', x_1', ..., x_n')], \tag{3}$$

provided that the propositions

$$(\exists x) \ \Phi(x) \tag{4}$$

and

$$(y)(\exists x) \ \Psi(y, x) \tag{5}$$

are true $[\![$that is, provable$]\!]$ in the theory T (Φ and Ψ may contain other variables $x_1, x_2, ..., x_n$[89]).

---

[86] $[\![$Herbrand seems here to be modifying his definition of 'truth in an infinite domain', since now the function replacing a restricted variable x has as arguments all the general variables superior to x, as well as the real variables of the proposition. See also *1931*, p. 229 below.$]\!]$

[87] $[\![$In *1931c*, pp. 290–294 below, Herbrand gives much clearer and simpler proofs for results (I) and (II) obtained immediately below.$]\!]$

[88] $[\![$That is, Theory 2 (p. 120 above).$]\!]$

[89] $[\![$This parenthetical remark is unclear. Formulas (4) and (5) contain no free variables other than $x_1, x_2, ..., x_n$, while their bound variables are x, y, and possibly others.$]\!]$

We shall prove the consistency [of this extended theory] on the very weak assumption that propositions (4) and (5) are true in the domain A (in other words, that they can be 'interpreted' in that domain). It suffices to observe that propositions (1) and (2) are true in the domain A when, first, as index functions of the [restricted] variables of these propositions we take the index functions of the corresponding variables of (4) and (5) and, second, we choose the values of the function $f(y, x_1, x_2, ..., x_n)$ in the following way: $f(0, x_1, x_2, ..., x_n)$ shall be the index function of x in (4); if the index function of x in (5) is $\varphi(y, x_1, x_2, ..., x_n)$, we shall take the value of $\varphi(f(y, x_1, x_2, ..., x_n), x_1, x_2, ..., x_n)$ for that of $f(y+1, x_1, x_2, ..., x_n)$; this completely defines the value of $f(y, x_1, x_2, ..., x_n)$ in the domain A. Proposition (3) is, of course, true in the domain.

II. *Introduction of the axiom of mathematical induction.* We recall (Chap. 4, 8.1) that propositions of the form

$$\{\Phi(0) \mathbin{\&} (x)[\Phi(x) \supset \Phi(x+1)]\} \supset (y)\,\Phi(y) \tag{6}$$

must be added to the hypotheses.[90]

When we attempt to prove the consistency of the theory thus obtained,[91] we are confronted with difficulties that we shall not try to resolve here, our goal being only to show the fruitfulness of the notion 'infinite domain'. If hypotheses of the form (6) are introduced among the hypotheses [referred to at the end of the preceding paragraph], we shall prove the consistency [of the theory thus obtained] only in either of the following two cases (which, however, as can easily be seen, are the principal cases in which the axiom of mathematical induction is used).

---

[90] [[These hypotheses are the axioms of Theory 2 together with propositions (1), (2), and (3) just given for the introduction of primitive recursive functions.]]

[91] [[This theory is full elementary number theory. To understand the difficulties with which "we are confronted", of whose true nature Herbrand had as yet no inkling, see *Gödel 1931* and *Herbrand 1931c*, § 4 (pp. 295–297 below); see also *Gentzen 1936* and *1938*, *Ackermann 1940*, and *Schütte 1951* and *1960*. Unlike Herbrand, Hilbert, Bernays, Ackermann and von Neumann (see *Bernays 1927* in *van Heijenoort 1967*, p. 489, and the editor's footnote 3 on the same page) thought – until they became acquainted with Gödel's incompleteness results – that their consistency arguments could readily be extended to full elementary number theory. Herbrand was clearly aware that attempts to so extend the arguments he gives would meet with difficulties.]]

(a) *Case in which $\Phi(a)$ is true in the domain A for every numeral a.*
It is then quite obvious that $(x)\,\Phi(x)$ is true in the domain A and can be added to the hypotheses without contradiction.

(b) *Case in which $\Phi(x)$ contains no apparent variable.*[92] Let us now assume that to the hypotheses we add all the propositions $P_1, P_2, ..., P_m$ obtained when in (6) we successively substitute $\Phi_1(x), \Phi_2(x), ..., \Phi_m(x)$ for $\Phi(x)$. Corresponding to the ⟦restricted⟧ quantifier (x) in P_i, $1 \leq i \leq m$, let us introduce the new index function $f_i(y_1, y_2, ..., y_{n_i})$, where $y_1, y_2, ...,$ y_{n_i} are the real variables of $\Phi_i(x)$ other than x. We seek to construct an infinite domain in which all the hypotheses of the theory under consideration are true. Hence we must show that, in addition to the original hypotheses (those of Chap. 4 and those due to the recursive definitions), each proposition

$$\{\Phi_i(0) \,\&\, [\Phi_i(f_i) \supset \Phi_i(f_i + 1)]\} \supset \Phi_i(y), \tag{7}$$

which results from the matrix of (6) when x is replaced by its index function, also can be made true. (Whenever we wish to exhibit all the real variables, $\Phi_i(x)$ will be written $\Phi_i(x, y_1, y_2, ..., y_{n_i})$.)

⟦For an arbitrary $p \geq 1$⟧ let E be the ⟦set of⟧ individuals of height not greater than p that are constructed from the constant 0, the original descriptive functions, and the new index functions.

We now have to construct an infinite domain in which all the hypotheses will come out true. The domain of order 0 will consist of a_0, and for each k the domain of order k will consist of letters from the domain A. Let Γ be the domain of order p ⟦in the infinite domain to be constructed⟧; every element of Γ is to be the value of an individual of E, and conversely every individual of E is to have a value in Γ. The hypotheses under consideration will be true in the infinite domain provided the following two conditions hold:

(1) The original descriptive functions have the same values as in A,

---

[92] ⟦Although in *1931c* Herbrand gives a much simpler proof of this result, the argument that he sketches here, once clarified, can be extended so as to establish the consistency of full elementary number theory (see *Dreben and Denton 1968* and *Dreben, Denton, and Scanlon 1972*). Moreover, the present argument is closely related to the argument for (c') in Note G, pp. 193–199 below.⟧

and the propositional function $x=y$ has the same logical value as in A;

(2) For each given sequence of n_i elements, $u_1, u_2, ..., u_{n_i}$, in Γ, the function $f_i(u_1, u_2, ..., u_{n_i})$ has the value 0 [[that is, a_0]] unless there is a $j>0$ such that

(α) a_j and a_{j+1} are in Γ,

(β) $\Phi_i(a_j, u_1, u_2, ..., u_{n_i})$ has the logical value 'true', and

(γ) $\Phi_i(a_{j+1}, u_1, u_2, ..., u_{n_i})$ has the logical value 'false',

in which case the function $f_i(u_1, u_2, ..., u_{n_i})$ has the value a_j.

Thus to actually construct the domain Γ we need only find the values that the new index functions have to take in Γ.

Every function (of whatever height) obtained from the original elementary descriptive functions will be called a function of the first kind; the new index functions (which are all of height 1) will be called functions of the second kind.

On any domain C [[contained in A]] in which the values of certain individuals of E are known, we shall perform, whenever possible, the following [[two-step]] operation:

(i) For each function of the first kind that is a function of individuals of E whose values in C are known, we add to C the value that this function has in the domain A (this value may or may not already occur in C; if it does, we simply have one more individual of E whose value in C is known);

(ii) Once this is done, for each function $f_i(y_1, y_2, ..., y_{n_i})$ of the second kind that is a function of individuals of E whose values $u_1, u_2, ..., u_{n_i}$ in C are known, we proceed thus:

(a) If $\Phi_i(0, u_1, u_2, ..., u_{n_i})$ is false in A, we assign the value 0 to $f_i(u_1, u_2, ..., u_{n_i})$;

(b) If there is a $j>0$ such that a_j and a_{j+1} are in C and $\Phi_i(a_j, u_1, u_2, ..., u_{n_i})$ has the logical value 'true' but $\Phi_i(a_{j+1}, u_1, u_2, ..., u_{n_i})$ has the logical value 'false', then we assign the value a_j to $f_i(u_1, u_2, ..., u_{n_i})$.

So let us start from the domain consisting of a_0 and perform the preceding operation a sufficient number of times; we obtain larger and larger domains, in which an ever-increasing number of individuals of E have values. It is quite obvious that we shall reach a point (after a number of operations at most equal to the number of individuals of E) where we have a domain Γ in which it is no longer possible to perform the preceding operation. The individuals of E will then fall into three sets:

(1) e_1, [the set of] those that have a value in the domain Γ;

(2) e_2, [the set of] those that are functions of the second kind of elements of e_1 but do not satisfy either (a) or (b) above;

(3) e_3, [the set of] those that are functions of elements of e_2.

To the elements of e_2 we assign the value 0. The elements of e_3 are functions of elements of e_2; in these functions we replace the elements of e_2 by 0. The elements of e_3 remain individuals of E, and their heights are not increased. To each of these elements of e_3 that thus become elements of e_1 or e_2 we assign the value of the individual of E into which it is transformed. For those that become other elements of e_3 we repeat the same transformation.

Thus we finally assign values in Γ to all the individuals of E. Hence we obtain the domain of order p that we were looking for. We observe immediately that this domain satisfies conditions (1) and (2) stated above [on page 185]; and so we come to the end of our proof.

This proof is a characteristic application of our method. We hope that our theorems will also enable us to prove the consistency of the theory that is obtained when the type of classes (Chap. 3, 2.3) and the corresponding axioms are added to arithmetic; the difficulties that we have encountered in this direction are similar to those presented by the general case of the axiom of mathematical induction and are, it seems to us, closely related to the questions raised by Hilbert's Lemma I (*1925*). We believe, moreover, that it may be possible by this approach to arrive at a general theorem of which a particular case would be: *transcendental methods will not enable us to prove in arithmetic any theorem that cannot be proved without their help.*[93] Our theorem of § 5, which provides a canonical form for every proof, would then enable us to give the purely arithmetic proof of these [arithmetic] theorems.

In the present § 6 we have given some simple applications of our theorems. We hope that in a paper soon to be written we shall be able to show their usefulness in the study of 'completely determined' theories

---

[93] We ascertained that this theorem could be proved if the decision problem were solved and we had a proof of the consistency of Russell and Whitehead's theory (with the assumption that the multiplicative axiom and the axiom of infinity are added to the theory). [[See *1931*, p. 257 below.]]

(Chap. 3, 2.1) and in that of the constructibility of mathematical objects.[94]

But it is quite certain that the most interesting line to pursue, and no doubt the most difficult, would be the one in which we search for a solution of the decision problem.[95] The solution of this problem would yield a general method in mathematics and would enable mathematical logic to play with respect to classical mathematics the role that analytic geometry plays with respect to ordinary geometry.

NOTE D

(footnote 12, p. 143 above)

Note that, for an arbitrary proposition P, not only is the proposition $(P \lor P) \equiv P$ provable in Q_H, but also each of the propositions $P \supset (P \lor P)$ and $(P \lor P) \supset P$ is provable in Q_H without the use of modus ponens.

(1) $P \supset (P \lor P)$ is an instance of $p \supset (p \lor q)$, a tautology in which each letter has at most one occurrence of each sign. Hence, by 2.13, p. 141 above, $P \supset (P \lor P)$ is a normal identity, hence is derivable without modus ponens (footnote 9, p. 141 above).

(2) $(P \lor P) \supset P$, however, is not necessarily a normal identity. For example, the instance

$$[(x)\,(\exists y)\,Fxy \lor (x)\,(\exists y)\,Fxy] \supset (x)\,(\exists y)\,Fxy$$

is not a normal identity. But consider $[(P \lor P) \supset P] \lor [(P \lor P) \supset P]$. This is an instance of $[(p \lor q) \supset p] \lor [(r \lor s) \supset q]$, a tautology in which each letter has at most one occurrence of each sign. Hence $[(P \lor P) \supset P] \lor [(P \lor P) \supset P]$ is a normal identity and therefore derivable without modus ponens; by the rule of simplification we have $(P \lor P) \supset P$.

Indeed, as was pointed out in Note B, all quantified tautologies can be obtained from quantifier-free tautologies just by the use of the rules of passage, universal

---

[94] [[Parts of Herbrand's subsequent papers (*1931* and *1931c*) touch upon these questions, but the paper that he contemplates was never written.]]

[95] [[See the last paragraph of the main text (p. 257 below) as well as the final Appendix (pp. 258–259 below) of *Herbrand 1931.*]]

generalization, existential generalization, and the following extended rule of simplification: from

$$\vdash : \Phi(x_1 x_1 x_2 \dots x_n) \lor \Phi(x_2 x_1 x_2 \dots x_n) \lor \dots \lor \Phi(x_n x_1 x_2 \dots x_n)$$

deduce

$$\vdash . (\exists y)\ \Phi(y x_1 x_2 \dots x_n).$$

(Note that in the absence of modus ponens this rule is not as strong as the rule: from $\vdash . P \lor P \lor \dots \lor P$ deduce $\vdash . P$; nor *a fortiori* as strong as the generalized rule of simplification that replaces modus ponens in the system Q'_H of Note F, p. 192 below.)

In addition, Herbrand's proof in Chap. 2, § 5 can be used to show that every quantified tautology P has a special form of property A: the normal type T associated with P can be derived from the scheme Σ associated with P, and in the associated equations a restricted variable y is equated to a general variable x only if x appears in T in a string of universal quantifiers that immediately precedes the string of existential quantifiers in which y appears.

We show this by an induction argument analogous to that appearing in Chap. 2, § 5, p. 83 above, and Note B, p. 99 above. That is, using the notation of that section, if the tautologous disjunction Q of

$$A[\Phi_1(x_i), \dots, \Phi_1(x_i);\ \Phi_1(x_{\alpha+1}), \dots, \Phi_1(x_{\alpha+\beta});\ \Phi_2, \dots, \Phi_n],$$

where i goes from $\alpha + 1$ to $\alpha + \beta$, has this special form of property A, then so does the tautology

$$A[(\exists x)\ \Phi_1(x), \dots, (\exists x)\ \Phi_1(x);\ (\exists x)\ \Phi_1(x), \dots, (\exists x)\ \Phi_1(x);\ \Phi_2, \dots, \Phi_n].$$

(Call the latter tautology R. In the Chap. 2 argument, to go from R to Q Herbrand uses a procedure of disjoining propositions obtained from R by replacing certain restricted variables by certain general variables; the proof we give here shows that in going from Q to R by reversing this procedure, the special form of property A is preserved.) For, let Σ be the scheme associated with Q, and let Σ_i $(i = 1, \dots, \beta)$ be the result of deleting from Σ all variables but those arising from the ith disjunct of Q. To get the appropriate scheme associated with R, define Σ' to be

$$+x_{\alpha+1}, +\cdots, +x_{\alpha+\beta} \begin{cases} -y_1^1, -\dots, -y_\alpha^1, \Sigma_1 \\ \vdots \\ -y_1^\beta, -\dots, -y_\alpha^\beta, \Sigma_\beta \end{cases}$$

Define T' to be $(+x_{\alpha+1}, +\cdots, +x_{\alpha+\beta})\ (-y_1^1, -\dots, -y_\alpha^1, -\dots, -y_1^\beta, -\dots, -y_\alpha^\beta)\ T$, where T is the normal type associated with Q. Since T is derived from Σ, clearly T' can be derived from Σ'. Moreover, by means of the associated equations that generate the quantifier-free tautology associated with Q, coupled with the new equations

$$y_j^1 = x_{\alpha+1}, \qquad y_j^2 = x_{\alpha+2}, \ \ldots, \qquad y_j^\beta = x_{\alpha+\beta},$$

for $j = 1, 2, \ldots, \alpha$, the same quantifier-free tautology can be associated with R. Hence R has the special form of property A.

NOTE E

(footnote 12, p. 143 above)

Herbrand's argument in this paragraph is ingenious but rather briefly expressed. Since it plays an essential role in his proof that modus ponens is eliminable from quantification theory (see 6.1 on p. 175 above as well as Note F below), it merits expansion.

Let P be a proposition that contains $n \geqslant 1$ bound variables $\pm x_1, \ldots, \pm x_n$, let $M(x_1, \ldots, x_n)$ be the matrix of P, and let P' be any proposition derived from P by a scheme Σ. Then $P \equiv P'$ is provable in Q_H.

Proof. Clearly, by the rules of passage, if Σ has but one line then the theorem holds. So assume that the theorem holds for all schemes with $k-1$ lines where $k \geqslant 2$, and let Σ be a scheme with k lines.

For each $i \leqslant k$, let the ith line of Σ be $S_i = \pm x_1^i, \ldots, \pm x_{r_i}^i, \pm x_{r_i+1}^i, \ldots, \pm x_n^i$, where $0 \leqslant r_i < n$, and the initial segment $\pm x_1^i, \ldots, \pm x_{r_i}^i$ is the longest initial segment common to both the ith and $(i-1)$th lines of Σ. (Take $r_1 = 0$. Footnote 14, p. 143, shows why nondisjoint lines are being considered.)

Now choose (the earliest) j, $2 \leqslant j \leqslant k$, such that $r_j \geqslant r_i$ for each $i \leqslant k$, and let $r = r_j$. Note that the variables $x_{r+1}^{j-1}, \ldots, x_n^{j-1}$ and $x_{r+1}^j, \ldots, x_n^j$ appear only in the $(j-1)$th and jth lines, respectively, of Σ.

Let P' be a proposition derived from P by Σ. The matrix of P' has the form $M(S_1) \vee \vee M(S_2) \vee \ldots \vee M(S_k)$; for elucidating Herbrand's text it is convenient to rewrite this matrix as $M(S_1) \vee \ldots \vee M(S_{j-2}) \vee M(S_{j+1}) \vee \ldots \vee M(S_k) \vee M(S_{j-1}) \vee M(S_j)$. Moreover, since all propositions derived from P by Σ differ only in their types and can be obtained from each other solely by use of the rules of passage, we can take the type T' of P' to be

$$(\pm x_1^j, \ldots, \pm x_r^j, \pm z_1, \ldots, \pm z_q, \pm x_{r+1}^{j-1}, \ldots, \pm x_n^{j-1}, \pm x_{r+1}^j, \ldots, \pm x_n^j),$$

where $z_1, \ldots, z_q$ are all the letters in Σ *not* appearing in the $(j-1)$th and jth lines.

Then, by the rules of passage, P' is provably equivalent to the proposition P^2

$$(\pm x_1^j, ..., \pm x_r^j) [(\pm z_1, ..., \pm z_q) (M(S_1) \vee ... \vee M(S_{j-2}) \vee M(S_{j+1})$$
$$\vee ... \vee M(S_k)) \vee (\pm x_{r+1}^{j-1}, ..., \pm x_n^{j-1}) M(S_{j-1})$$
$$\vee (\pm x_{r+1}^j, ..., \pm x_n^j) M(S_j)].$$

But, by once again using the rules of passage, we can make the disjunct $(\pm x_{r+1}^{j-1}, ..., \pm x_n^{j-1}) M(S_{j-1})$ identical with the disjunct $(\pm x_{r+1}^j, ..., \pm x_n^j) M(S_j)$. Hence, P becomes provably equivalent to the proposition P^3

$$(\pm x_1^j, ..., \pm x_r^j) [(\pm z_1, ..., \pm z_q) (M(S_1) \vee ... \vee M(S_{j-2}) \vee M(S_{j+1})$$
$$\vee ... \vee M(S_k)) \vee (\pm x_{r+1}^j, ..., \pm x_n^j) M(S_j) \vee (\pm x_{r+1}^j, ..., \pm x_n^j) M(S_j)].$$

But, for any proposition R, $\vdash(R \vee R) \equiv R$ (see Note D, p. 188). Hence, by the theorem of Chap. 2, 6.1 (p. 86 above),

$$\vdash P^3 \equiv P^4,$$

where P^4 is

$$(\pm x_1^j, ..., \pm x_r^j) [(\pm z_1, ..., \pm z_q) (M(S_1) \vee ... \vee M(S_{j-2}) \vee M(S_{j+1})$$
$$\vee ... \vee M(S_k)) \vee (\pm x_{r+1}^j, ..., \pm x_n^j) M(S_j)].$$

Hence, $\vdash P^2 \equiv P^4$; hence $\vdash P' \equiv P^4$.

But P^4 is generated from P by a scheme with $k-1$ lines. Hence, by the induction hypothesis, $\vdash P \equiv P^4$. Hence,

$$\vdash P \equiv P'.$$

In Herbrand's text (p. 143 above), the proposition P^2 is written as

$$(\pm x_1, ..., \pm x_r) [A(x_1, ..., x_r) \vee (\pm x_{r+1}, ..., \pm x_n) M(x_1, ..., x_r,$$
$$x_{r+1}, ..., x_n) \vee (\pm y_{r+1}, ..., \pm y_n) M(x_1, ..., x_r, y_{r+1}, ..., y_n)],$$

and the proposition P^4 is written as

$$(\pm x_1, ..., \pm x_r) [A(x_1, ..., x_r) \vee (\pm x_{r+1}, ..., \pm x_n) M(x_1, ..., x_r,$$
$$x_{r+1}, ..., x_n)].$$

Q.E.D.

(The above proof is adapted from an unpublished proof by George Huff who, with Theodore Hailperin, showed that the argument in Note C in the first printing of *van Heijenoort 1967*, pp. 569–570, is fallacious.)

Note that, by an argument similar to that of Chap. 2, § 4 (see footnote 9, p. 141 above, and the first part of Note D), $P \supset P'$ can easily be shown to be a normal identity, and hence provable in Q_H. Thus Herbrand's primary concern in the present argument is to show that $P' \supset P$ is provable in Q_H.

NOTE F

(footnote 16, p. 144 above)

If a proposition P has property A, then there is, in Herbrand's system Q_H, a formal proof of P that can be divided into two parts. Part 1 is a proof of some prenex normal identity P'. Part 2 is a proof of P from P'. (In general, P' is assumed to be derivable from P by some scheme Σ. But any such derivation is not part of the formal proof of P in Q_H.)

Clearly (see footnote 9), Part 1 can always be put into a simple standard form consisting of a quantifier-free identity followed by the results of successive applications of the rules of generalization.

However, the discussion in Note E shows us that we can also give Part 2 a standard form if to the system Q_H we add, as a new primitive rule of inference (see p. 175 above) the following *generalized rule of simplification*:

If a proposition R is like a proposition Q except for containing an occurrence of the subproposition P where Q contains an occurrence of the subproposition $P \vee P$, then from Q we can infer R.

For assume that P^3 is proved in Q_H (see Note E). It has the form

$$(\pm x_1, ..., \pm x_r) [A(x_1, ..., x_r) \vee (\pm x_{r+1}, ..., \pm x_n) M(x_1, ..., x_n)$$
$$\vee (\pm x_{r+1}, ..., \pm x_n) M(x_1, ..., x_n)].$$

Hence, by the generalized rule of simplification, we prove P^4 of the form

$$(\pm x_1, ..., \pm x_r) [A(x_1, ..., x_r) \vee (\pm x_{r+1}, ..., \pm x_n) M(x_1, ..., x_n)].$$

But then, as Herbrand says in 6.1, a proposition P that has property A can be proved from a quantifier-free identity just by the use of the two rules of generalization, the rules of passage, and the generalized rule of simplification. The rule of implication (that is, modus ponens) is not needed. (In § 5, pp. 168–174 above, Herbrand shows constructively that a proposition is provable in Q_H if and *only if* it has property A. Hence Q_H is equivalent to a system Q'_H that is just like Q_H except for containing the generalized rule of simplification in place of both the rule of simplification and the rule of implication. This constructively proved equivalence between Q_H and Q'_H is the basic result of Herbrand's thesis.)

NOTE G

(footnote 44, p. 160 above)

The following example, taken from *Dreben, Andrews, and Aanderaa 1963* shows that the first half of (c) is false. Indeed, it shows that to calculate, in general, a number q from a number p such that P_2 has property C of order q when P_1 has property C of order p we must know more about P_1 than just the number p. (P_2 contains $(x) [\Phi(x) \vee Z]$ in one place where P_1 has $(x) \Phi(x) \vee Z$. We use 'Z' instead of 'p' as a syntactic variable over propositions.)

For each $p \geq 3$ let A_p be

$$(y_2) (y_3) \ldots (y_{p+1}) [\sim W(y_2, y_3) \vee \sim W(y_3, y_4) \vee \ldots \vee \sim W(y_{p-1}, y_p)$$
$$\vee \sim H(y_2, y_{p+1}) \vee (\exists x_3) H(y_p, x_3)],$$

let $P_{1,p}$ be

$$A_p \vee (\exists x_1) (\exists x_2) \sim [\sim W(x_1, x_2) \vee (x) \sim H(x_1, x) \vee (\exists y_1) H(x_2, y_1)],$$

and let $P_{2,p}$ be

$$A_p \vee (\exists x_1) (\exists x_2) \sim \{\sim W(x_1, x_2) \vee (x) [\sim H(x_1, x) \vee (\exists y_1) H(x_2, y_1)]\}.$$

Now, for each $p \geq 3$, $P_{1,p}$ has property C of order 3 and $P_{2,p}$ has property C of order p but of *no* smaller order.

We shall soon see, however, that the only additional information needed about P_1 to obtain q is the number of quantifiers and descriptive functions occurring in P_1. For, by combining Herbrand's argument with certain ideas of Hilbert, Ackermann, and Bernays (see *Hilbert 1927, Bernays 1927, Hilbert and Bernays 1939*, pp. 93–130, and *Ackermann 1940*, as well as *van Heijenoort 1967*, pp. 485–486, and pp. 184–187 above), we can prove:

(c′) Let P_1 be any proposition that contains no real variable but does contain j quantifiers and d descriptive functions, $j, d \geq 0$. Let P_2 be like P_1 except for containing $(x) [\Phi(x) \vee Z]$ in one negative occurrence where P_1 contains $(x) \Phi(x) \vee Z$. Assume that P_1 has property C of order p. Then P_2 has property C of some order less than or equal to $p(1 + N^j)^p$, where $N = n_p$ is the cardinality of $G_p^{(1)} = C_1^{(1)} \cup \ldots \cup C_p^{(1)}$. But then, since N can obviously be bounded by a primitive recursive function $\zeta(j, d, n_1)$, where n_1 is the cardinality of $C_1^{(1)}$, there is a primitive recursive function $\gamma(j, d, p, n_1)$ such that, if P_1 has property C of order p, then P_2 has property C of some order less than or equal to $\gamma(j, d, p, n_1)$.

Proof (adapted from *Dreben and Denton 1966*). We begin by defining the notion of a *standard expansion of a proposition*.

DEFINITION I. Let P be any proposition of height $h \geqq 0$. If y is any real or general variable of P, and $x_1^y, \ldots, x_{r_y}^y$, with $r_y \geqq 0$, are the restricted variables of P superior to y, call $f_y(x_1^y, \ldots, x_{r_y}^y)$ the *superiority index function correlated with y.*

Let $E(P)$ be the elementary proposition that we obtain from P by deleting all the quantifiers of P and replacing each real and each general variable of P with its correlated superiority index function. Call $E(P)$ the *elementary proposition associated with P* and note that the real variables of $E(P)$ are the restricted variables of P.

For each $c \geqq 1$, let $G(P, c)$ be the union of the domains $C_1, C_2, \ldots, C_c$ generated by a set of functions among which are all the descriptive functions of P and all the superiority index functions correlated with the general variables of P. (In the present Note we write $G(P, c)$ rather than G_c.)

Let K be either $E(P)$ or a subproposition of $E(P)$. A *substitution instance of K over* $G(P, p)$ is the elementary proposition that we obtain from K by first replacing each real variable of K with some member of $G(P, p)$ and then replacing each function in the resulting expression with its value in $G(P, p+h+1)$. If $x_1, \ldots, x_k$ are all the real variables of K and $a_1, \ldots, a_k$ are any (not necessarily distinct) members of $G(P, p,)$ then write $K[a_1, \ldots, a_k]$ for the substitution instance of K that we obtain by replacing x_i with a_i for $i = 1, \ldots, k$.

Now let $R(P, p)$ be the disjunction (in some order henceforth assumed fixed) of all the distinct substitution instances of $E(P)$ over $G(P, p)$, and call $R(P, p)$ the *standard expansion of P over* $G(P, p)$, or the *standard expansion of P of order p.* (End of Definition I.)

On p. 227 below, and in footnote 40 to *1931*, p. 244 below, Herbrand introduced both the notion of an elementary proposition associated with P and that of a standard expansion of P. (The expression 'elementary proposition associated with P' comes from Herbrand. It is what we call the strict validity functional form of P on p. 8 above and in Note J below. He had no name for a standard expansion; but see footnote 47 above.) Herbrand did not show that the (far more perspicuous) notion of standard expansion is interchangeable with the notion of expansion given on pp. 153–154 above. But, if we take into account the associative and distributive laws, it is not hard to see that the standard expansion of P over $G(P, p)$ is truth-functionally equivalent to the second expansion of P over $G(P, p)$. (For the term 'second expansion of P' see footnote 32 above.) Hence a proposition P has property C of order p if and only if $R(P, p)$ is an identity. But then to prove (c′) above it suffices to prove that, if $R(P_1, p)$ is an identity, $R(P_2, u)$, where $u = p(1 + N^j)^p$, is also an identity.

Let $r \geqq 1$ be the number of restricted quantifiers in P_1 and let $n \geqq 0$ be the number of restricted quantifiers $\pm x_1, \ldots, \pm x_n$ in P_1 within whose scopes $(x) \Phi(x) \vee Z$ lies.

(Note that $n \leqq r \leqq j$.) Let $t \geqq 0$ be the number of restricted quantifiers in Φ and let $m \geqq 0$ be the number of restricted quantifiers in Z. We shall assume that Φ and Z each contains at least one general quantifier. (This innocuous assumption simplifies our notational conventions. Also, if Z contains no general quantifier, $E(P_1)$ and $E(P_2)$ are identical, and so P_2 obviously has property C of order p.) Let us write $\Phi_1 \vee Z_1$ for what $(x)\,\Phi(x) \vee Z$ becomes in $E(P_1)$, and $\Phi_2 \vee Z_2$ for what $(x)\,[\Phi(x) \vee Z]$ becomes in $E(P_2)$. When we wish to exhibit the real variables of Φ_1 and Φ_2, Φ_1 will be written $\Phi_1(x_1, ..., x_n, x, x_{n+1}, ..., x_{n+t})$ and Φ_2 will be written $\Phi_2(x_1, ..., x_n, x, x_{n+1}, ..., x_{n+t})$. Finally, if S is any set, let us write $[S]^k$ for the k-fold Cartesian product of S, $k \geqq 0$ ($[S]^0$ is the unit set of the null set, and an ordered 0-tuple is the null set).

By hypothesis, $R(P_1, p)$ is an identity. Let $q = p(1 + N^n)^p$. Since $n \leqq r \leqq j$, to prove (c') is suffices to prove that $R(P_2, q)$ is an identity. This we shall now do. The argument turns on three main definitions and two lemmas. (In what follows, the term 'truth value' is used for Herbrand's 'logical value', the term 'truth-value assignment' for Herbrand's 'system of logical values', and the sign '1' for the first element of $C_1^{(1)} = C_1^{(2)}$.)

DEFINITION II. Let A be any truth-value assignment to $R(P_2, q+p)$. A function α from $[G(P_2, q+p)]^n$ into $G(P_2, q)$ is said to be A-admissible if and only if, for each ordered n-tuple $\langle a_1, ..., a_n \rangle$ in $[G(P_2, q+p)]^n$, either $\alpha(a_1, ..., a_n) = 1$ or there is some ordered t-tuple $\langle a_{n+1}, ..., a_{n+t} \rangle$ in $[G(P_2, q)]^t$ such that A falsifies the substitution instance

$$\Phi_2[a_1, ..., a_n, \beta, a_{n+1}, ..., a_{n+t}]$$

of $\Phi_2(x_1, ..., x_n, x, x_{n+1}, ..., x_{n+t})$, where $\beta = \alpha(a_1, ..., a_n)$.

By an inductive construction on the orders of the elements we can easily associate with each function α from $[G(P_2, q+p)]^n$ into $G(P_2, q)$ a unique one-to-one mapping $\varDelta_\alpha$ of $G(P_1, p+h+1)$ into $G(P_2, q+p+h)$ that satisfies the following three conditions:

(1) $\varDelta_\alpha(a_e) = a_e$ for each element a_e in $C_1^{(1)} = C_1^{(2)}$.

(2) Let $\pm y^1$ be any general quantifier in P_1 and let $\pm y^2$ be the corresponding general quantifier in P_2.

(i) Assume that $\pm y^1$ does not occur in Z. If $b_1, ..., b_{r_y1}$ are any r_{y^1} members of $G(P_1, p)$ and if $b = f_{y^1}(b_1, ..., b_{r_y1})$, then $\varDelta_\alpha(b) = f_{y^2}[\varDelta_\alpha(b_1), ..., \varDelta_\alpha(b_{r_y1})]$.

(ii) Assume that $\pm y^1$ does occur in Z and lies within the scopes of s_{y^1} restricted quantifiers also occurring in Z. If $b_1, ..., b_n, b_{n+1}, ..., b_{n+s_y1}$ are any $n + s_{y^1}$ members of $G(P_1, p)$ and if

$$b = f_{y^1}(b_1, ..., b_n, b_{n+1}, ..., b_{n+s_y1}),$$

then

$$\Delta_\alpha(b) = f_{y^2}[\Delta_\alpha(b_1), ..., \Delta_\alpha(b_n), \beta, \Delta_\alpha(b_{n+1}), ..., \Delta_\alpha(b_{n+s_y 1})],$$

where $\beta = \alpha[\Delta_\alpha(b_1), ..., \Delta_\alpha(b_n)]$.

(3) Let $f(x_{i_1}, ..., x_{i_\theta})$ be any descriptive function of height $v \leqq h$ occurring in P_1. If $b_1, ..., b_\theta$ are any members of $G(P_1, p)$ and if $b = f(b_1, ..., b_\theta)$, then $\Delta_\alpha(b) = f[\Delta_\alpha(b_1), ..., \Delta_\alpha(b_\theta)]$.

DEFINITION III. For each A-admissible function α, call the one-to-one mapping Δ_α of $G(P_1, p+h+1)$ into $G(P_2, q+p+h)$ that satisfies the above three conditions an *A-admissible α-mapping*.

Note that, since Δ_α maps $G(P_1, p+h+1)$ into $G(P_2, q+p+h)$, Δ_α maps $G(P_1, p+1)$ into $G(P_2, q+p)$ and not merely into $G(P_2, q+p+1)$.

We now come to our basic definition.

DEFINITION IV. An A-admissible α-mapping Δ_α is said to be an *A-resolvent* if and only if the following two conditions are satisfied:

(1) Δ_α maps $G(P_1, p+h+1)$ into $G(P_2, q+h)$;

(2) For each ordered n-tuple $\langle b_1, ..., b_n \rangle$ in $[G(P_1, p)]^n$, if A falsifies $\Phi_2[\Delta_\alpha(b_1), ..., \Delta_\alpha(b_n), \Delta_\alpha(b^*), a_1^*, ..., a_t^*]$ for some element b^* in $G(P_1, p)$ and for some ordered t-tuple $\langle a_1^*, ..., a_t^* \rangle$ in $[G(P_2, q)]^t$, then A falsifies $\Phi_2(\Delta_\alpha(b_1), ..., \Delta_\alpha(b_n), \beta, a_1, ..., a_t]$ for $\beta = \alpha[\Delta_\alpha(b_1), ..., \Delta_\alpha(b_n)]$ and for some ordered t-tuple $\langle a_1, ..., a_t \rangle$ in $[G(P_2, q)]$.

LEMMA I. Let $R(P_1, p)$ be an identity. Let A be any truth-value assignment to $R(P_2, q+p)$. If A possesses an A-resolvent Δ_α, then A verifies $R(P_2, q)$.

Proof. Let $A(\Delta_\alpha)$ be the truth-value assignment induced on $R(P_1, p)$ by A and Δ_α thus: for each k-adic predicate letter W of P_1 and any k members $b_1, ..., b_k$ of $G(P_1, p+h+1)$, $A(\Delta_\alpha)$ assigns to the atomic proposition $W[b_1, ..., b_k]$ the same truth value that A assigns to $W[\Delta_\alpha(b_1), ..., \Delta_\alpha(b_k)]$. By hypothesis, $R(P_1, p)$ is an identity. But it is also a disjunction. Hence $A(\Delta_\alpha)$ must verify at least one disjunct of $R(P_1, p)$, say the substitution instance $E(P_1)[b_1, ..., b_r]$. Using $E(P_1)[b_1, ..., b_r]$ and Δ_α, we shall specify a disjunct of $R(P_2, q)$ that A verifies.

Let

$$\Phi_1[b_{c_1}, ..., b_{c_n}, b^*, b_{c_{n+1}}, ..., b_{c_{n+t}}] \vee Z_1[b_{c_1}, ..., b_{c_n}, b_{u_1}, ..., b_{u_m}],$$

abbreviated $\Phi_1^1 \vee Z_1^1$, be the substitution instance of $\Phi_1 \vee Z_1$ that occurs in $E(P_1)[b_1, ..., b_r]$. Consider now the substitution instance $E(P_2)[\Delta_\alpha(b_1), ..., \Delta_\alpha(b_r)]$ of $E(P_2)$ over $G(P_2, q)$. Then

$$\Phi_2[\Delta_\alpha(b_{c_1}), ..., \Delta_\alpha(b_{c_n}), \Delta_\alpha(b^*), \Delta_\alpha(b_{c_{n+1}}), ..., \Delta_\alpha(b_{c_{n+t}})]$$
$$\vee Z_2[\Delta_\alpha(b_{c_1}), ..., \Delta_\alpha(b_{c_n}), \Delta_\alpha(b^*), \Delta_\alpha(b_{u_1}), ..., \Delta_\alpha(b_{u_m})],$$

abbreviated $\Phi_2^1 \vee Z_2^1$, is the substitution instance of $\Phi_2 \vee Z_2$ that occurs in $E(P_2) [\Delta_\alpha(b_1), ..., \Delta_\alpha(b_r)]$. We see at once that Φ_2^1 takes the same truth value under A as Φ_1^1 takes under $A(\Delta_\alpha)$. More generally, we see at once that

(†) If φ is any atomic proposition in $E(P_1) [b_1, ..., b_r]$ not occurring just in Z_1^1 and if χ is any homologously occurring atomic proposition in $E(P_2) [\Delta_\alpha(b_1), ..., \Delta_\alpha(b_r)]$, then A assigns to χ the same truth value as $A(\Delta_\alpha)$ assigns to φ.

However, we cannot see at once that A assigns to Z_2^1 the same truth value as $A(\Delta_\alpha)$ assigns to Z_1^1. For, by Definition III, $A(\Delta_\alpha)$ assigns to Z_1^1 the same truth value as A assigns to

$$Z_2^2 = Z_2 [\Delta_\alpha(b_{c_1}), ..., \Delta_\alpha(b_{c_n}), \beta, \Delta_\alpha(b_{u_1}), ..., \Delta_\alpha(b_{u_m})],$$

where $\beta = \alpha[\Delta_\alpha(b_{c_1}), ..., \Delta_\alpha(b_{c_n})]$, and we have no right to assume that $\Delta_\alpha(b^*) = \beta$.

Nevertheless, it follows from (†) that A verifies $E(P_2) [\Delta_\alpha(b_1), ..., \Delta_\alpha(b_r)]$ provided that A assigns to $\Phi_2^1 \vee Z_2^1$ the same truth value as $A(\Delta_\alpha)$ assigns to $\Phi_1^1 \vee Z_1^1$. Moreover, it follows from (†) that A verifies $E(P_2) [\Delta_\alpha(b_1), ..., \Delta_\alpha(b_r)]$ provided that A falsifies $\Phi_2^1 \vee Z_2^1$ and $A(\Delta_\alpha)$ verifies $\Phi_1^1 \vee Z_1^1$. For, since $\Phi_1 \vee Z_1$ occurs negatively in $E(P_1)$, the substitution instance $\Phi_1^1 \vee Z_1^1$ occurs negatively in $E(P_1) [b_1, ..., b_r]$. Hence, if we replace $\Phi_1^1 \vee Z_1^1$ in $E(P_1) [b_1, ..., b_r]$ by any proposition that is false under $A(\Delta_\alpha)$, the resulting proposition Θ is still true under $A(\Delta_\alpha)$. But then, since $\Phi_2^1 \vee Z_2^1$ occurs negatively in $E(P_2) [\Delta_\alpha(b_1), ..., \Delta_\alpha(b_r)]$ and is assumed to be false under A, the propositions Θ and $E(P_2) [\Delta_\alpha(b_1), ..., \Delta_\alpha(b_r)]$ will agree in truth value. Hence A verifies $E(P_2) [\Delta_\alpha(b_1), ..., \Delta_\alpha(b_r)]$.

Thus we need consider only the case in which $A(\Delta_\alpha)$ falsifies $\Phi_1^1 \vee Z_1^1$ but A verifies $\Phi_2^1 \vee Z_2^1$. But here A falsifies Φ_2^1 and also Z_2^2. Hence, since Δ_α is an A-resolvent, A falsifies some substitution instance, namely

$$\Phi_2^2 = \Phi_2 [\Delta_\alpha(b_{c_1}), ..., \Delta_\alpha(b_{c_n}), \beta, a_1, ..., a_t],$$

where $\langle a_1, ..., a_t \rangle$ is some ordered t-tuple in $[G(P_2, q)]^t$ and $\beta = \alpha[\Delta_\alpha(b_{c_1}), ..., \Delta_\alpha(b_{c_n})]$. Obviously, A falsifies $\Phi_2^2 \vee Z_2^2$. So, let $E^*(P_2)$ be the substitution instance of $E(P_2)$ over $G(P_2, q)$ that results from $E(P_2) [\Delta_\alpha(b_1), ..., \Delta_\alpha(b_r)]$ when we put $\Phi_2^2 \vee Z_2^2$ for $\Phi_2^1 \vee Z_2^1$. But then we see from (†) that A verifies $E^*(P_2)$. Q.E.D.

LEMMA II. Let A be any truth-value assignment to $R(P_2, q+p)$. Then A possesses an A-resolvent Δ_α.

Proof. We shall construct by induction a sequence $\sigma = \langle \alpha_1, \alpha_2, ..., \alpha_{q/p} \rangle$ of q/p (not necessarily distinct) A-admissible functions and then show that for some $z < q/p$ there is a function α_z in σ that determines an A-resolvent.

If α is any A-admissible function and $\varDelta_\alpha$ is the mapping determined by α, let η_α be the maximum of the orders of the elements in the range of α, and let δ_α be the maximum of the orders of those elements in the range of $\varDelta_\alpha$ that are images of elements in $G(P_1, p+1)$. Call η_α the *order* of α, and δ_α the *order* of $\varDelta_\alpha$. Now $\eta_\alpha \leqq q$. So $\delta_\alpha \leqq \eta_\alpha + p \leqq q + p$. (For the remainder of the proof of Lemma II we shall write $\varDelta_d$, η_d, and δ_d in place of $\varDelta_{\alpha_d}$, η_{α_d}, and δ_{α_d}, respectively, when $d = 1, ..., q/p$.)

Begin the construction of σ by letting α_1 be the A-admissible function that assigns **1** to all n-tuples in $[G(P_2, q+p)]^n$. Since **1** is of order 1, the mapping $\varDelta_1$ has the order $p+1$. Continue inductively as follows.

Consider successively each $g < q/p$ and assume that the A-admissible function α_g has an order $\eta_g \leqq p(g-1)+1$. Then the mapping $\varDelta_g$ has an order $\delta_g \leqq p(g-1) + 1 + p = pg + 1$. But $g < q/p$. So $pg + 1 \leqq q$ and then $\delta_g \leqq q$. If $\varDelta_g$ is an A-resolvent, let $\alpha_{g+1} = \alpha_g$. Then $\varDelta_{g+1}$ coincides with $\varDelta_g$ and is also an A-resolvent. If, however, $\varDelta_g$ is not an A-resolvent, since $\delta_g \leqq q$, there must be an ordered n-tuple $\langle b_1, ..., b_n \rangle$ in $[G(P_1, p)]^n$ such that,

(1) For some element b^* in $G(P_1, p)$ and some ordered t-tuple $\langle a_1^*, ..., a_t^* \rangle$ in $[G(P_2, q)]^t$, A falsifies $\varPhi_2 [\varDelta_g(b_1), ..., \varDelta_g(b_n), \varDelta_g(b^*), a_1^*, ..., a_t^*]$, but

(2) For $\beta = \alpha_g [\varDelta_g(b_1), ..., \varDelta_g(b_n)]$ and *each* ordered n-tuple $\langle a_1, ..., a_t \rangle$ in $[G(P_2, q)]^t$, A verifies

$$\varPhi_2 [\varDelta_g(b_1), ..., \varDelta_g(b_n), \beta, a_1, ..., a_t].$$

Hence $\varDelta_g(b^*) \neq \beta$. Moreover, since the function α_g is assumed to be A-admissible, it follows from Definition II that $\beta = \mathbf{1}$. Let α_{g+1} be the function that assigns $\varDelta_g(b^*)$ to the ordered n-tuple $\langle \varDelta_g(b_1), ..., \varDelta_g(b_n) \rangle$ and agrees with α_g on all other elements of $G(P_2, q+p)$. But the order of $\varDelta_g(b^*)$ is less than or equal to $\delta_g \leqq q$. So $\eta_{g+1} \leqq q$, and α_{g+1} is A-admissible.

Now, in the sequence $\sigma = \langle \alpha_1, \alpha_2, ..., \alpha_{q/p} \rangle$ just constructed, a function α_g is identical with the function α_{g+1} if and only if the mapping $\varDelta_g$ is an A-resolvent. Hence, to complete the proof of Lemma II, we have only to show that there is at least one α_z in σ such that $\alpha_z = \alpha_{z+1}$.

For each $g \leqq q/p$ and each $k \leqq p$, let $\xi(g, k)$ be the number of ordered n-tuples $\langle b_1, ..., b_n \rangle$ in $[G(P_1, k)]^n$ such that $\alpha_g [\varDelta_g(b_1), ..., \varDelta_g(b_n)] = \mathbf{1}$, and let the *index* of α_g, abbreviated $\mathrm{ind}(\alpha_g)$, be the ordered p-tuple $\langle \xi(g, 1), \xi(g, 2), ..., \xi(g, p) \rangle$. Then, for each g and each $m \leqq q/p$, write $\mathrm{ind}(\alpha_g) < \mathrm{ind}(\alpha_m)$ if and only if, for some $k \leqq p$ and for all $j < k$, $\xi(g, k) < \xi(m, k)$ but $\xi(g, j) = \xi(m, j)$. We shall now establish:

($\star$) For each $g < q/p$ either $\alpha_g = \alpha_{g+1}$ or $\mathrm{ind}(\alpha_{g+1}) < \mathrm{ind}(\alpha_g)$.

By the construction of σ, if $\alpha_g \neq \alpha_{g+1}$, there is a unique ordered n-tuple $\langle b_1, ...,$

$b_n \rangle$ in $[G(P_1, p)]^n$ such that

$$\alpha_g[\Delta_g(b_1), ..., \Delta_g(b_n)] = 1$$

but

$$\alpha_{g+1}[\Delta_g(b_1), ..., \Delta_g(b_n)] \neq 1.$$

Moreover, the functions α_g and α_{g+1} agree on all other ordered n-tuples in $[G(P_2, q+p)]^n$. Hence, by the construction of an A-admissible α-mapping, if $k \leq p$ is the maximum of the orders of $b_1, ..., b_n$, then, for each element b in $G(P_1, k)$, $\Delta_g(b) = \Delta_{g+1}(b)$. Therefore, for all $j < k$, $\xi(g+1, j) = \xi(g, j)$. Also,

$$\alpha_{g+1}[\Delta_g(b_1), ..., \Delta_g(b_n)] = \alpha_{g+1}[\Delta_{g+1}(b_1), ..., \Delta_{g+1}(b_n)] \neq 1.$$

So $\xi(g+1, k) < \xi(g, k)$, and $\text{ind}(\alpha_{g+1}) < \text{ind}(\alpha_g)$. Thus ($\star$) holds.

But from ($\star$) Lemma II is proved. For there are fewer than $(1 + N^n)^p = q/p$ different possible indices. Hence, for some $z < q/p$, $\alpha_z = \alpha_{z+1}$. But then Δ_z is an A-resolvent.

Q.E.D.

Thus, with Lemmas I and II, we have proved that, if $R(P_1, p)$ is an identity, every truth-value assignment to $R(P_2, q)$ verifies $R(P_2, q)$. But then $R(P_2, q)$ is an identity. Hence (c′) is proved, since $q = p(1 + N^n)^p \leq p(1 + N^j)^p$.

NOTE H

(footnote 45, p. 160 above)

Corollary 3.31 is false, since the lemma in 3.3. is false with respect to property C. Indeed, the following argument, based on an example due to Stål Aanderaa, shows that for each $p \geq 3$ and each $q \geq p$ we can construct a proposition $P_{p, q}$ that has property C of order p but no prenex form of which has property C of order less than q. For $q \geq p$ let P_q be the proposition

$$(y_2)(y_3)...(y_q) \; [[G(y_2, y_3) \,\&\, G(y_3, y_4) \,\&\, ... \,\&\, G(y_{q-1}, y_q)]$$
$$\supset \{[(\exists x_8)(\exists x_9) M(y_q, x_8, x_9) \,\&\, W(z)] \vee [(\exists x_6)(\exists x_7) \sim M(y_2, x_6, x_7)$$
$$\&\, \sim W(z)] \vee [(\exists x_{10}) \sim M(y_2, y_2, x_{10}) \,\&\, W(z)] \vee [(\exists x_{11}) M(y_q, x_{11},$$
$$y_q) \,\&\, \sim W(z)]\}] \vee (\exists x_1)(\exists x_2) [G(x_1, x_2) \,\&\, (\exists x) \{[(\exists x_3) M(x_1, x, x_3)$$
$$\vee \sim W(z)] \,\&\, [(y) M(x_1, x, y) \vee W(z)]\} \,\&\, (\exists x_4) \{[(y_1) \sim M(x_2, y_1, x_4)$$
$$\vee \sim W(z)] \,\&\, [(\exists x_5) \sim M(x_2, x_5, x_4) \vee W(z)]\}].$$

The proposition P_q has property C of order 3, but no prenex form of P_q has property C

of an order less than q. Now, for each $p \geqq 3$ and each $q \geqq p$ let $P_{p,q}$ be the conjunction $P_q \& P_{2,p}$, where $P_{2,p}$ is the proposition defined at the beginning of Note G, p. 193 above. Then $P_{p,q}$ has property C of order p, but no prenex form of $P_{p,q}$ has property C of an order less than q.

Thus, whenever Corollary 3.31 is cited in Herbrand's text, it should be replaced by the relevant part of the following:

3.31′. Let P contain j quantifiers and d descriptive functions, and let the cardinality of C_1 be $n_1 \geqq 1$. Let $\gamma(j, d, p, n_1)$ be the primitive recursive function introduced in Note G, p. 193 above, and let $\delta(j, d, p, n_1)$ be the primitive recursive function defined thus:

For every $i \geqq 1$, let

$$\gamma_1(j, d, p, n_1) = \gamma(j, d, p, n_1),$$
$$\gamma_{i+1}(j, d, p, n_1) = \gamma(j, d, \gamma_i(j, d, p, n_1), n_1);$$

then set

$$\delta(j, d, p, n_1) = \gamma_{j^2}(j, d, p, n_1).$$

(i) If P has property C of order p, it has property B of order p.

(ii) If P has property C of order p, any prenex form of P has property C of some order less than or equal to $\delta(j, d, p, n_1)$.

(iii) If P has property B of order p, it has property C of some order less than or equal to $\delta(j, d, p, n_1)$.

Part (i) of 3.31′ follows at once from the correct part of the lemma in 3.3 (in its original statement by Herbrand). Part (ii) follows from the lemma in 3.3 as emended (see Note G, p. 193 above) and the fact that to get any prenex form of P we need no more than j^2 crucial passages from $(x) \Phi(x) \vee Z$ to $(x) [\Phi(x) \vee Z]$, that is, passages in which $(x) \Phi(x) \vee Z$ occurs negatively and Z contains a general quantifier. (We are also using the fact that, if a proposition has property C of order p, it has property C of order q for each q greater than p. But this was justified in footnote 40.) Part (iii) follows from part (ii), the correct part of the lemma in 3.3 (as stated by Herbrand), and the fact that properties B and C are identical for a proposition in canonical form.

NOTE I

(footnote 63, p. 172 above)

Lemma 3 in 5.3 is false, and unlike the lemma in 3.3 it remains false even when property B replaces property C. For consider the following example (adapted from Example 2 in *Dreben and Aanderaa 1964*), in which properties B and C coincide:

For each $s \geqq 4$ let P_s be

$$[(y_1) \sim H_1(y_1) \vee (\exists x_1) H_1(x_1)] \And [(y_2) \sim H_2(y_2) \vee (\exists x_2) H_2(x_2)]$$
$$\And \ldots \And [(y_s) \sim H_s(y_s) \vee (\exists x_s) H_s(x_s)],$$

and let Q_s be

$$(\exists x)(y) \{H_s(y) \vee \sim H_1(y) \vee [H_1(x) \And \sim H_2(y)] \vee [H_2(x) \And \sim H_3(y)]$$
$$\vee \ldots \vee [H_{s-1}(x) \And \sim H_s(y)]\}.$$

Now, for each $s \geqq 4$, P_s has property C of order 2, $P_s \supset Q_s$ has property C of order 3, and Q_s has property C of order s but of no smaller order.

Herbrand's argument for the lemma, however, goes wrong in only one point. Relying on the false Corollary 3.31 (see Note H, p. 199 above), Herbrand assumes that, since the conjunction $P \And (P \supset Q)$ has property C of order p, a certain prenex form of this conjunction has property C of order p (see the second and third sentences of his argument). So Herbrand does succeed in proving the very interesting sublemma:

5.3′. If a certain prenex form (specified in the third sentence of his argument) of $P \And (P \supset Q)$ has property C of order q, then Q has property C of order q.

Hence, if we now use part (ii) of 3.31′ (see Note H), then from 5.3′ we obtain as a replacement for Lemma 3 in 5.3:

5.3″. Let P contain j quantifiers and d descriptive functions. Let Q contain k quantifiers and e descriptive functions. (Both P and Q are assumed to contain no real variables.) If both P and $P \supset Q$ have property C of order p, then Q has property C of some order less than or equal to $\delta(2j + k, 2d + e, p, n_1)$.

NOTE J

(footnote 84, p. 182 above)

Call any proposition *proper* if it contains no index functions. Clearly, if P is any proposition without real variables and R is any proper proposition, the same strict validity functional form can be associated with both $P \supset R$ and $F^S(P) \supset R$, where $F^S(P)$ is the satisfiability functional form of P (for the definitions of these functional forms, see the Introduction, pp. 8 and 11 above). Hence, by the Fundamental Theorem, if R is proper, $P \supset R$ is provable in Herbrand's Q_H if and only if $F^S(P) \supset R$ is provable in Q_H. But $F^S(P) \supset \mathscr{F}^S(P)$ is obviously provable in Q_H, and $F^S(P)$ is provable in $Q_H + \mathscr{F}^S(P)$, where $\mathscr{F}^S(P)$ is the strict satisfiability functional form of P (p. 11 above). Thus, for any *proper* theory T, that is, the system Q_H with proper propositions added as hypotheses, we can constructively find a conservative extension all of whose hypotheses are quantifier-free, namely, the theory T' that we obtain from T by replacing each hypothesis H by the strict satisfiability functional form of the universal closure of H, or of H itself if H lacks real variables. (See the discussion of *symbolische Auflösung* in *Hilbert and Bernays 1939*, pp. 1–18 and 130–137.)

Hilbert and Bernays's proof of this theorem rests on their ε-Theorems. However, as was mentioned in the Introduction, p. 19 above, the analogue for Q_H of the First ε-Theorem is also a corollary of the Fundamental Theorem.

If a proper quantifier-free formula $B(x_1, ..., x_n)$ is derivable from proper quantifier-free axioms by the rules of Q_H, then we can find a proper quantifier-free derivation of $B(x_1, ..., x_n)$ from these axioms.

Proof. Let $A(y_1, ..., y_m)$ be the conjunction of the proper quantifier-free axioms from which $B(x_1, ..., x_n)$ is derived. (Here $y_1, ..., y_m$ are all the real variables in $A(y_1, ..., y_m)$ and $x_1, ..., x_n$ are all those in $B(x_1, ..., x_n)$. Both $A(y_1, ..., y_m)$ and $B(x_1, ..., x_n)$ may contain descriptive functions and constants.) Since $B(x_1, ..., x_n)$ is derivable from $A(y_1, ..., y_m)$, the formula

$$(y_1) ... (y_m)\, A(y_1, ..., y_m) . \supset B(x_1, ..., x_n)$$

is derivable in Q_H (see Chap. 3, pp. 107–108 above). Hence, by the Fundamental Theorem, some finite disjunction of instances $A(b_1, ..., b_m) \supset B(a_1, ..., a_n)$ is truth-functionally valid, where $a_1, ..., a_n$ are the constants replacing $x_1, ..., x_n$ in the validity functional form of $B(x_1, ..., x_n)$, and $b_1, ..., b_m$ are terms constructed from the a_i and the function signs and constants appearing in $A(y_1, ..., y_m)$ and $B(x_1, ..., x_n)$. This disjunction is equivalent to a formula of the form

$$A_1 \& ... \& A_k . \supset B(a_1, ..., a_n), \tag{1}$$

where the A_i are variable-free instances of $A(y_1, ..., y_m)$. If in (1) we replace all occurrences of $a_1, ..., a_n$ by occurrences of the variables $x_1, ..., x_n$, we obtain a formula

$$A'_1 \& ... \& A'_k . \supset B(x_1, ..., x_n), \tag{2}$$

where the A'_i are instances of $A(y_1, ..., y_m)$; formula (2) is truth-functionally valid. Hence, $B(x_1, ..., x_n)$ can be derived from the axioms whose conjunction is $A(y_1, ..., y_m)$ by using the rule of substitution, the truth-functionally valid formula (2), and the rules of truth-functional logic; this derivation is proper and quantifier-free. (Thus the analogue to the First ε-Theorem follows at once from the fact that the validity functional form of $(y_1) ... (y_m)\, A(y_1, ..., y_m) . \supset B(x_1, ..., x_n)$ contains only 0-place index functions.)

Q.E.D.

VI

THE PRINCIPLES OF HILBERT'S LOGIC

(1930a)

During the past several years, a new doctrine of logic has been developed under the aegis of the German mathematician Hilbert. It is claimed that this doctrine is capable of examining and resolving all the problems and difficulties regarding the foundations of mathematics that have arisen in the last forty years. We feel it to be of interest to point out briefly the fundamental ideas on which it rests and the manner in which it makes use of these. We do not claim to explain Hilbert's own ideas in these pages; the instrument he forged is independent of this presentation. We wish only to present the principles of his theory in a form which we shall try to make clearer and less subject to objections than some of those which have been selected up until now.

The characteristic of this new doctrine – which its founder has called 'metamathematics', hoping to express by this that all questions of principle concerning mathematics would be included under it – is that it has as its object of study not the objects with which mathematicians usually concern themselves, but rather the very sentences which can be pronounced about these objects. Thus, the doctrine takes into consideration the propositions which can be stated in a theory, and seeks their characteristic properties. It is, in a sense, a mathematics of language.

To attain this goal, metamathematics could have taken ordinary language and studied the sentences which can be formed with its words. But this language is really much too poorly suited for mathematics; it is infinitely more convenient to use a special language which possesses all the desired simplicity, and in which are expressible all sentences having a sense in mathematics. Indeed, such languages had already been created, due to the efforts of the logicians. In their well-known work *Principia Mathematica*, Russell and Whitehead exhibited a particularly simple one, in which only an extremely limited number of signs is needed. All such languages used since then have been derived from theirs.

In order to understand clearly the principles of this language we must first remember what a mathematical theory comprises: it takes into consideration certain categories of objects and, within these, certain particular objects, certain properties that these objects can have,[1] and certain relations that can exist between them. For example, in arithmetic we study the positive integers; the fundamental relation that we consider holds between two numbers when the second is obtained from the first by adding *one*. Similarly, in geometry we study points and the fundamental relation which holds between three points when they are on the same straight line. We are able to show that all propositions we can imagine can be stated using only these objects and this relation. Henceforth we shall designate objects and fundamental properties and relations by letters (as is done in algebra or for points in geometry). In particular, certain letters, which we shall call 'variables', will be considered to be indeterminates, and will represent an *arbitrary* object of a certain category of objects (they will play the same role as variables in algebra). When we wish to translate a determinate theory into our language, these letters will always be the same for the same object, the same property, or the same relation. The sentence 'the object a has the property Φ' will be translated as $\Phi(a)$; the sentence 'the object a bears the relation R to the object b' will be translated as Rab; and so on. Thus, we have a certain number of propositions, the atomic propositions of the theory, such that every other proposition that we could ever have to state in this theory can be constructed starting from them.

It results from the investigations of Russell and Whitehead[2] that to do this it is necessary to introduce only the following three signs (and their number could be reduced still further): the sign $\vee$ means 'or', the

[1] We shall wish to speak of properties which can be true or not for a determinate object. For example, the property of a number of being different from 0. In this way, a relation between two objects is a property of this pair of objects.

[2] All the mathematicians who have occupied themselves with these questions have used different (although equivalent) methods in the exposition of this symbolic language and the rules of reasoning. Here we use the method which seems to us to be the simplest.

sign ∼ means 'it is false that', the sign (∃x), where x is a variable, means 'there is an object x such that'.[3] (For example, if P and Q are propositions, P ∨ Q means 'P or Q' and ∼P means 'it is false that P'; finally, if Φ(x) is a proposition containing the variable x, (∃x) Φ(x) means 'there exists an object x such that Φ(x)'.)

In addition, it is necessary to introduce systems of dots which replace the punctuation marks of ordinary language. A system of two dots is a stronger punctuation mark than a system of one dot, and in general an arbitrary system of dots is stronger than a system of a smaller number of dots. (Thus, in the above examples it would have been necessary, in order to be correct, to follow the ∼ sign with a number of dots larger than that of any system of dots appearing in P, and similarly for the signs ∨ and (∃x). In practice, however, we employ rules that are a little more complicated in order to avoid having to use too large a number of dots in propositions.)

The authors of *Principia Mathematica* then show how all sentences can be translated using these signs. For example, 'P implies Q' is translated as ∼P . ∨ Q (it is false that P, or Q). Henceforth we shall write P ⊃ Q instead of ∼P . ∨ Q, thus introducing the new sign ⊃. But this sign is not essentially different from the others; it must be considered an abbreviation and is always implicitly assumed to be replaced by its definition. Similarly, 'P and Q' is translated as ∼ : ∼P . ∨ . ∼Q (it is false that P is false or Q is false), and we write P & Q in abbreviation. 'Whatever x is, Φ(x)' is translated as ∼ : (∃x) . ∼Φ(x) (it is false that there is an x for which Φ(x) is false), and is abbreviated (x).Φ(x). We cannot indicate in any more detail how we proceed in all cases; but we do come to the conclusion that it would be useless to introduce signs other than ∼, ∨, and (∃x) in order to translate all possible propositions. Henceforth we shall implicitly suppose that all mathematical propositions that we consider are written in this language.

Now that we possess a more convenient and simpler instrument than ordinary language, we should ask ourselves under what conditions a proposition is true in a given theory; in other words, we should analyze the rules of reasoning. The largest part of this work was also accomplished by Russell and Whitehead. First, let us recall that all reasoning which a

---

[3] [[In the French text, Herbrand uses '(Ex)' rather than '(∃x)' and ' × ' instead of '&'.]]

mathematician can make in a given theory can be carried out by supposing certain propositions to be true – these propositions, fixed beforehand, depend on the theory and are called the 'hypotheses' of the theory (or the 'axioms' of the theory; these two words will always have the same sense for us) – and by deducing other true propositions from these by purely logical methods, by universal rules of reasoning which are independent of the theory under consideration. Let us suppose that all the hypotheses are written in our new language. There may be a finite number of these; it is essential to note that there can also be an infinity of them. An example of this is what is called the 'axiom of mathematical induction' in arithmetic; it states that if a property is true for 0 and if whenever it is true for x it is also for $x+1$, then the property is true for every number.[4] When this axiom is used, it is used only for certain determinate properties; hence the axiom must be considered as giving rise to as many axioms as there are possible properties to which it is applied, and hence as a matrix of an infinity of axioms rather than as an axiom proper.

It remains for us to find all the universal rules of reasoning. The authors of *Principia Mathematica* showed that these could be reduced to a very small number, and their investigations allow us to show that all reasoning can be conducted by using only the following rules; all others can be deduced from them.

RULE 1. True propositions are obtained by replacing p, q, and r in the following propositions by any propositions whatsoever:

$$p \vee p . \supset p, \quad p \supset . p \vee q, \quad p . \vee . q \vee r : \supset : q . \vee . p \vee r,$$
$$q \supset r . \supset : p \vee q . \supset . p \vee r.$$

RULE 2. If P is true and if $P \supset Q$ is true then Q is true, where P and Q denote propositions.

RULE 3. If $\Phi(x)$ is a true proposition, where x is a variable, then $(x).\Phi(x)$ is another true proposition.

RULE 4. If $\Phi(xy)$ is a proposition containing the objects x and y (where x is a variable and y a determinate object or a variable) which becomes

---

[4] In our symbolic language:

$$\Phi(0) \&: (x).\Phi(x) \supset \Phi(x+1) .: \supset : (x).\Phi(x).$$

true when x is replaced by y, then $(\exists x).\Phi(xy)$ is another true proposition.

RULE 5. A proposition remains true when within it $(\exists x).\Phi(x) \vee p$ is changed into $(\exists x)\,\Phi(x)\,.\vee p$, or $(\exists x).\Phi(x)\,\&\,p$ into $(\exists x)\,\Phi(x)\,.\&\,p$, or conversely, where p is a proposition not containing x and $\Phi(x)$ a proposition containing x.

Let us suppose, for example, that we seek the propositions that are true when there are no hypotheses; in a sense, then, these are the ones that are true no matter what atomic propositions they are formed from. These are called 'identities'; propositions that are true according to Rule 1 are examples of this.[5] We see that all other identities can be formed starting with these by using the other four rules. A mathematical theory is now characterized by its hypotheses, and all theorems true in this theory can be obtained starting from the hypotheses and from the identities furnished by Rule 1, by using Rules 2, 3, 4, and 5.

Consequently, we can reason with the signs of our language without referring at each moment to their meaning in ordinary language. We can operate in a purely mechanical manner, without concerning ourselves with the origin of the symbols dealt with; we arrive at a sort of algebra in which all mathematics can be done.

This is the first step which must be taken – moreover, not at all due to Hilbert, who here borrowed from his predecessors – in order to pose clearly the fundamental problems of metamathematics. An objection arises with respect to this: we can ask ourselves how we can be assured that *all* sentences which can be formed in a mathematical theory are combinations of signs, and that *all* rules of reasoning which can be used are the rules indicated above. We must recognize that we have only an experimental certainty about these facts, which is essentially due to the existence of *Principia Mathematica* – the authors of this work having succeeded in reconstructing all the foundations of mathematics and even in developing certain theories in a rather advanced manner. Of course, we have no *a priori* reason to believe that these rules will suffice in every case; but we have a nearly absolute certainty that every argument considered correct up until now in mathematics can be carried out using them. Furthermore, if some mathematician, too exacting or not exacting enough, wishes to change them, the principle of the above methods will

---

[5] [[Regarding the use of the term 'identity', see the Note to *1928*, p. 32 .above.]]

always remain applicable to the theories he constructs; only their usage will be modified. But at present we limit ourselves to theories that are used ordinarily, and we can be assured that for these we have succeeded in carrying out a faithful and certain translation.

So far we have only replaced ordinary language with another more convenient one, but this does not help us at all with respect to the problems regarding the principles of mathematics. Hilbert sought to resolve the questions which can be posed by applying himself to the study of collections of signs which are translations of propositions true in a determinate theory. But he wished this study to satisfy requirements of the most absolute rigor. He wished to be subject to none of the objections which the severest critics of ordinary mathematical methods have raised. He restricted himself to employing only modes of reasoning so immediate that they carry conviction with them in all cases in which they must be used.

The following is the general type of reasoning which will be used: let us consider a determinate mathematical theory, and let us seek to assure ourselves that all propositions true in this theory have a certain property A (this property is different in each particular case, and characterizes the case). First we shall require that we always be able to determine whether or not any determinate proposition has this property, and even that we should take care to actually indicate the operations that must be carried out to determine this. Then it will be necessary to show that all the hypotheses of the theory, and all the propositions that are identities according to the first rule of reasoning, have property A; this must be shown by an argument which is described in detail and which can actually be repeated for any arbitrary one of these propositions. Finally, it will be shown that if some propositions have property A, then so do those propositions derivable from them by an application of any of Rules 2–5; this also is to be shown by an argument which may actually be repeated in each particular case. Now let us consider an argument made in this theory: it consists of starting with hypotheses and arriving at a conclusion by the repeated use of the rules of reasoning. For each intermediate true proposition introduced in this argument, property A holds; and this can actually be verified for each step of the argument. At the end of a certain number of steps, which depends on the length of the argument, we arrive at the conclusion, which hence also has property A. Hence all propositions true in this theory have this property.

We can establish this for every definite argument, and this metamathematical proof is at bottom nothing but a practical method – a manual of operations – which unquestionably permits us to carry out the verification.

All metamathematical reasoning is done on the above model, by choosing suitable properties A. We shall examine two of the principal problems that arise in the study of mathematical theories in light of this method: we are speaking of consistency and of the excluded middle. First, let us define two terms we shall use often. We say a theory is *inconsistent* if it is possible to prove in it both a theorem and its negation; hence, if for some proposition P, both P and $\sim P$ are true in the theory. We can easily see that if we could prove both P and $\sim P$ for a definite proposition P, then we could deduce from this the truth of any other proposition.[6] Thus, if P is true in a theory, then by adding $\sim P$ to the hypotheses of the theory we obtain a theory in which every proposition is true. This is often translated by saying that every result, true or false, can be deduced from a false result.

We say that a theory is *complete* if for any proposition P we can prove either P or $\sim P$.[7] Our knowing a theory not to be complete means that we can find a proposition P such that neither P nor $\sim P$ is true in the theory. Then we can prove that two other theories, both consistent, are obtained by adding either P or $\sim P$ to the hypotheses. Conversely, if we can do this, then the theory under consideration is not complete. We are thus led back to a problem of consistency in order to show that a theory is not complete.

In order to show that a theory is consistent, we must find a property A satisfying the conditions indicated above, and moreover such that if P has this property, then $\sim P$ cannot have it. Then we could never construct arguments allowing us to prove both a proposition P and its negation $\sim P$; for we could then verify, as we said above, that P and $\sim P$ would both have this property A, which is impossible.

On the other hand, if we wish to prove that a theory is inconsistent, we must find a proposition P such that both P and $\sim P$ are provable;

---

[6] For, as Russell and Whitehead proved, $P \supset : \sim P . \supset Q$ is an identity. Consequently, it suffices to apply the second rule of reasoning in order to arrive at the conclusion of the text.

[7] [[Here P cannot contain any free variables.]]

to prove that a theory is complete, we must find a procedure always permitting us, given a proposition P, to prove either P or $\sim P$. Hence, we now have method permitting us to investigate whether a theory is inconsistent or not, and complete or not. We shall now show under what conditions we shall have to apply these methods.

The view is often taken that in order for a mathematical theory not to be a vain game of symbols, a pure algebra, as we said above, it should be the translation of something real; it should be concerned with objects that can actually be conceived by the understanding. Thus, the study of numbers gave birth to arithmetic, that of space to geometry, that of the continuum to analysis, and that of sets to set theory. In this case, the atomic propositions of the theory should correspond to the fundamental properties that the objects under consideration can have and the fundamental relations that can hold between them; the hypotheses should correspond to the fundamental propositions true for them. However, it is quite necessary to be on guard; for we can never be sure that this translation is not unfaithful and will not reveal itself to be insufficient at some moment. Set theory furnished well-known examples of this, and showed that it is necessary to be prudent before affirming that such-and-such a property is intuitively true for the objects under consideration. The question of Euclid's postulate showed this already a century earlier, although perhaps in a less urgent way. The first example furnishes us with a case in which consistency proofs would be quite useful to dissipate the last doubts; the second example furnishes one in which it was necessary to show that a theory is not complete, and which had been resolved without the help of metamathematics,[8] although in an insufficient manner, by showing that the two geometries of Euclid and Bolyai were either both inconsistent or both consistent. But nothing has shown us that similar problems do not arise for theories which appear most perfect to us, like arithmetic.

Is it possible then that arithmetic is inconsistent? We know that

---

[8] A certain number of arguments that we now consider as metamathematical had already been made, in a more or less complete manner, before the invention of metamathematics. These usually consist of showing that certain theories are consistent or incomplete if other theories, like arithmetic, are assumed to be consistent. But only metamathematics permits us to pose these problems clearly in all cases.

Brouwer asserts that it is illegitimate to reason about the set of all integers; it seems to him that this notion is not sufficiently clear in itself, nor sufficiently present to our intuition. Consequently, it is not impossible that reasoning carried out by using it could lead to some contradiction. We can also ask ourselves whether arithmetic is a complete theory. For example, consider the famous theorem of Fermat, which asserts that it is impossible to find four integers x, y, z and n (n greater than 2) such that $x^n + y^n = z^n$. It would not be absurd that it is impossible to prove this theorem and also impossible to prove that it is false. This simply would show us that we do not have a sufficiently precise notion of the totality of all integers, and we could conclude from this that it is possible to develop two arithmetics, both consistent, such that Fermat's theorem is assumed true in one and not true in the other. Of course, in one of these theories we would be led to assume that there are four numbers x, y, z, and n such that $x^n + y^n = z^n$, with n greater than 2, without being able to give the values of these four numbers; but it would not be inconsistent to assume they exist. Similar problems arise in set theory, and in a much more urgent manner than in arithmetic. Until now, only metamathematical methods have permitted these questions to be taken into consideration and to begin to have answers brought to them.

The problem of consistency also appears in another point of view, which is purely mathematical. Let us consider Fermat's theorem again; assume that we have proved it by using certain arguments which Brouwer considers illegitimate, and which, however, mathematicians use all the time; for example, by bringing to bear the collection of all integers, or of all rational or irrational numbers. Also, let us assume that we have succeeded in proving metamathematically that the theory obtained by using these notions is consistent. We would then be sure that it is impossible to actually find four numbers such that $x^n + y^n = z^n$, where n is greater than 2; for this would entail the inconsistency of this system, and an argument which satisfies all of Brouwer's requirements has shown this to be impossible. We must conclude from this that we have the right to use these prohibited notions, since every result proved using them as intermediate steps could not be false. Only these notions should be considered by Brouwer as elements without real meaning, as ideal elements, as Hilbert says. In this way, the founder of metamathematics feels himself to have conciliated the requirements of the intuitionists who share the ideas of Brouwer and those of the mathematicians who do not wish to abandon any of their usual methods.

The question of the excluded middle is also treated easily. The principle of the excluded middle asserts that given a proposition P, either P is true or else P is false. That is, $P \vee \sim P$ is a true proposition in every theory. Indeed, this results without difficulty from our rules of reasoning, which permit the use of this principle in every theory. In general, the principle is used in the following way: we assume successively that P is true and then that P is false, and show that in either case we can deduce a proposition Q from the assumption. From this we conclude that Q is true in this theory. Hence, we may use this principle in any theory in which our rules of reasoning do not lead to a contradiction. But it does not result from this that either P is provable or else $\sim P$ is: the theory may be incomplete. In other words, it is quite possible that neither P nor $\sim P$ be true; however, we can successively assume P true and then P false in any argument. We are led to two quite distinct senses of the excluded middle: one purely mathematical, translated by the fact that $P \vee \sim P$ is an identity; and the other metamathematical, leading to the question of whether a theory is complete.

Such is the general form of this new logic. It seeks only to examine already existing theories, and studies the characteristics of propositions true in them. It does not take part in the discussions to which these theories give rise, and does not seek to disparage them. It limits itself to indicating that the results obtained by reasoning in such-and-such a manner have such-and-such properties. We have indicated above only its application to usual mathematical theories. But suppose we are working in a theory for which the ordinary rules of reasoning have been modified; then, as we pointed out above, once these rules are formulated, the methods of metamathematics remain applicable and permit us to study these theories. At no time does metamathematics seek to know whether a given theory describes the properties of a particular object suitably, or whether it corresponds to something real; moreover, it could not do this. From the metamathematical viewpoint, all theories have an equal right to be cited.

This agnostic position displeases many; but it should not be hidden that perhaps the role of mathematics is merely to furnish us with arguments and forms, and not to find out which of these apply to which objects. Just as the mathematician who studies the equation of wave propagation no longer has to ask himself whether waves satisfy this equation in nature, so no longer in studying set theory or arithmetic should he ask whether the sets or numbers of which he intuitively thinks satisfy the hypotheses of the theory he is considering. He ought to concern himself with developing the consequences of these hypotheses and with presenting them in the most suggestive manner; the rest is the role of the physicist or the philosopher.

The results obtained so far with these new methods are yet rather sparse; there are many more hopes than realizations. We should attribute this only to the extreme difficulty of the problems that arise. Of all the usual mathematical theories, only arithmetic has been shown consistent, and this only with certain restrictions with regard to the use of the axiom of mathematical induction. Five years ago Hilbert announced that he had proved the consistency of full analysis and even of set theory plus a well-known set-theoretic hypothesis, the continuum hypothesis; but his proofs were not published and there still seem to be serious difficulties in them. However, there is another viewpoint from which work can be done and in which encouraging results have already been obtained: the study of what the Germans call the *Entscheidungsproblem*, which consists of seeking a method allowing us to recognize with certainty (at the end of a number of operations which can be determined beforehand) whether or not a given proposition is an identity, and if it is to find a proof of the proposition. The solution of this problem would allow us to recognize whether a proposition is true in any determinate theory which has a finite number of hypotheses, for it can easily be shown that if the proof of a proposition P in a theory makes use of only the hypotheses H_1, $H_2, ..., H_n$, then H_1 & H_2 & ... & H_n . $\supset P$ is an identity, and conversely if such a proposition is an identity, then P is true in the theory under consideration. In particular, we would then be able to recognize whether or not the theory is consistent.[9] And in general, we can contrive so as to make all usual mathematical arguments in theories that have only a determinate finite number of hypotheses. Thus we can see the importance

---

[9] Let P be a proposition true in the theory. From what we said in the definition of consistency, it is necessary and sufficient for the theory to be inconsistent that $\sim P$ be true in the theory.

of this problem, whose solution would allow us to decide with certainty with regard to the truth of a proposition in a determinate theory. This would furnish a general method for mathematics which would permit mathematical logic to play the same role with respect to ordinary mathematics as does analytic geometry vis-à-vis Euclidean geometry. This problem is far from resolved; only particular cases have been treated up until now. In any case, the problem can be reduced to a purely arithmetical one, and a profound study of this reduction furnishes curious results about the structure of all mathematical proofs and the related questions of the paradoxes that are obtained by considering the 'set' of all numbers definable by a finite number of words.[10] But we cannot investigate these questions here without overstepping the limits we have imposed upon ourselves.

These are the methods of metamathematics and the directions in which it is heading. So far only the first steps have been taken; immense regions remain unexplored. But the several results obtained suffice to show the immense value of this doctrine; only metamathematics suffices to bring decisive answers to the questions which have seemed until now to escape any positive treatment. Perhaps its influence will extend little by little to all branches of mathematics, and provide methods for them. The realization of its true grand ambition, the solution of the *Entscheidungsproblem*, will have a considerable repercussion, perhaps as much by its practical consequences as by the questions of principle whose resolution it would permit. However, it does not seem that this goal is to be obtained in the near future; all efforts made in this direction have succeeded only in making the difficulty of the problem more precise. But this science dates from yesterday, and its beginnings already allow us to predict the role which it can be called upon to play.

[10] Here we are alluding to the paradox of Skolem according to which every mathematical theory can be carried out by considering only the objects of a denumerable set. But a discussion of the importance and the correct sense of this proposition would lead us much too far. Supplementary details about this question can be found in the work of Hilbert and Ackermann (*1928*, p. 80), which also contains a complete bibliography, and in Chap. 5 of our thesis, which will appear soon (*1930*). These two works and the articles of Hilbert can be consulted for a detailed exposition of metamathematics; furthermore, our *1929b* can be consulted with regard to the *Entscheidungsproblem*.

VII

ON THE FUNDAMENTAL PROBLEM OF
MATHEMATICAL LOGIC

(1931)

⟦This paper is a sequel to *1930*. Herbrand wrote it during September 1929, but added an appendix in April 1931 dealing with the effect of the results of *Gödel 1931* on Herbrand's work in Chap. 3. The paper is self-contained: the first chapter presents a formulation of quantification theory and explains the Fundamental Theorem of *1930*, Chap. 5. The formulation differs from what we called Q_H in two ways: the rules of simplification and modus ponens are replaced by the generalized rule of simplification (see above, p. 175), so that as a result of the Fundamental Theorem, modus ponens becomes a derived rule; and the formulation allows different types of variables, that is, it is a many-sorted system. (However, Herbrand does not formulate the rules of inference with the appropriate conditions for many-sorted systems. For example, Rule 2 (p. 225 below) should read: "If $\Phi(aa)$ is a true proposition, so is $(\exists x)\, \Phi(xa)$, where x is a variable of the same type as a.") The notation is practically the same as that used in the first four chapters of *1930* (except for some differences in the use of commas); see p. 45 above for a short exposition of it.

The Fundamental Theorem is also formulated somewhat differently here. First, Herbrand always takes the function sign correlated with a general variable x of a proposition P to have as arguments all the restricted variables *superior* to x (not dominating x); see p. 138 above. (Thus, his statement of the Theorem is based on Property C, not Property B). In addition, the construction of the domains is carried out differently; compare pp. 227–229 below with *1930*, Chap. 5, 3.1 (p. 148 above) and 4.2 (p. 166 above). It is not difficult to see that these constructions yield equivalent results (given the first difference just explained regarding which function signs are used). Herbrand also no longer considers the notion of expansion defined on p. 154 above (the 'second expansion'); instead he defines the "elementary proposition associated with P" (which we called in the Introduction, p. 8 above, the "strict validity functional form of P"), and considers disjunctions of instances of this elementary proposition. Thus, he deals essentially with the standard expansion; see footnote 40, p. 244 below, and the Introduction, p. 9 above. Finally, his definitions of "true in an infinite domain" and "false in an infinite domain" no longer involve an explicit construction of the infinite domain; compare p. 230 below with pp. 164ff. above.

The body of the paper is devoted to consequences of the Fundamental Theorem. In Chap. 2 Herbrand presents several reductions of the decision problem: he shows that the problem for any theory can always be reduced to that for a theory without function signs or constants, for a theory with only dyadic predicate letters (a result which in nonconstructive form was obtained in *Löwenheim 1915*), and for a theory with only one ternary predicate letter. Chap. 3 contains solutions to the decision problem for various classes of formulas of quantification theory, and also the result that for any proposition P the problem of whether P is provable in Q_H is equivalent to an arithmetical problem. Finally, Chap. 4 is entitled 'Consequences of the solution of the decision problem', and includes remarks on first-order arithmetic and a formalized completeness proof for Q_H. Despite the fact that, as we now know, the decision problem is not effectively solvable, several interesting results can be extracted from Herbrand's work here (see Note N, p. 265 below).]]

TABLE OF CONTENTS

MEANING OF THE LETTERS EMPLOYED

Certain of these letters are always abbreviation signs (that is, each denotes an arbitrary letter of the sort representing the category of objects for which the sign is an abbreviation). We designate such letters by the words: Abbr. Signs. Whenever other letters are used, they have a precise sense.

Numerals	Abbr. Signs: i, j, h, l, m, n, p
Individuals	Abbr. Signs: a, b, c
Variables	$x, y, z, \xi, \eta, \zeta$; Abbr. Sign: t
Functions	f; Abbr. Sign: f
Constants	Abbr. Sign: C
Type	Abbr. Sign: τ
Atomic proposition	H, V, R, ε; Abbr. Signs: φ, ψ
Proposition	Abbr. Signs: P, Q, R, Ψ, Φ
Hypothesis	Abbr. Sign: H
Product of hypotheses	Abbr. Sign: $\mathscr{H}$
Theory	Abbr. Sign: T

CHAPTER 1

INTRODUCTION

1. Preliminaries

Mathematical language, as is well known,[1] can be replaced by another language, which requires only a very limited number of signs and in which a sentence is composed of an assemblage of such signs placed one after another on the same line. Some of these assemblages (namely, those having a meaning) are called *propositions*; we shall see later on under what conditions an assemblage is a proposition. Our language will be such that

1. Every sentence having a meaning in mathematics can be translated into a proposition;

---

[1] The fundamental ideas on which the present paper is based are those presented by Hilbert in his papers on the new foundations of mathematics; see also the short bibliography in *Herbrand 1930*.

2. Every proposition is the translation of a sentence having a meaning in mathematics.

We can then investigate the conditions under which a proposition is the translation of a theorem true in a given mathematical theory. In order to do that, it will first be necessary to state rules permitting us to assert that certain propositions are true, in such a way that every true proposition is the translation of a true theorem and every true theorem is translated as a true proposition. The fundamental problem of mathematical logic is then to look for a procedure that permits us to recognize infallibly whether a proposition is true or not in a given theory. We shall not solve this problem, but we shall study it as thoroughly as possible.

We shall use for this purpose a theorem that is one of the main results of a previous paper,[2] to which we shall frequently refer. It is not necessary, however, to have read that paper to understand what follows; we shall summarize in the present chapter everything that will be used hereafter. A number of the results obtained in Chaps. 2 and 3 were already known; we thought, nevertheless, that it was useful to present them again, either because (as in Chap. 2) it seemed to us that previous proofs were not rigorous or even correct or because (as in Chap. 3), in addition to the fact that we consider the current proof of dubious rigor, the proof we present is simpler and can be generalized. Finally, all this will give us an opportunity to point out the numerous applications of the theorem just mentioned.

2. SIGNS

The signs used[3] will be letters, parentheses, commas, sets of dots, and special signs.

---

[2] *Herbrand 1930*; see also *Herbrand 1928, 1929, 1929a, 1929b*. We take this opportunity to correct an error that slipped into the last of these notes in the formulation of Problem B [[p. 42 above]]: instead of

$$'f_i(b_{j_1} b_{j_2} ... b_{j_{n_i}}) = f_{i'}(b_{j'_1}, b_{j'_2} ... b_{j'_{n_i}})'$$

read

$$'f_i(b_{j_1} b_{j_2} ... b_{j_{n_i}}) = c_m \quad \text{or} \quad f_i(c_{j_1} c_{j_2} ... c_{j_{n_i}}) = b_m \quad \text{or} \quad b_i = c_j'.$$

[3] It follows from the investigations of Russell and Whitehead (see *Principia Mathematica*) that the signs we are going to introduce suffice to translate all mathematical propositions.

A *letter* is any letter of the Greek or Roman alphabet, with or without indices.

In order to talk about these signs we shall use other signs, called *abbreviation signs*, which will have the property of being indeterminate; that is, in every given particular case, taking the context into consideration, we shall replace these signs by one of the signs or notions of the collection for which they are the abbreviation.

In the text we shall also use numerals and arithmetical signs, giving them the meaning they have in ordinary arithmetic. The corresponding abbreviation signs will be one of the letters i, j, k, l, m, n, and p, with or without indices; these letters will denote 'any given number'.

A. Letters. These are of several kinds.

(α) *Individuals.* An *individual* is a set of letters and parentheses formed according to the rules below. Their abbreviation signs will be a, b, and c, with or without numerical indices.[4] These individuals will be divided into different *types*,[5] each individual belonging to a definite type. The abbreviation sign for a type will be τ. Moreover, to each individual we shall assign a number called its degree.

Elementary individuals are of degree 0 or 1, and they include:

1. *Variables*, which will be one of the letters x, y, z, ξ, η, and ζ; their abbreviation sign is t; their degree is 0;

2. *Elementary descriptive functions*[6] (or, for short, elementary functions). They will be denoted by a sign of the form $f(t_1 t_2 \ldots t_n)$, where each of the t_i, as well as $f(t_1 t_2 \ldots t_n)$, is of a definite type. Their degree is 1 (n may be 0; the function is then simply of the form f; in this special case its degree is 0).

Let us denote by $\overset{h}{[}$ any set of k signs "(" placed one after another (k may be 0), and by $\overset{h}{]}$ any set of k signs ")" one after another, k being any number at least equal to h.

---

[4] Let us state once for all that every time a sign is used for a kind of object it can also be used with one or more numerals (or letters) as upper or lower indices.

[5] In a given mathematical theory each kind of individual will determine a type (in geometry we have the type of points, the type of straight lines, and so on).

[6] The descriptive functions translate the ordinary functions of mathematics.

1. If $a_1, a_2, ..., a_n$ are individuals of types $\tau_1, \tau_2, ..., \tau_n$, and of degrees $h_1, h_2, ..., h_n$, respectively, and if $f(t_1 t_2 ... t_n)$ is a function of type τ (t_1, $t_2, ..., t_n$ being of types $\tau_1, \tau_2, ..., \tau_n$, respectively), then $f(\overset{h_1}{[}a_1\overset{h_1}{]}\ \overset{h_2}{[}a_2\overset{h_2}{]} ... \overset{h_n}{[}a_n\overset{h_n}{]})$ is also an individual of type τ and of degree $k+1$, k being the largest number of parentheses contained in any one of the signs $\overset{h_i}{[}$ or $\overset{h_i}{]}$.

2. Every individual either is an elementary individual or is formed from elementary individuals according to the above rule.

Any individual is said to be a *descriptive function* (or a *function*) of the variables it contains, which are called its *arguments*. There are functions, whether elementary or not, that contain no variables; they are the *constants*, and their abbreviation sign will be C. An elementary function of no arguments is called a *primitive constant*. From now on, unless otherwise indicated, $f(t_1 t_2 ... t_n)$ will be the abbreviation sign for an arbitrary function.

(β) *Atomic propositions*.[7] A *proposition* is a set of signs formed according to the rules we are going to state.

An atomic proposition is a set of signs of the form $\varphi(a_1, a_2, ..., a_n)$ (or $\psi(a_1, a_2, ..., a_n)$), where each a_i is an individual of a certain type, always the same when φ (or ψ) appears in propositions considered at a given moment. There are also atomic propositions containing no individuals. We agree to omit the commas between the a_i whenever no ambiguity results, particularly whenever each a_i is represented by just one letter (variable or abbreviation sign). In the following chapters we shall also use the signs

$$Hab, Vab, a = b, Rab, a \in b, abc$$

to denote atomic propositions.

B. Signs and dots. Dots will occur in sets containing a definite number of them. The abbreviation sign for a set of m dots will be $[m]$.

Signs will be of two kinds:

---

[7] In a given mathematical theory atomic propositions translate the fundamental relations that may exist between the objects considered in the theory.

1. Signs of the first kind: $\vee$, &, $\supset$, $\equiv$,[8] each sign being preceded and followed by a set of dots (which may be empty);

2. Signs of the second kind, of the form: $\sim$, (t), $(\exists t)$, each sign being followed by a set of dots (which may be empty).

To every sign of the first kind occurring in a proposition we shall assign two propositions, its *scopes*; to every sign of the second kind, one proposition, its *scope*.

To every proposition we shall assign a number, its *degree*, which is the largest of the numbers of dots in the sets of dots following signs of the second kind and the numbers of dots, plus one in the sets of dots preceding and following signs of the first kind. Moreover, the degree of an atomic proposition will be -1.

1. If m and n are positive numbers greater than or equal to the degrees of the propositions P and Q, respectively, then

$$P[m] \vee [n]Q, \quad P[m] \& [n]Q, \quad P[m] \supset [n]Q,$$
$$P[m] \equiv [n]Q$$

are new propositions; the scopes of the signs already occurring in P and Q are the same as in P and Q, and the scopes of the new signs $\vee$, &, $\supset$, $\equiv$, are P and Q.

2. If m is greater than the degree of the proposition P (in case this degree is zero, m is any arbitrary number), then $\sim [m] P$ and, in case t is not an apparent variable of P, $(t) [m] P$ and $(\exists t) [m] P$ are new propositions; the scopes of the signs occurring in P are the same as in P, and the scope of the new signs $\sim$, (t), and $(\exists t)$ is P.

3. Every proposition either is an atomic proposition or can be constructed from atomic propositions by the preceding rules.

Moreover, we shall make the following conventions:[9]

1. We shall omit sets of dots between two consecutive signs (t) and $(\exists t)$ whenever the scope of the left one extends to the right exactly as

---

[8] We are modifying here slightly the notations used in *Herbrand 1930*. The sign '&' will mean 'and' and will replace the systems of dots used there for this purpose. The meanings of the other signs are given at the end of the present section (p. 224). [[In the French text, Herbrand uses ' $\times$ ' rather than '&'.]]

[9] These conventions differ very slightly from those made in *Herbrand 1930*, the main differences being the introduction of the sign $\times$ and a slight difference in convention 1.

far as the scope of the right one. For example, we write

$$(y)(\exists x).\Phi(x) \lor \Psi(y)$$

instead of

$$(y):(\exists x).\Phi(x) \lor \Psi(y).$$

2. Instead of writing

$$P_1 \lor [m_1]P_2 \lor [m_2]P_3 \lor \cdots \lor [m_{k-1}]P_k$$

with $k-1$ $\lor$ signs and with the m_i decreasing as the index increases, we shall write

$$P_1 \lor [m_{k-1}]P_2 \lor [m_{k-1}]P_3 \lor \cdots \lor [m_{k-1}]P_k.$$

We call this proposition the *disjunction* of $P_1, P_2, ..., P_k$, these propositions being the *terms* of the disjunction.

3. Same remark, with $\lor$ replaced by &, and 'disjunction' by 'product'.

4. Instead of writing

$$(t_1)(t_2)...(t_n)[m]\Phi,$$

where Φ is a proposition, we shall write

$$(t_1 t_2 ... t_n)[m]\Phi.$$

5. Instead of writing

$$(\exists t_1)(\exists t_2)...(\exists t_n)[m]\Phi,$$

where Φ is a proposition, we shall write

$$(\exists t_1 t_2 ... t_n)[m]\Phi.$$

6. We consider the letter representing an apparent variable to be arbitrary, keeping in mind however the restriction made above on this point; this will allow us, for example, to assume sometimes that all the variables occurring in a proposition are different letters.

We readily see that it is always possible to check whether or not an assemblage of signs is a proposition according to the preceding rules; we also see that a proposition can be constructed by the preceding rules from the atomic propositions occurring in it in essentially just one way.

To construct a proposition P from atomic propositions we must use the preceding rules a certain number of times and this leads to a number of intermediate propositions. Whenever one of these rules is applied, we can see that the number of dots in the set of dots that has to be introduced has only a lower bound and can always be increased; we shall always consider this number to be arbitrary. Let us assume, on the other hand, that we replace the atomic propositions of P by other propositions; it may happen that, in order to obtain the intermediate propositions by the use of the same rules, we have to increase the number of dots; we shall always assume that this has been done.[10] Similarly, we shall use propositions that contain abbreviation signs standing for propositions; we shall write the proposition as if these last propositions were atomic; but it must be understood that, in each particular case, it will be necessary to restore the exact number of dots.[11]

To prove that a proposition has a certain property, we have to prove that the atomic propositions have the property and that each of the rules of construction preserves it (*proof by recursion on the construction of the proposition*).

All of the preceding applies when 'proposition' is replaced by 'individual', 'atomic proposition' by 'elementary individual', and 'dot' by 'parenthesis'.

Among the variables occurring in a proposition, we shall call those occurring in one of the signs (t) or $(\exists t)$ *apparent* variables, and the others *real* variables; the latter are also called the *arguments* of the proposition. A proposition with no apparent variables is said to be *elementary*.

An abbreviation sign for a proposition will often be followed by a number of individuals of definite types in a definite order; we shall thus have abbreviation signs of the form P, Q, R, $\Phi(a_1, a_2, ..., a_n)$, $\Psi(a_1, a_2, ..., a_n)$,[12] and, in a special case to be mentioned later, H and $\mathcal{H}$. We may denote by $\Phi(t_1 t_2 ... t_n)$ or $\Psi(t_1 t_2 ... t_n)$ any proposition whose apparent variables do not include the t_i; but, unless we specify the contrary, other variables than the t_i may also occur among its real variables (they are then contained in the abbreviation sign), and it is also possible that some

---

[10] This calls for an example: If in $p \vee q$ we replace p by $q \supset r$, we do not obtain $q \supset r \vee q$, which is not a proposition, but rather $q \supset r . \vee q$.

[11] For example, in footnote 10 the letter p may be an abbreviation sign.

[12] Concerning the use of commas we make the same convention as for atomic propositions.

t_i do not occur among the real variables (they are *fictitious* variables). In other words, we write in the abbreviation sign only the variables, occurring or not in each given case, to which we wish to draw attention. $\Phi(a_1 a_2 \dots a_n)$ will denote the propositions obtained when we replace in any of the propositions $\Phi(t_1 t_2 \dots t_n)$ each t_i by the individual a_i.

Here we shall not point out what the correspondence between sentences of ordinary language and propositions is. The possibility of this correspondence is an experimental fact. We shall simply state the meanings of the signs $\vee$, &, $\supset$, $\equiv$, $\sim$, (t), and $(\exists t)$, which are, respectively: or, and, implies, is identical with, it is false that, for any individual of the type of t, there exists an individual of the type of t such that.

3. RULES OF REASONING

3. We shall call a set of rules of the kind described below a *theory*; according to these *rules of reasoning* we apply to certain propositions the epithet *true in this theory*.[13] The abbreviation sign for a theory will be T. The rules of reasoning of a theory are as follows.

Preliminary rule 1. All propositions considered in a theory will be constructed from atomic propositions and certain elementary functions, to the exclusion of all other such functions. It follows from this that certain types will exist and others not.

Preliminary rule 2. To ascertain the truth of a proposition in a theory we first eliminate the signs $\supset$, &, $\equiv$ that the proposition contains by using the following procedure:

Replace

$$
\begin{array}{lll}
P \supset Q & \text{by} & \sim P . \vee Q, \\
P \& Q & \text{by} & \sim . \sim P \vee \sim Q, \\
P \equiv Q & \text{by} & P \supset Q . \& . Q \supset P.
\end{array}
$$

(Here the reader should recall the remarks made above (p. 223) about sets of dots and abbreviation signs.) We readily see that the order in which we make these substitutions does not change the final result (by using recursion on the construction of the proposition).

---

[13] As we have shown in *Herbrand 1930*, it follows from the investigations of Russell and Whitehead that all methods of proof can be reduced to the rules we are going to state.

Therefore we shall *always* assume from now on that the propositions considered do not contain the signs $\supset$, &, $\equiv$.

Rule 1. If $\Phi(t)$ is a true proposition, so is $(t).\Phi(t)$.

Rule 2. If $\Phi(aa)$ is a true proposition, so is $(\exists t).\Phi(ta)$.

Rule 3.[14] A proposition remains true if in it we replace

$\sim.(t)\,\Phi(t)$	by	$(\exists t).\sim\Phi(t)$	and conversely,
$\sim.(\exists t)\,\Phi(t)$	by	$(t).\sim\Phi(t)$	and conversely,
$(t)\,\Phi(t).\vee P$	by	$(t).\Phi(t)\vee P$	and conversely,
$P\vee.(t)\,\Phi(t)$	by	$(t).P\vee\Phi(t)$	and conversely,
$(\exists t)\,\Phi(t).\vee P$	by	$(\exists t).\Phi(t)\vee P$	and conversely,
$P\vee.(\exists t)\,\Phi(t)$	by	$(\exists t).P\vee\Phi(t)$	and conversely,

where P does not contain the variable t.

Rule 4. If within a true proposition we replace $P\vee P$ by P, we obtain a true proposition.[15]

Rule 5. Let us consider an elementary proposition R; to every atomic proposition occurring in it we assign, arbitrarily, one of the two signs T and F; we then assign to every elementary proposition constructed from these atomic propositions one of these two signs according to the following convention: If T (or F) is assigned to Q, F (or T) is assigned to $\sim Q$; F is assigned to $P\vee Q$ if and only if F is assigned to P and to Q. If, by these rules, T is assigned to R, no matter which way T and F have been assigned to the atomic propositions, then P is true.

From now on the signs T and F will be called 'logical values'; if to a proposition P we assign T (or F), we shall say that this proposition has the logical value 'true' (or 'false') [under this assignment].

Rule 6. In a theory we shall consider as true certain propositions without real variables; they will be called hypotheses and we shall have special rules to decide whether any given proposition is a hypothesis or not. The abbreviation sign for a hypothesis is H and that for a product of hypotheses is $\mathscr{H}$.

---

[14] The rules of passage given in Chap. 2, § 2 of *Herbrand 1930* (p. 74 above) must be completed and stated in the form of Rule 3.

[15] [[This is the generalized rule of simplification, introduced in *Herbrand 1930* on p. 175 above. See also Note F, p. 192 above.]]

Rule 7. If H is a hypothesis and $H \supset P$ is a true proposition, then P is a true proposition.

DEFINITION. A proposition true in the theory in which we have at our disposal all the constants, functions, and atomic propositions we wish and *in which there are no hypotheses* is called an *identity*.

From now on the *proof* of a proposition P true in a theory will be the sequence of true intermediate propositions that we have to consider in order to come to the conclusion that P is true by using the preceding rules.

To prove a property of propositions true in a theory we will have to show that it holds of propositions that are true by Rules 5 and 6 and that it still holds when Rules 1, 2, 3, 4, and 7 are used (*proof by recursion on the proof of a proposition*).

The problem of recognizing whether a proposition is true in a theory and, if so, of proving it, is the *decision problem* [[*Entscheidungsproblem*]] [16] for this theory. The problem of recognizing whether a proposition is an identity and, if so, of proving it, will be called the *decision problem in the restricted sense.*

REMARK 1. Once all the symbols (t) and $(\exists t)$, as well as the dots accompanying them, have been removed from a proposition, we readily see that we have a new proposition, the *matrix* of the first. Rule 3 allows us to substitute for the investigation of the truth of a proposition P that of the truth of a proposition P' in which all the symbols (t) and $(\exists t)$ are at the left of the matrix. Let us assume that in P different variables are denoted by different letters; let P be transformed into P'; an apparent variable t of P is said to be *general* if [[in P']] it occurs in a symbol (t) and *restricted* if it occurs in a symbol $(\exists t)$.

It is possible to prove that in P a variable is general (restricted) if the corresponding symbol either is (t) and occurs in the scopes of an even (odd) number of $\sim$ signs, or is $(\exists t)$ and occurs in the scopes of an odd (even) number of $\sim$ signs.

4. THE FUNDAMENTAL THEOREM

THEOREM 1. *If P is an identity, we obtain another identity by replacing the atomic propositions and the elementary functions of P by other proposi-*

---

[16] This definition differs slightly from the usual one.

tions or other functions (provided, of course, that the dots and parentheses of P are such that the new assemblage of signs is a proposition; recall the remarks in § 2 (p. 223 above)).[17]

This is an important theorem, particularly in conjunction with Rule 5.

THEOREM 2. (Fundamental theorem). The present paper is devoted to the consequences of this theorem. Its proof can be found in the paper cited at the beginning;[18] it provides us with a criterion for recognizing whether a proposition is an identity. The various ways of stating it necessitate certain preliminary remarks.

(a) Let P be a proposition in which each variable is denoted by a different letter. Let us introduce new elementary functions and new constants, so that the following one-to-one correspondence can be established:

(1) To each real variable of P we assign one of these constants of its type;

(2) To each general variable t of P whose quantifier is included in the scopes of the quantifiers of the restricted variables $t_1, t_2, ..., t_n$ we assign a function $f_i(t_1 t_2 ... t_n)$ (if there are no such variables t_i, then we assign a constant).

In the matrix of P let us replace each real or general variable by the corresponding function (or constant),[19] called the *index function* of this variable. We obtain an elementary proposition Π which will be said to be *associated* with P.[20]

(b) We shall consider sets of letters; they will be called *domains*, and the letters will be called the *elements* of the domain. We shall also consider elementary descriptive functions, which will be said to *generate* the domain. Each letter of the domain will be considered as being of a definite type, that is, of one of the types occurring in these functions. These elementary functions allow us to construct other functions by the procedure described in § 2. If $f(t_1 t_2 ... t_n)$ is one of the functions generating the domain, t_i being of type τ_i and f of type τ, then with certain symbols $f(\alpha_1 \alpha_2 ... \alpha_n)$ (where each α_i is a letter of the domain of type τ_i) we shall associate a

---

[17] [[See Chap. 2, § 5 of *1930*, p. 83 above, and Note B, p. 98 above.]]

[18] Chapter 5, § 5.

[19] As we mentioned in § 2, we must introduce in addition the necessary parentheses.

[20] [[The elementary proposition associated with P is what is called in the Introduction, p. 8 above, the "strict validity functional form of P".]]

letter of the domain of type τ, called the *value* of $f(\alpha_1\alpha_2\ldots\alpha_n)$. In particular, to each constant there will correspond a definite element of the domain. Starting with the values of the elementary functions, we define the values of the nonelementary functions by the following rules.

Let φ_i be the functions in which all the arguments have been replaced by letters of the domain; if $\varphi_1, \varphi_2, \ldots, \varphi_n$ have the values $\alpha_1, \alpha_2, \ldots, \alpha_n$ and if $f(\alpha_1\alpha_2\ldots\alpha_n)$ has the value β, then the value of $f(\varphi_1\varphi_2\ldots\varphi_n)$ is β. We therefore know the value of some of the symbols $f(\alpha_1\alpha_2\ldots\alpha_n)$ whether f is an elementary function or not.

To state that $f(\alpha_1\alpha_2\ldots\alpha_n)$ has the value β, we shall often write $f(\alpha_1 \alpha_2\ldots\alpha_n)=\beta$.

We shall associate with every function a number that we shall call its 'height'. An elementary function will be of height 1; if the height of the function having the greatest height among the functions $f_1, f_2, \ldots, f_n$ is h, then the height of $f(f_1 f_2\ldots f_n)$ (where $f(t_1 t_2\ldots t_n)$ is an elementary function) will be $h+1$.

A domain is said to be *of order k* if, for each type, there are letters of the domain, called *initial elements*, such that all functions of height k of these letters have a value in the domain and that there are functions of height $k+1$ for which this is not the case.

An element is said to be *of order k* if it is the value of a function of height k of the initial elements and is not the value of any function of smaller height.

A domain is said to be *canonical* of order k if it is a domain of order k and if every element is the value of one and only one function of the initial elements (there is a one-to-one correspondence between the functions of height k at most ⟦of the initial elements⟧ and the elements of the domain).

(c) In a domain we shall also consider atomic propositions $\varphi_i(x_1 x_2\ldots x_n)$ (namely, those that occur in P); we shall assign a logical value to each symbol $\varphi_i(\alpha_1\alpha_2\ldots\alpha_n)$ where α_i is of the type of x_i.

Let us begin with Π; assume that we have a domain of order k generated by functions among which occur the elementary functions occurring in Π; assume also that we have logical values for the atomic propositions occurring in Π. Let us replace in a specified way the real variables of Π (which were restricted in P) by elements $\alpha_1, \alpha_2, \ldots, \alpha_n$ of the domain. We can transform the proposition thus obtained by replacing in it any function of elements of the domain by its value; if the α_i are not of too great height and if k is greater than the height of the function of greatest height occurring in Π, we shall obtain a proposition that no longer contains any functions and with which a logical value will be associated.

If, for every choice of $\alpha_1, \alpha_2, ..., \alpha_n$ such that this operation is possible, the logical value thus obtained is the value 'false', P is said to be *false in the domain* (it is understood that this is for the system of logical values considered).[21]

If $\sim P$ is false in a domain, P is said to be true in the domain (in this domain the index functions are associated with the *restricted* variables of P).

We shall say that a canonical domain of order k is the domain *associated* with P if it is generated by the descriptive functions and the index functions of P and *by no others*. This domain is then well-defined.

Our theorem can now be stated as follows:

1. *If [[for some k]] there is no system of logical values making P false in the associated canonical domain of order k, then P is an identity.*[22]

2. *If P is an identity, then there is a number k obtainable from the proof of P, such that there is no system of logical values making P false in every associated canonical domain of order equal to or greater than k.*

(d) From a domain C we can obtain another domain C' by *equating* some elements of the domain. For example, let α_i and α_j be elements of C; they are replaced in C' by just one element. This is what is meant by equating them; but, to obtain C', it is also necessary to equate the values of all functions with arguments taken in C with the following relation: they differ only by their systems of arguments, and we can pass from one system of arguments to the other merely by replacing α_i by α_j or α_j by α_i. This leads to equating a number of elements of C. Moreover, if there are logical values in C such that two atomic propositions $\varphi(\alpha_1 \alpha_2 ... \alpha_n)$ and $\varphi(\beta_1 \beta_2 ... \beta_n)$ have the same logical value when each α_i is identical with the corresponding β_i or is going to be equated to it in

---

[21] [[Thus P can be made false in a domain of order k if and only if the standard expansion of P over this domain (see the Introduction, p. 9 above, Note G, p. 194 above, and footnote 40 on p. 244 below) is not truth-functionally valid.]]

[22] We have shown the means of proving this (*Herbrand 1930*, Chap. 5, 5.1).

order to obtain C', then a system of logical values can be obtained in C'.[23]

After these preliminary remarks, we can easily show that our theorem can be stated in a form that we shall often use:

1. *If P is not an identity, then for every number k there is a domain of order k in which P can be made false.*

2. *If, for every number k, P can be made false in a domain of order k, then P is not an identity.*

We shall often say that P can be made false in an infinite domain if, for every k, it can be made false in a domain of order k.[24] We can then say:

For P to be an identity, it is necessary and sufficient that it cannot be made false in an infinite domain.

To justify this way of speaking, we observe that the elements of a canonical domain of order k (with corresponding values for the functions) can be considered as a part of the elements of a canonical domain of higher order, and that the elements of all the canonical domains can be put together to form an 'infinite canonical domain' composed of letters having a one-to-one correspondence with all the functions of the initial elements that we can form by starting from the functions that generate the domain. For every k, we can then extract the domain of order k; it will be composed of the elements that correspond to the functions of the initial elements whose height is at most k.

(e) We shall often consider several propositions in the same domain simultaneously; we shall then suppose implicitly that all the descriptive functions and all the index functions to which these propositions give rise occur among the functions generating the domain.

Thus H_1 & H_2 & ... & $H_n . \supset P$ can be false only in a domain in which P is false and $H_1, H_2, ..., H_n$ are true.

---

[23] [[See *Herbrand 1930*, Chap. 5, 3.11 and 3.211, and the footnotes to these paragraphs, and *Herbrand 1931c*, p. 284 below.]]

[24] [[This definition of 'false in an infinite domain' differs from that in *Herbrand 1930*, Chap. 5, § 4 in that there Herbrand replaces each general variable x by a functional term $f(y_1 ... y_n)$, where $y_1, ..., y_n$ *dominate* x (p. 138 above), and he explicitly constructs an 'infinite domain'. Given the Fundamental Theorem and the fact that if P is false in a domain of order k, then it is false in the canonical domain of order k, the two definitions of 'false in an infinite domain' are equivalent.]]

COROLLARY 1. *If P and P ⊃ Q are propositions true in a theory, then so is Q.*

The proof of this very important corollary can be found in *Herbrand 1930* (Chap. 5, 6.1 ⟦rather 5.3⟧). Numerous consequences can be deduced from it.

(α) The system of rules of reasoning we have chosen can easily be proved to be equivalent to that of Russell and Whitehead in *Principia Mathematica*, which gives us an experimental proof of the fact that this system of rules is complete.[25]

(β) Together with Theorem 1 and Rule 5, it gives the following results: Since $P \equiv Q . \supset . Q \equiv P$ is an identity, we see that if $P \equiv Q$ is true, so is $Q \equiv P$. Similarly, it can be proved that if $P \equiv Q$ and $Q \equiv R$ are true, so is $P \equiv R$; if $P \equiv Q$ and P are true, so is Q. If $P \equiv Q$ is true in a theory, we shall say that P is *identical* with Q in the theory; we see that this relation is symmetric and transitive.

It can also be seen that a disjunction (or a product) is identical with the disjunction (or product) obtained by permuting its terms; and that, if a product is true, all of its terms are true, and conversely; this permits us to replace the hypotheses of a theory by their product.

(γ) $\Phi(t) \supset \Phi(t)$ is true by Theorem 1 and Rule 5; therefore (by Rule 2) $(\exists x).\Phi(x) \supset \Phi(t)$ is true, as well as (by Rule 3) $(x)\,\Phi(x) . \supset \Phi(t)$; therefore, if $(x)\,\Phi(x)$ is true, so is $\Phi(t)$. Hence, by Rule 1, proving $\Phi(t)$ amounts to the same as proving $(x).\Phi(x)$.

We can always assume, therefore, that the propositions to be proved have no real variables. In particular, we can always state the hypotheses with real variables; they can be transformed immediately into other propositions with no real variables. In the following chapter we shall always implicitly assume that this transformation has been made.

COROLLARY 2. In applying our theorem to elementary propositions, we see that

The necessary and sufficient condition for an elementary proposition to be an identity is that it be an identity by application of Rule 5 only.

5. Here are two more theorems we shall use:

THEOREM 3. *If P is a proposition true in a theory, it is possible, once its proof is known, to find a product $\mathcal{H}$ of hypotheses such that $\mathcal{H} \supset P$ is*

---

[25] ⟦See p. 48 above, and Note N, p. 265 below.⟧

an identity. If there is only a finite number of hypotheses, we can take $\mathscr{H}$ to be the product of all the hypotheses.

THEOREM 4. *If, in a theory, an atomic proposition is equivalent to another proposition having the same arguments, then, replacing the first by the second in a proposition, we obtain another proposition 'identical' with this last proposition.*

Theorem 3 is easily proved by recursion on the proof, and Theorem 4 by recursion on the construction of the proposition under consideration.[26]

CHAPTER 2

REDUCTIONS OF THE DECISION PROBLEM

1. METHODS

1. It follows from the very statements of Theorems 2 and 3 that the necessary and sufficient condition for a proposition P to be true in a theory is that it be true in a theory differing from the first simply by containing only the hypotheses necessary for the proof of P and the types, functions, constants, and atomic propositions contained in these hypotheses and in P.

This remark will allow us henceforth to leave implicit the types, functions, constants, and atomic propositions of a theory. We shall always implicitly assume in the present chapter that, when we wish to prove the truth of a proposition in a theory, we shall use only the elements that occur in the hypotheses of the theory and in the proposition considered.

We shall say that a theory T_2 is a *simple extension* of T_1 if every proposition of T_1 is a proposition of T_2 and if the necessary and sufficient condition for a proposition of T_1 to be true in T_2 is that it be so in T_1.[27] It follows from the preceding that we obtain a simple extension of T_1

---

[26] [[For the proof of Theorem 3 see *Herbrand 1930*, Chap. 3, 2.4, p. 107 above, and for that of Theorem 4, Chap. 2, 4.2, p. 80 above. Theorem 4 also holds for two equivalent propositions even when neither of them is atomic and they do not have the same arguments.]]

[27] [[In more usual terminology, T_2 is said to be a *conservative extension* of T_1.]]

by adding only some new types, functions, constants, or atomic propositions. Here are some other examples.

Method 1. We add a new atomic proposition $\varphi(x_1 x_2 \ldots x_n)$ and a new hypothesis of the form

$$\varphi(x_1 x_2 \ldots x_n) \equiv \Phi(x_1 x_2 \ldots x_n),$$

where $\Phi(x_1 x_2 \ldots x_n)$ is a proposition of the former theory.

The new theory is a simple extension of the former; for let P be a proposition [[of the former theory]] true in the new theory, and $\mathscr{H}$ a product of hypotheses of the former theory such that

$$\mathscr{H} \,\&.\, \varphi(x_1 x_2 \ldots x_n) \equiv \Phi(x_1 x_2 \ldots x_n) :\supset P$$

is an identity by Theorem 3. We still obtain an identity when we replace φ by Φ (Theorem 1). Now by Rule 5 and Theorem 1, $\mathscr{H} \,\&.\, p \equiv p :\supset P$ $:.\supset. \mathscr{H} \supset P$[28] is an identity; hence, by corollary 1 of Theorem 2, $\mathscr{H} \supset P$ is also an identity and P is true in the former theory (Theorem 3).

Method 2. Let $H_1, H_2, \ldots, H_n$ be hypotheses of T_1, and $P_1, P_2, \ldots, P_m$ propositions of T_1 such that $H_1 \,\&\, H_2 \,\&\, \ldots \,\&\, H_n. \equiv .P_1 \,\&\, P_2 \,\&\, \ldots \,\&\, P_m$ is a proposition true in T_1. We obtain a simple extension of T_1 by replacing the hypotheses $H_1, H_2, \ldots, H_n$ by $P_1, P_2, \ldots, P_m$.

The proof is easy.[29]

This method will be used, in particular, if $m=n$ and if, for every i, $H_i \equiv P_i$ is a proposition true in T_1 (since by Theorem 4 we can deduce that then $H_1 \,\&\, H_2 \,\&\, \ldots \,\&\, H_n. \equiv .P_1 \,\&\, P_2 \,\&\, \ldots \,\&\, P_m$ is another true proposition).

Method 2a. We obtain a simple extension of a theory by adding to the hypotheses propositions that are true in the theory.

The proof is easy (besides, it is a particular case of the preceding).

Method 3. Assume that in a theory T_1 we add hypotheses $H_1, H_2, \ldots,$ and H_n. We thus obtain a theory T_2. Every proposition true in T_1 is

---

[28] [[The French text has $\mathscr{H} \,\&\, p \equiv p :\supset P :.\mathscr{H} \supset P$, which is an oversight.]]

[29] [[For this method to be correct, the equivalence $H_1 \,\&\, \ldots \,\&\, H_n. \equiv .P_1 \,\&\, \ldots \,\&\, P_m$ must be provable in T_1 without use of the hypotheses $H_1, \ldots, H_n$. For, using these hypotheses we can prove $H_1 \,\&\, \ldots \,\&\, H_n. \equiv .p \vee \sim p$, but clearly the theory with $p \vee \sim p$ instead of $H_1 \,\&\, \ldots \,\&\, H_n$ is not in general a simple extension of T_1. In the uses Herbrand makes of this method, however, this restriction is observed.]]

true in T_2. By Theorem 3, if a proposition P is true in T_2, there is a product $\mathscr{H}$ of hypotheses of T_1 such that $\mathscr{H}$ & H_1 & H_2 & ... & $H_n \supset P$ is an identity. If P is not true in T_1, $\mathscr{H} \supset P$ is not an identity and therefore can be made false in an infinite domain. If in this domain in which P is false and $\mathscr{H}$ true, we can make H_1, H_2,..., and H_n true, we can deduce that P cannot be true in T_2 (see Chap. 1, § 4), and T_2 will be a simple extension of T_1 (by Theorem 2). Therefore, when this method is used, *it is necessary to make the new hypotheses true in every infinite domain in which the former ones are true.*[30]

We will succeed in doing so, in particular, if, after the necessary new functions have been introduced without introducing new elements in the domains, the order of a domain remains the same (or at least if the order of the new domain increases indefinitely with that of the former).

Assume, for example, that in a theory in which, for the sake of simplicity, there is only one type we introduce a new atomic proposition $x = y$, which we call 'equality', along with the hypotheses

$$
\begin{aligned}
&x = x, \\
&x = y \,.\supset.\, y = x, \\
&x = y \,\&\, y = z \,.\supset.\, x = z,
\end{aligned}
\tag{1}
$$

and the hypotheses

$$
x_1 = y_1 \,\&\, x_2 = y_2 \,\&\, \cdots \,\&\, x_n = y_n \\
.\supset.\, \varphi\,(x_1 x_2 \ldots x_n) \equiv \varphi\,(y_1 y_2 \ldots y_n)
\tag{2}
$$

for every atomic proposition φ, and

$$
x_1 = y_1 \,\&\, x_2 = y_2 \,\&\, \cdots \,\&\, x_n = y_n \\
.\supset.\, f\,(x_1 x_2 \ldots x_n) = f\,(y_1 y_2 \ldots y_n)
\tag{3}
$$

for every elementary function f.

---

[30] [[Because he had a nonconstructive analogue to the Fundamental Theorem (see the Introduction, p. 12 above), Skolem arrived at a procedure similar to Method 3 (*1929*, §§ 5–6). However, since his theorem is concerned with model-theoretic, rather than proof-theoretic, notions he used the procedure to prove relative satisfiability, that is, if a given set of hypotheses has a model, then so does the extension.

We note in addition that Herbrand's procedure allows us to find a proof of a proposition in the original theory if we are given a proof of it in the new theory (see *Herbrand 1930*, Chap. 5, 6.6, p. 181 above).]]

We can make these hypotheses true in every infinite domain by making $\alpha_i = \alpha_j$ true only if α_i and α_j are identical. Therefore, the new theory is a simple extension of the first.

Let us take advantage of this example to make two important remarks.

(a) In a theory that contains the preceding hypotheses, propositions (2) and (3) are also true when φ is an arbitrary (not atomic) proposition and f an arbitrary (not elementary) function. Theorem 4 of Chap. 1 remains true if we replace the term 'atomic proposition' by 'elementary function', 'identical' by 'equal', and 'dot' by 'parenthesis'.

(b) In a domain in which the preceding hypotheses are true and in which we have, moreover, a system of logical values, we can 'equate' (see Chap. 1, p. 229) to one another all elements α_j such that $\alpha_j = \alpha_i$ has the logical value 'true'. We readily see that we have a new domain in which the former system of logical values is transformed into a new system of logical values, and in which the only element α_j such that $\alpha_j = \alpha_i$ has the logical value 'true' is α_i itself.[31]

We have proved in the paper already mentioned that we can limit ourselves to solving the decision problem for theories with only one type (see Chap. 3, § 3 [p. 108 above]); we shall not return to this, but shall go on to study subsequent simplifications.

2. ELIMINATION OF DESCRIPTIVE FUNCTIONS (AND CONSTANTS)

Let T_1 be a theory with only one type. First we introduce the new atomic proposition $x = y$ with hypotheses 1, 2, and 3. Then we introduce new atomic propositions in such a way that to each [elementary] descriptive function $f(x_1 x_2 \ldots x_n)$ there corresponds such a proposition $\psi(y x_1 x_2 \ldots x_n)$ with the hypotheses

$$\psi(y x_1 x_2 \ldots x_n) \equiv y = f(x_1 x_2 \ldots x_n). \tag{4}$$

It is easily proved that in the theory thus obtained the following prop-

---

[31] Since, on reflection, this is not altogether obvious, we intend to return to it in a note for *Comptes rendus hebdomadaires des séances de l'Académie des Sciences* (Paris) [[never published, but see footnote 1 to *Herbrand 1931c*, p. 284 below]].

ositions are true:

$$y = y' \mathbin{\&} x_1 = x'_1 \mathbin{\&} \cdots \mathbin{\&} x_n = x'_n$$
$$.\supset. \psi(yx_1x_2 \cdots x_n) \equiv \psi(y'x'_1x'_2 \cdots x'_n) \qquad (5)$$

as well as

$$(\exists y)(z).\psi(zx_1x_2 \ldots x_n).\equiv.z = y. \qquad (6)$$

Let us add these propositions to the hypotheses.

By Methods 1 and 2a of the preceding section, we see that the theory obtained is a simple extension of the first. In it, every proposition is equivalent to a proposition containing no descriptive functions; indeed, it is easily proved that in the theory $\Phi(f(a_1a_2 \ldots a_n), b_1, b_2, \ldots, b_p)$ is equivalent to

$$(\exists x).\psi(xa_1a_2 \ldots a_n) \mathbin{\&} \Phi(xb_1b_2 \ldots b_p).$$

(This is the essence of Russell and Whitehead's theory of descriptions (see *Principia Mathematica*, *13).) By applying the procedure often enough we finally replace every proposition by an equivalent proposition that does not contain any descriptive functions.

Consider a proposition P; let us transform it in the manner just described; this yields Q; let us transform in the same way the hypotheses of T_1; this yields a theory T_2. For P to be true in T_1 it is necessary and sufficient that Q be true in $T_2+1, 2, 3, 4, 5, 6$. (This abbreviation, which we shall use from now on, denotes the theory obtained when hypotheses 1, 2, 3, 4, 5, and 6 are added to T_2.)

Now, by method 2a, $T_2+1, 2, 3, 4, 5, 6$ is a simple extension of T_2+1, 2, 4, 5, 6, because proposition 3 is true in the latter theory, as is easily seen.

We must now show by method 3 that $T_2+1, 2, 4, 5, 6$ is a simple extension of $T_2+1, 2, 5, 6$. For that, let us consider a domain of order k in which 1, 2, 5, 6 are true. We give to $f(x_1x_2 \ldots x_n)$, for every value of $x_1x_2 \ldots x_n$, the same value as the index function of y has in (6).[32] Then (4) becomes true in the domain, and obviously the order of this domain is not changed.

Finally, we arrive at the conclusion that *the truth of P in T_1 is equivalent to that of Q in $T_2+1, 2, 5, 6$. But the hypotheses of this new theory and Q no longer contain any descriptive function or any constant.*

---

[32] [[Since we are dealing with *truth* in the infinite domain, the index functions are associated with restricted variables.]]

REMARK. It is useless to eliminate the constants of a theory; it does not simplify the decision problem in any way. For it is easily proved that, if $\Phi(C_1 C_2 \ldots C_n)$ is an identity in which the elementary constants C_1, $C_2, \ldots, C_n$ appear, then, replacing every elementary constant by a distinct real variable that does not occur in Φ, we have another identity (by recursion on the proof of $\Phi(C_1 C_2 \ldots C_n)$).

3. ELIMINATION OF ATOMIC PROPOSITIONS OF MORE THAN TWO ARGUMENTS[33]

Suppose, for example, that we wish to replace a theory T_1 in which the atomic proposition $\varphi(xyz)$ occurs but in which no descriptive function occurs by another theory, also without any descriptive functions, in which neither $\varphi(xyz)$ nor any new atomic proposition of more than two arguments occurs. The methods we use for that would also permit us in every case to reduce the number of arguments of atomic propositions of more than two arguments.

We introduce first the atomic proposition $x = y$ and hypotheses 1 and 2 of § 1; next a new type (the variables of this type will be denoted by ξ, η, and ζ, while x and y will be reserved for the original type); and then the atomic propositions

$$\xi = \eta, \quad Rx\xi, \quad H\xi\eta, \quad V\xi\eta$$

with the following hypotheses:

$$
\left.
\begin{aligned}
H\xi\eta \ \& \ \xi = \xi' \ \& \ \eta = \eta' \ . \supset \ H\xi'\eta' \\
V\xi\eta \ \& \ \xi = \xi' \ \& \ \eta = \eta' \ . \supset \ V\xi'\eta' \\
Rx\xi \ \& \ x = x' \ \& \ \xi = \xi' \ . \supset \ Rx'\xi'
\end{aligned}
\right\}
\begin{aligned}
\text{(hypotheses} \\
\text{of equality)}
\end{aligned}
\tag{3}
$$

$$
\left.
\begin{aligned}
Rx\xi \ \supset \ H\xi\xi \\
Rx\xi \ \& \ Ry\xi \ . \supset \ x = y \\
Rx\xi \ \& \ Rx\eta \ . \supset \ \xi = \eta
\end{aligned}
\right\}
\tag{4}
$$

$$(\exists \xi) . Rx\xi \tag{5}$$

$$H\xi\xi \ \supset \ (\exists x) . Rx\xi \tag{6}$$

---

[33] Löwenheim (1915) published a proof of the result stated in this section. In *Herbrand 1930* (Chap. 5, 6.2) we pointed out that there are serious gaps in his proof. We take up his fundamental idea here, but modify his method considerably.

(these are the properties of $Rx\xi$ that establish a one-to-one correspondence between the objects of the first type and those of the second type for which $H\xi\xi$ is true);

$$\left.\begin{array}{l} H\xi\xi \equiv V\xi\xi, H\xi\eta \supset H\eta\eta, V\xi\eta \supset V\eta\eta \\ H\xi\eta \;\&\; H\xi\eta' .\supset \eta = \eta' \\ V\xi\eta \;\&\; V\xi\eta' .\supset \eta = \eta' \\ H\xi\eta \;\&\; V\xi\zeta \;\&\; H\xi'\eta \;\&\; V\xi'\zeta .\supset \xi = \xi' \end{array}\right\} \quad (7)$$

$$(\xi)(\exists\eta).H\xi\eta \tag{8}$$

$$(\xi)(\exists\eta).V\xi\eta \tag{9}$$

$$(\eta\zeta)(\exists\xi).H\xi\eta \;\&\; V\xi\zeta \tag{10}$$

(these last hypotheses state that there is a one-to-one correspondence between the objects of the second type and the pairs of objects for which $H\xi\xi$ is true; if, in this correspondence, the pair (η, ζ) corresponds to ξ, then η is the only object for which $H\xi\eta$ is true and ζ the only object for which $V\xi\zeta$ is true).

For each atomic proposition $\varphi_i(x_1 x_2 \ldots x_{n_i})$ of the original theory other than $\varphi(xyz)$, we introduce an atomic proposition $\psi_i(\xi_1\xi_2 \ldots \xi_{n_i})$; furthermore, we introduce the atomic proposition $\psi\xi\eta$ with the following hypotheses: first, all the hypotheses

$$Rx_1\xi_1 \;\&\; Rx_2\xi_2 \;\&\; \cdots \;\&\; Rx_{n_i}\xi_{n_i}$$
$$.\supset. \varphi_i(x_1 x_2 \ldots x_{n_i}) \equiv \psi_i(\xi_1\xi_2 \ldots \xi_{n_i}), \quad (11)$$

then the hypothesis

$$Rx\xi \;\&\; Ry\eta_1 \;\&\; Rz\eta_2$$
$$\&\; H\zeta\eta_1 \;\&\; V\zeta\eta_2 .\supset. \varphi(xyz) \equiv \psi\xi\zeta. \quad (12)$$

(Therefore, in the new type we have replaced an atomic proposition with three arguments by one with two arguments.)

Finally, we add the hypotheses

$$\left.\begin{array}{l} \xi_1 = \xi_1' \;\&\; \xi_2 = \xi_2' \;\&\; \cdots \;\&\; \xi_{n_i} = \xi_{n_i}' \\ \qquad .\supset. \psi_i(\xi_1\xi_2 \ldots \xi_{n_i}) \equiv \psi_i(\xi_1'\xi_2' \ldots \xi_{n_i}'), \\ \xi = \xi' \;\&\; \eta = \eta' .\supset. \psi\xi\eta \equiv \psi\xi'\eta' \end{array}\right\} \quad (13)$$

which are, moreover, a consequence of the preceding ones.

Every proposition without real variables in the former theory is equivalent in this new theory to a proposition of the new theory containing only variables of the new type. In fact, let $\Phi(x_1 x_2 \ldots x_n)$ be a proposition of the former theory with the real variables $x_1, x_2, \ldots, x_n$ and the apparent variables $x_{n+1}, x_{n+2}, \ldots, x_{n+p}$. In Φ we replace each x_i by ξ_i; then, in the assemblage of signs thus obtained, we replace $\varphi(\xi_i \xi_j \xi_k)$ by

$$(\exists \eta) . \psi \xi_i \eta \ \& \ H \xi_j \eta \ \& \ V \xi_k \eta \ \& \ H \xi_i \xi_i$$

and $\varphi_i(\xi_1 \xi_2 \ldots \xi_{n_i})$ by $\psi_i(\xi_1 \xi_2 \ldots \xi_{n_i})$. We thus obtain a proposition $\Psi(\xi_1 \xi_2 \ldots \xi_n)$, and the proposition

$$Rx_1 \xi_1 \ \& \ Rx_2 \xi_2 \ \& \ \cdots \ \& \ Rx_n \xi_n$$
$$. \supset . \ \Phi(x_1 x_2 \ldots x_n) \equiv \Psi(\xi_1 \xi_2 \ldots \xi_n)$$

is true in the new theory. This can be proved without difficulty by recursion on the construction of Φ. We have the desired result for a proposition without real variables.

Let T_2 be the theory obtained when we transform the hypotheses of T_1 in this manner. Let us prove that (with the notation of the preceding section) $T_1 + (1\text{--}13)$ is a simple extension of T_1, and that $T_2 + (1\text{--}13)$ is a simple extension of $T_2 + 3, 7, 8, 9, 10, 13$. If the transformation mentioned above changes P (which, we can assume, has no real variables) into Q, we shall have proved (by using method 2)[34] that the necessary and sufficient condition for P to be true in T_1 is that Q be so in $T_2 + 3$, 7, 8, 9, 10, 13. Now in the hypotheses of this theory and in Q the atomic propositions are $\psi_i(\xi_1 \xi_2 \ldots \xi_{n_i})$, $\psi \xi \eta$, $H \xi \eta$, $V \xi \eta$, and $\xi = \eta$; we therefore have three propositions with two arguments for which there are no corresponding propositions in T_1; but we have replaced a proposition of three arguments $\varphi(xyz)$ by one with two arguments $\psi \xi \eta$, which is the result we desired. If we repeat this procedure enough times, we finally have only atomic propositions with two arguments, which is Löwenheim's theorem.

1. $T_1 + (1\text{--}13)$ *is a simple extension of* T_1.

Let $\alpha_0, \alpha_1, \ldots, \alpha_n$ be a domain of order k in which all the hypotheses of T_1 that we must consider when using Method 3 are true (the elements

---

[34] [[The restriction of footnote 29 is observed here, since the equivalence of each hypothesis of T_1 and its transform can be proved using only hypotheses 1–13. Hence $T_2 + (1\text{--}13)$, which results from $T_1 + (1\text{--}13)$ by replacing each hypothesis of T_1 by its transform, is a simple extension of $T_1 + (1\text{--}13)$.]]

being arranged in order of nondecreasing height and α_0 being the initial element). The elements of the new type in the new domain will be denoted by β_{ij} (i and j going from 0 to n); those of the former type will remain $\alpha_0, \alpha_1, ..., \alpha_n$, with the same logical values and the same values for the functions as in the former domain. We shall make the new hypotheses true in this domain by proceeding as follows:

$R\alpha_i\beta_{jk}$ will be true only if $i=j=k$,

$H\beta_{ij}\beta_{kl}$ will be true only if $i=k=l$,

$V\beta_{ij}\beta_{kl}$ will be true only if $j=k=l$,

$\beta_{ij}=\beta_{kl}$ will be true only if $i=k$ and $j=l$,

$\alpha_i=\alpha_j$ will be true only if $i=j$.[35]

$\psi_j(\beta_{i_1 i'_1}\beta_{i_2 i'_2}...\beta_{i_{n_j} i'_{n_j}})$ will be true only if, for every l, $i_l=i'_l$, and if $\varphi_j(\alpha_{i_1}\alpha_{i_2}...\alpha_{i_{n_j}})$ is true.

$\psi\beta_{ii'}\,\beta_{jj'}$ will be true only if $i=i'$ and $\varphi(\alpha_i\alpha_j\alpha_{j'})$ is true.

In (5) we have an index function $f_1(x)$; we shall set $f_1(\alpha_i)=\beta_{ii}$.

In (6) we have an index function $f_2(\xi)$; we shall set $f_2(\beta_{ij})=\alpha_0$ if $i\neq j$ and $=\alpha_i$ if $i=j$.

In (8) we have an index function $f_3(\xi)$; we shall set $f_3(\beta_{ij})=\beta_{ii}$.

In (9) we have an index function $f_4(\xi)$; we shall set $f_4(\beta_{ij})=\beta_{jj}$.

In (10) we have an index function $f_5(\eta\xi)$; we shall set $f_5(\beta_{ij}\beta_{i'j'})=\beta_{00}$ unless $i=j$ and $i'=j'$, in which case it is equal to $\beta_{ii'}$.

With these values we have a new domain which is of order k (we can prove this by showing that the largest subscript of the values of our new functions is never greater than the largest subscript of the values of the arguments); and one sees immediately that all the new hypotheses are true in the new domain.

2. $T_2+(1-13)$ *is a simple extension of* $T_2+3, 7, 8, 9, 10, 13$.

Let us denote by γ_i the elements of the domain of order k (in which all the hypotheses of $T_2+3, 7, 8, 9, 10, 13$ are true) that we must consider when following method 3; we begin by equating to one another all elements γ_i and γ_j for which $\gamma_i=\gamma_j$ has the logical value 'true' (as is explained at the end of § 1). We observe that by hypotheses 7, 8, 9, and 10, which are true in this domain, we can classify the elements in a sequence

---

[35] [[If T_1 already contained the atomic proposition $=$, we must first transform the original domain into one in which $\alpha_i=\alpha_j$ has the logical value 'true' only if $i=j$ (see above, p. 235).]]

with double index β_{ij} (i and j perhaps not taking *all* pairs of values) in such a way that $H\beta_{ij}\beta_{i'j'}$ and $V\beta_{ij}\beta_{i'j'}$ are true only under the conditions stated above and that, keeping the same name for the index functions as above, the values of f_3, f_4, and f_5 are as above; we note in particular that, if there exists a pair of elements β_{ii} and β_{jj} of order at most equal to $k-1$, then there exists a β_{ij}, and that, if there is a β_{ij} of order at most equal to $k-1$, then there exist a β_{ii} and a β_{jj}. Let $\beta_{i_1 k_1}$ be an initial element. $\beta_{i_1 i_1}$ is therefore of order 1 or 0; we now introduce new letters $\alpha_{i_1}, \alpha_{i_2}, \ldots$, the indices $i_1, i_2, \ldots$ being those of the β_{ii} present in the domain; and we give the following values to the functions f_1 and f_2:

$$f_1(\alpha_i) = \beta_{ii}, \quad f_2(\beta_{ij}) = \alpha_{i_1} \quad \text{if} \quad i \neq j$$
$$= \alpha_i \quad \text{if} \quad i = j.$$

It follows from this that the heights of the elements α_i and β_{ii} differ by at most 1.

Finally, we shall give the logical value 'true'

to $\alpha_i = \alpha_{i'}$ only if $i = i'$ is true;

to $\varphi_j(\alpha_{i_1}\alpha_{i_2} \ldots \alpha_{i_{n_j}})$ only if $\psi_j(\beta_{i_1 i_1}\beta_{i_2 i_2} \ldots \beta_{i_{n_j} i_{n_j}})$ is true;

to $\varphi(\alpha_i \alpha_j \alpha_{j'})$ only if $\psi(\beta_{ii}\beta_{jj'})$ is true.

As above, all the hypotheses ⟦of $T_2 + (1–13)$⟧ are true in this domain. Moreover, this domain is of order k; to prove this, note that the only new functions introduced are f_1 and f_2; in the type of the letters α let us take α_{i_1} as an initial element; we define a pseudo-order equal to the original order for the β_{ij} and, for any α_i, to the order of β_{ii} less 1. It can be proved immediately, by recursion on the construction of the function, that the pseudo-order of the value of a function is at most equal to the height of this function; since every function of height 1 (see the definition of height, Chap. 1, § 4 (b)) having as arguments elements of pseudo-order at most equal to $k-1$ has a value in the domain, it follows that our domain is of height k ⟦rather, order k⟧. This proves our assertions.

4. FURTHER REDUCTIONS

We can therefore limit ourselves to theories in which the atomic propositions have only two arguments; let $\varphi_i xy$ be these atomic propositions ($i = 1, 2, \ldots, n, \ldots$). We can continue the reduction further; let us begin with such a theory T_1.

1. We introduce constants C_i and a new atomic proposition $\psi(xyz)$, with the hypotheses

$$\psi(xyC_i) \equiv \varphi_i xy. \tag{1}$$

This new theory is a simple extension of the former one, as is easily seen by Method 3. In this theory it is quite obvious, by Theorem 4 (p. 232 above), that every proposition P is equivalent to a proposition Q that no longer contains the atomic propositions $\varphi_i xy$ but contains the constants C_i. Let us transform the hypotheses of T_1 in this manner; we obtain a theory T_2. It is also proved without difficulty by Method 3 that $T_2 + 1$ is a simple extension of T_2. By Method 2 the necessary and sufficient condition for P to be true in T_1 is then that Q be true in T_2.[36] Since, furthermore, by the remark of § 2 we need not concern ourselves with constants in the solution of the decision problem, we see that we are brought back to a theory containing no more than one atomic proposition of three arguments.

2. If we again apply the method of the preceding section, we seem to be brought back to a theory with four atomic propositions each having two arguments; but we can reduce this to three such propositions. Let us use the same notation again – we no longer deal with the atomic propositions $\psi_i(x_1 x_2 \ldots x_{n_i})$ – let us consider the following proposition, which we shall denote by $\xi \equiv \xi'$:[37]

$$(\eta) . \psi \xi \eta \equiv \psi \xi' \eta \ .\&.\ \psi \eta \xi \equiv \psi \eta \xi' \ .\&.\ H \xi \eta \equiv H \xi' \eta$$
$$.\&.\ H \eta \xi \equiv H \eta \xi' \ .\&.\ V \xi \eta \equiv V \xi' \eta \ .\&.\ V \eta \xi \equiv V \eta \xi'.$$

Let P be the proposition we are considering in T_1, and Q the proposition by which we replace it in $T_2 + 3$, 7, 8, 9, 10, 13 (a theory that we shall henceforth denote by T_3). In T_3, $\xi = \eta \ .\supset.\ \xi \equiv \eta$ is true. Neither Q nor the hypotheses of T_3, except, however,[38] 3, 7, and 13, contain the atomic proposition $\xi = \eta$. When we replace the atomic proposition $\xi = \eta$ by $\xi \equiv \eta$ in these propositions, 3 and 13 become (as is easily seen) iden-

---

[36] [[The transformation of T_1 into T_2 uses no hypotheses except (1). Hence it is in accord with the restriction on Method 2.]]

[37] There will be no occasion to confuse this sign with that already used to denote the equivalence of propositions.

[38] We denote here by k the product of the hypotheses numbered k.

tities, and 7 becomes a proposition $7'$ such that $7 \supset 7'$. We shall call T_4 the theory $T_2 + 7'$, 8, 9, 10. If Q is true in T_4, it is therefore true in T_3. Conversely, let us assume that Q is true in T_3; then by Theorem 3 we see that 3 & 7 & 8 & 9 & 10 & 13 & $\mathscr{H} . \supset Q$ is an identity, where $\mathscr{H}$ is some suitable product of hypotheses of T_2. In this identity we replace the atomic proposition $x = y$ by $x \equiv y$; it is then easily deduced[39] by Theorem 1 that $7'$ & 8 & 9 & 10 & $\mathscr{H} . \supset Q$ is an identity; therefore Q is true in T_4.

Therefore, for Q to be true in T_3, it is necessary and sufficient that it be true in T_4; but Q and the hypotheses of T_4 contain only the atomic propositions $H\xi\eta$, $V\xi\eta$, and $\psi\xi\eta$.

The method of § 3 can be modified in this manner every time there is only a finite number of different atomic propositions in the hypotheses of T_1.

THEOREM. *To solve the decision problem in a theory, it suffices to solve it in a theory containing not more than one type, no functions (but perhaps containing constants), and including only one atomic proposition of three arguments or three atomic propositions of two arguments.*

Theorem 3 and the remark at the end of § 2 of the present chapter yield the following *Corollary*:

To solve the decision problem in a theory having only a finite number of hypotheses, it suffices to solve it in the restricted sense, with propositions having only one type, no functions or constants, and including only one atomic proposition of three arguments or three atomic propositions of two arguments.

CHAPTER 3

SPECIAL CASES OF THE DECISION PROBLEM

1. PRELIMINARIES

In this chapter we wish to consider some special cases of the decision problem in the restricted sense; we therefore want to find the necessary and sufficient condition for a given proposition to be an identity. Our Fundamental Theorem will give us a convenient procedure for this

---

[39] Because $P_1 \supset :: P_2 \supset :. P_1$ & P_2 & $P_3 . \supset Q : \supset . P_3 \supset Q$ is an identity by Rule 5.

purpose. We assume, to simplify (nothing essential is involved) that there is only one type of variable in the propositions.

Let us consider then a proposition P; let $\varphi_i(x_1 x_2 \ldots x_{n_i})$ be the atomic propositions it contains. To see whether it is an identity, we shall try to make it false in the corresponding infinite canonical domain. We can consider the infinite domain constructed in advance: $\alpha_0, \alpha_1, \ldots, \alpha_p, \ldots$. Let us consider the elementary proposition associated with P; it contains the variables $x_1, x_2, \ldots, x_n$ [which were restricted variables in P]; we shall denote it by $\Pi(x_1 x_2 \ldots x_n)$. The problem consists in trying to make any arbitrary number of propositions $\Pi(\alpha_{p_1} \alpha_{p_2} \ldots \alpha_{p_n})$ false, or else finding a system of propositions of that form which cannot all be made false, because Theorem 2 shows that in the first case P cannot be an identity and in the second case it is one. Conversely, if we know that P is not an identity, we know that we can make false an arbitrary number of these propositions, and if we know the proof of P, we can construct a system of such propositions that cannot all be made false.[40] We are therefore brought back to a purely arithmetical problem, equivalent to the decision problem; this problem is the determination of the logical values that must be given to the $\varphi_i(\alpha_{i_1} \alpha_{i_2} \alpha_{i_3} \ldots [\![\alpha_{i_{n_i}}]\!])$ to make the $\Pi(\alpha_{p_1} \alpha_{p_2} \ldots \alpha_{p_n})$ false.

It can be presented in the following form: for each system $\alpha_{p_1}, \alpha_{p_2}, \ldots, \alpha_{p_n}$, let us consider the different systems of possible logical values for the atomic propositions of $\Pi(\alpha_{p_1} \alpha_{p_2} \ldots \alpha_{p_n})$[41] such that this last proposition has the logical value 'false'; assume that there are k such systems. We shall assign to the system $\alpha_{p_1}, \alpha_{p_2}, \ldots, \alpha_{p_n}$ the number $1, 2, \ldots$, or k, according as the first, the second, $\ldots$, or the kth of those systems comes up for $\Pi(\alpha_{p_1} \alpha_{p_2} \ldots \alpha_{p_n})$ in the domain in which we are trying to make P false. We should therefore try to assign to each system $\alpha_{p_1}, \alpha_{p_2}, \ldots, \alpha_{p_n}$

---

[40] We can state our Fundamental Theorem in such a way that these facts are emphasized; let $\Pi(x_1 x_2 \ldots x_n)$ be the matrix of P (see Remark 1 on p. 226). If P is an identity, then there is a certain disjunction of propositions of the form $\Pi(\alpha_{p_1} \alpha_{p_2} \ldots \alpha_{p_n})$ that is a [[truth-functional]] identity; and this disjunction is such that from the fact of its being an identity we can deduce that P is an identity. Compare *Herbrand 1930*, Chap. 5, 5.1. [[This disjunction is what we have called the standard expansion of P in the Introduction p. 9 above, Note G, p. 194 above, and footnote 21, p. 229 above.]]

[41] We shall always assume implicitly that all the functions in $\Pi(\alpha_{p_1} \alpha_{p_2} \ldots \alpha_{p_n})$ have been replaced by their values in the domain, so that no function occurs in it.

one of these numbers in such a way that no contradiction arises between the logical values of the atomic propositions with arguments taken in a domain of order k; for the case in which the initial proposition does not contain any descriptive functions we see immediately that the problem can be stated as follows:[42]

Given any collection of a finite number of systems [[that is, n-tuples]] *$\beta_1, \beta_2, ..., \beta_n$ in a definite order, the β_i being taken in a canonical domain, can we assign to each system of the collection one of the numbers $1, 2, ..., k$ in such a way that a number of conditions of the following form are fulfilled?*

Let $f_i(x_1 x_2 ... x_{n_i})$ be the functions with which the canonical domain is constructed, let $\beta_1, \beta_2, ..., \beta_n$ and $\gamma_1, \gamma_2, ..., \gamma_n$ be any two systems of the collection, identical or distinct; when certain definite conditions of one of the forms

$$f_i(\beta_{j_1}\beta_{j_2} ... \beta_{j_{n_i}}) = \gamma_m \quad \text{or} \quad f_i(\gamma_{j_1}\gamma_{j_2} ... \gamma_{j_{n_i}}) = \beta_m \quad \text{or} \quad \beta_i = \gamma_j$$

hold, the numbers corresponding to $\beta_1, \beta_2, ..., \beta_n$ and $\gamma_1, \gamma_2, ..., \gamma_n$ can only be chosen among certain pairs of numbers.

If this correspondence is impossible for certain collections of systems, can we find these collections?

However, in the special cases that follow, we shall not consider the question this way. We shall show that, if a sufficient number of $\Pi(\alpha_{p_1}\alpha_{p_2}... \alpha_{p_n})$ have been made false, we can obtain an infinite domain and logical values for which P is false; hence, there is a number k such that if P can be made false in the canonical domain of order k, then P cannot be an identity. Therefore, the necessary and sufficient condition for P to be an identity is that it be true [[rather, not false]] in the canonical domain of order k. By a remark made in the statement of Theorem 2, we see that the condition, once put in this form, provides in addition a proof of P [[if P is an identity]]. However, we shall put the condition in different, though equivalent, forms in the various special cases.

In particular, we shall consider some finite domain; these are domains with a finite number of individuals such that we have in them the value of every function that has arguments taken in the domain. We shall show that, if P can be made false in a canonical domain of a sufficiently

---

[42] See also *Herbrand 1929b* [[p. 41 above]] and footnote 2 above.

high order k, there is a finite domain of n elements in which P is false; by the second statement of Theorem 2, P cannot be an identity;[43] and we obtain again that the necessary and sufficient condition for P to be an identity is that P is true in a domain of n elements.

It is because of the special cases considered that the condition can be put in such a simple form; although in the general case we can hope to find a condition of the first form, we must not count on finding one of the second form. The only case known hitherto in which the condition of truth does not take this last form is the one whose solution has led to the conclusion that arithmetic is not contradictory.[44]

2. FOUR SPECIAL CASES

We merely mention the classical case in which all n atomic propositions have just one argument. If there are n atomic propositions, it is necessary and sufficient that the proposition be true in a domain of 2^n elements.[45]

FIRST CASE. *Propositions*

$$(y_1 y_2 \ldots y_m)(\exists x_1 x_2 \ldots x_p) \cdot \Phi(y_1 y_2 \ldots y_m x_1 x_2 \ldots x_p)$$

without descriptive functions.[46]

The infinite domain that has to be considered according to the Fundamental Theorem is here a domain of m individuals. Therefore, for

---

[43] A direct proof can be found in *Herbrand 1930*, Chap. 2, § 8. [[See Note K, p. 259 below.]]

[44] See *Herbrand 1930*, Chap. 4.

[45] See, for example, *Herbrand 1930*, Chap. 2, 9.2. We take this opportunity to correct an inaccuracy in the last part of the argument, which was pointed out to us by Bernays. The argument is in fact faulty if $r = 0$. It should be modified as follows: it is necessary and sufficient for P to be an identity that $p_1 \vee p_2 \vee \ldots \vee p_q \cdot \supset \cdot A(p_1, p_2, \ldots, p_q)$ be an identity. It is sufficient because $\vdash . p_1 \vee p_2 \vee \ldots \vee p_q$, whence, if the former proposition is true, $\vdash . A(p_1, p_2, \ldots, p_q)$ and the conclusion as in the text. It is necessary because, if the former proposition were not an identity, we could give to the p_i logical values making it false, therefore such that $A(p_1, p_2, \ldots, p_q)$ would have the logical value 'false' and one of the p_i the logical value 'true'. It suffices then to take up the argument of the text.

[46] This is a classical case; see, for example, *Bernays and Schönfinkel 1928*.

this proposition to be an identity it is necessary and sufficient that it be true in a domain of m individuals (one individual if $m=0$).[47]

SECOND CASE. *Propositions whose matrix is a disjunction of atomic propositions and negations of atomic propositions, with (or without) descriptive functions.*

Let us consider the elementary proposition associated with such a proposition P; call it Π. We shall assume that all its variables have been replaced by the elements α_i of the infinite domain; then what we must make false is a disjunction of terms of the form $\varphi_i(a_1 a_2 \ldots a_n)$ or $\sim \varphi_i(a_1 a_2 \ldots a_n)$.[48] Now consider $\varphi_i(\alpha_{p_1} \alpha_{p_2} \ldots \alpha_{p_n})$; we must find the values of the variables of Π for which it will be identical with $\varphi_i(a_1 a_2 \ldots a_n)$. This is easily done. Hence, if φ_i occurs only once in Π, or if it occurs several times either preceded everywhere or preceded nowhere by the $\sim$ sign, we obtain the logical value of $\varphi_i(\alpha_{p_1} \alpha_{p_2} \ldots \alpha_{p_n})$; on the other hand, if we have in Π among the terms of the disjunction a term $\varphi_i(a_1 a_2 \ldots a_n)$ and a term $\sim \varphi_i(b_1 b_2 \ldots b_n)$, it may be that for some values of the α_i each b_j becomes identical with each a_j; this is the only case in which Π cannot be made false in the domain. We therefore have a criterion allowing us to recognize whether P is an identity; it is easy to transform this criterion so that the necessary and sufficient condition for P to be an identity is that it be true in a domain having a specific number of elements; however, it is useless to do so because in practice the new criterion would be more complicated than the first.[49]

THIRD CASE. *Propositions of the form*

$$(x_1 x_2 \ldots x_m)(\exists y)(z_1 z_2 \ldots z_p) . \Phi(x_1 x_2 \ldots x_m y z_1 z_2 \ldots z_p)$$

without descriptive functions.

Let P be a proposition of this form and assume that it has no variables other than those actually exhibited.

This case has already been considered by Ackermann (*1928*); but we believe we can reproach his proof for a lack of rigor (see *Herbrand 1930*,

---

[47] [[That is, the canonical domain is generated by m elements of order 1 (the constants replacing the y_i) and no functions; hence, it has only m individuals.]]

[48] a_i and b_i here denote functions of the α_i.

[49] [[See Note L, p. 262 below.]]

Chap. 5, 6.3 [[rather, 6.4]]), and we present here a proof that is considerably simplified and can easily be generalized.

An element α_i of the domain is assigned to each of the x_i; an index function $f_i(\alpha)$ of *one* argument is assigned to each z_i. We can then put the infinite canonical domain in the following form (what Ackermann calls a "Stammbaum" and what we called a "scheme" in *1930*[50]):

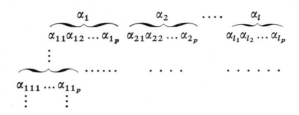

where $\alpha_{ijl...mn}$ is the value of $f_n(\alpha_{ijl...m})$. Let us assume that P is false in this domain. For each element x of the domain we shall consider the logical values of the atomic propositions having arguments taken from among x, the α_i and the $f_j(x)$. We shall call every sequence of elements of the form $\alpha_i, \alpha_{ij}, \alpha_{ijk}, ..., \alpha_{ijk...l}, \alpha_{ijk...lm}, ...$ a line. In every line there are two elements, $\alpha_{ij...l}$ and $\alpha_{ij...l...mn}$, for which the above-mentioned system of logical values is the same; it is easy to assign an upper bound to the heights of these elements. We shall replace the infinite domain considered by a finite domain obtained by stopping each line at the individual $\alpha_{ij...l...m}$ and by taking $f_n(\alpha_{ij...l...m})=\alpha_{ij...l}$;[51] in this finite domain if we take the same logical values as in a canonical domain of sufficiently high order to contain all these letters, P is evidently false.

Let us assume that P includes atomic propositions with $1, 2, ..., k$ arguments and that there are μ_i propositions of i arguments. Replacing the arguments of the atomic propositions by $\alpha_1, \alpha_2, ..., \alpha_m, x, f_1(x), ..., f_p(x)$, in any way whatsoever, we have $\sum \mu_i C_{p+l+1}^i$ distinct propositions;[52]

---

[50] Instead, we could just as easily consider what is called in group theory a free group.

[51] [[This proof contains an error; see Note M, p. 263 below.]]

[52] $C_n^m = \dfrac{n(n-1)...(n-m+1)}{m!}$ is the binomial coefficient. [[The French text has 'C_{p+l+i}' in two places instead of 'C_{p+l+1}^i'. In any case, because of the error in the proof, the bound given is incorrect.]]

hence there are $h = 2^{\Sigma \mu_i C^i_p + l + 1}$ systems of distinct logical values. Therefore, in the above procedure, we can stop the line after the element of height h at most.

Now the number of elements of the domain that are of height h at most is:

$$1 + lp + \cdots + lp^h = l \frac{p^{h+1} - 1}{p - 1}$$

Therefore, *for the proposition under consideration to be an identity it is necessary and sufficient that it be true in a domain of* $l(p^{h+1} - 1)/(p-1)$ *individuals, where* $h = 2^{\Sigma \mu_i C^i_p + l + 1}$ (We can also say: *it is necessary and sufficient that the proposition cannot be made false in the canonical domain of order h.*)

FOURTH CASE. Our method can immediately be generalized to the case of propositions of the form

$$(x_1 x_2 \ldots x_m) : (\exists y_1) . (z_1^1 z_2^1 \ldots z_{p_1}^1) \, \Phi_1 \, (x_1 x_2 \ldots x_m y_1 z_1^1 z_2^1 \ldots z_{p_1}^1)$$
$$. \vee . (\exists y_2) . (z_1^2 z_2^2 \ldots z_{p_2}^2) \, \Phi_2 \, (x_1 x_2 \ldots x_m y_2 z_1^2 z_2^2 \ldots z_{p_2}^2)$$
$$. \vee . \ldots$$
$$. \vee . (\exists y_k) . (z_1^k z_2^k \ldots z_{p_k}^k) \, \Phi_k \, (x_1 x_2 \ldots x_m y_k z_1^k z_2^k \ldots z_{p_k}^k)$$

and without descriptive functions. This time we have $p_1 + p_2 + \ldots + p_k$ index functions of one argument, and the reasoning is exactly the same; however, the formula for the number of elements of the domain is now more complicated, and we do not think it is necessary to write it down.[53]

The general case of the decision problem presents difficulties that have not yet been surmounted. The preceding case, which seems to have some generality, nevertheless does not permit us to realize the difficulties of the general case, since we are concerned there with index functions of only one argument. This fact allows us to give the domain a remarkable

---

[53] [[This case is not an extension of the one immediately above, for by using the equivalence $(\exists y_1) \, \Phi(y_1) \vee (\exists y_2) \, \Phi(y_2) . \equiv : (\exists y_1) . \Phi(y_1) \vee \Phi(y_2)$, we can always find a proposition of the form $(x_1 \ldots x_m) (\exists y) (z_1 \ldots z_p) \, \Psi$ equivalent to one of the form shown here.]]

form; when this is no longer the case, the structure of the domain is very complex (it is no longer 'simply connected', so to speak); and this circumstance makes a thorough study of the problem essentially very difficult.

3. APPENDIX

Consider an infinite canonical domain generated by the functions $f_k(x_1 x_2 \ldots x_{n_k})$ $(k = 1, 2, \ldots, p)$. We can prove that it can be put in the form $\alpha_0, \alpha_1, \alpha_2, \ldots, \alpha_m, \ldots$ in such a way that $f_k(\alpha_{i_1} \alpha_{i_2} \ldots \alpha_{i_{n_k}})$ has the value α_j, where j is, for each value of k, a polynomial in $i_1, i_2, \ldots, i_{n_k}$. If we recall the statement to which we reduced the decision problem [[p. 245 above]], we see that we are finally brought back to a problem that is a simple generalization of the problem of effectively solving a system of diophantine equations.

Proof. It suffices to show that we can assign, in a *bijective* manner, to every system k, $i_1, i_2, \ldots, i_{n_k}$ (where k takes only the values $1, 2, \ldots, p$; the n_k are fixed; and the i take arbitrary integral values, positive or zero) an integer (positive or zero) that is the value of a polynomial $\varphi_k(i_1, i_2, \ldots, i_{n_k})$ and is greater than each i_j (unless they are all 0 and $k = 1$), in such a way that every integer is the value of one and only one of these functions. Thus we see that by giving the value $\alpha_{\varphi_k(i_1, i_2, \ldots, i_{n_k})}$ to $f_k(\alpha_{i_1} \alpha_{i_2} \ldots \alpha_{i_{n_k}})$ we shall have an infinite canonical domain.

To construct these polynomials we consider first the case in which the n_k are equal to 1. Here it suffices to note that we can assign, in a bijective manner, to every system of two integers i and j an integer k that is the value of a polynomial $\varphi(i, j)$; we can take $\varphi(i, j) = \frac{1}{2}(i+j)(i+j+1) + i$.[54]

In the case in which $n_k = 1$, we take $\varphi_k(i) = ip + k$.

[54] [[Herbrand shows in this paragraph that we can deal with the case $p = 1$; that is, there is one function of n_1 arguments. φ is a pairing function; by iterating it $n_1 - 1$ times, we can associate systems $i_1, i_2, \ldots, i_{n_1}$ of integers bijectively with integers. Thus, using φ we first reduce all functions to functions of one argument, and then apply the coding $\varphi_k(i) = ip + k$ so as to reduce the number of functions to one, where p is the total number of functions.]]

CHAPTER 4

SOME CONSEQUENCES OF THE SOLUTION OF THE DECISION PROBLEM

1. The Arithmetization of Mathematical Theories

Our fundamental theorem poses the decision problem[55] in an essentially arithmetical form. But we can even show that it is a direct generalization of classical problems of arithmetic. Consider, for example, Fermat's theorem, which will provide the occasion for some curious remarks.

Take a theory with one constant, 0, and four descriptive functions, one with one argument, $x+1$, and three with two arguments, $x+y$, xy, x^y, and with the hypotheses[56]

$$x = x, \quad x = y \supset y = x, \quad x = y \,\&\, y = z .\supset. x = z,$$
$$\sim. x + 1 = 0, \quad x = y.\equiv.x + 1 = y + 1,$$

$$\left.\begin{array}{l} x + 0 = x \\ x + (y + 1) = (x + y) + 1 \end{array}\right\} \text{ (defines } x + y) \tag{1}$$

$$x + y = x .\supset. y = 0$$

$$\left.\begin{array}{l} x \cdot 0 = 0 \\ x (y + 1) = xy + x \end{array}\right\} \text{ (defines } xy)$$

$$\left.\begin{array}{l} x^0 = 1 \\ x^{y+1} = x \cdot x^y \end{array}\right\} \text{ (defines } x^y)$$

$$x = x' \,\&\, y = y' .\supset. x + y = x' + y' \,\&\, xy = x'y' \,\&\, x^y = x'^{y'}.$$

---

[55] Concerning this chapter, see the appendix at the end of the paper. Henceforth we shall always mean the decision problem in the restricted sense (how to recognize whether a proposition is an identity, or, what amounts to the same thing by the corollary at the end of Chap. 2, how to recognize whether a proposition is true in a theory having only a finite number of hypotheses).

[56] For the statement of the hypotheses we make the convention indicated on p. 231, before Corollary 2. Concerning their statement one may want to consult *Herbrand 1930*, Chap. 4 and Chap. 5, 6.4.

Let us consider the proposition

$$(\exists xyzn) . x^n + y^n = z^n \,\&\, \sim n = 0 \,\&\, \sim n = 1 \,\&\, \sim n = 2,$$
(2)

n denoting a variable for the moment.

To see whether this proposition is true in our theory, we must try (by Chap. 1, § 4 (e)) to construct an infinite domain in which hypotheses (1) are true and proposition (2) is false.

If we take the remarks concluding § 1 of Chap. 2 into account, we readily see that this infinite domain can be put precisely in the form of the sequence of integers, with the ordinary values of the functions of arithmetic; and that, therefore, proposition (2) is not true in the theory under consideration unless we can *actually* find numbers x, y, z, and n such that $x^n + y^n = z^n$, where n is greater than 2.

Here the decision problem is reduced to the effective solution of the equation $x^n + y^n = z^n$.

Suppose now that to hypotheses (1) we add other hypotheses, such as the axiom of mathematical induction:

$$\Phi(0) \,\&. (x) . \Phi(x) \supset \Phi(x+1) : \supset . (x) . \Phi(x) . \,^{[57]}$$
(1a)

We now have to deal with new functions in constructing the infinite domain; hence the problem changes. If under these conditions, (2) were true without being so before the introduction of the new hypotheses, then we could prove that there exist numbers x, y, z, and $n > 2$ such that $x^n + y^n = z^n$; but it would be *impossible to actually find* four such numbers. Although by reasoning in a mathematical way on the infinite domain originally considered we come to the conclusion that its construction cannot be pursued indefinitely, it is clear that metamathematically this is of no importance, since we shall never be stopped in this construction.

On the other hand, *assume that the decision problem has been solved.* Applied to the theory originally considered, which has only a finite

---

[57] Let us recall that this axiom should be considered the source of an infinite number of hypotheses, these hypotheses being obtained whenever $\Phi(x)$ is replaced by a definite proposition.

number of hypotheses, the solution will provide an intuitionistic reasoning [58] by which we shall be able to prove that it is always the case that $x^n + y^n \neq z^n$ for $n > 2$ or to find four numbers x, y, z, and $n > 2$ such that $x^n + y^n = z^n$; we come finally to the conclusion that

If the decision problem can be solved, either Fermat's theorem is true or else we can actually find four numbers such that $x^n + y^n = z^n$ (with $n > 2$).[59]

This remarkable fact is easily generalized and we then come to the following conclusion: if the decision problem can be solved, we can construct the objects whose existence we have been able to prove; but this fact presents itself then in a much more complex manner, on which we shall not dwell here.

We see that Fermat's theorem, and diophantine problems in general, undergo little or no change in aspect when we apply our Fundamental Theorem to them. But, besides the fact that this theorem regains all its strength when there are general variables in the identities to be proved (which was not the case in the original example above), it allows us to pose from an entirely different viewpoint every question relative to a theory that considers nondenumerable sets of objects; for it reduces such questions to the consideration of infinite domains that, considered arithmetically, are denumerable.[60] It reveals the remarkable fact that in a given theory we consider at one time only a finite number of constants, variables, and functions, and that the set of those that we might even be led to consider is 'denumerable' in some way. It effectuates, in this sense, the arithmetization of every mathematical theory.

But the very fact that the general arithmetical problem to which it reduces every question is itself reduced, when we particularize the data,

---

[58] [[Herbrand is using 'intuitionistic' here and below in the sense of 'metamathematical', rather than in relation to any special doctrines of Brouwer. See Jean van Heijenoort's introduction to *1931c*, p. 282 below.]]

[59] It suffices to assume in this result that the decision problem has been solved for the proposition obtained when we write that the product of propositions (1) implies proposition (2).

[60] In the sense in which Borel, for example, says that the set of real numbers is denumerable. [[See also the Introduction, p. 16 above.]]

to the solution of diophantine equations gives us an estimate of the difficulty of the problem: it must be considered, in its generality, as beyond the present means of analysis.

2. REFLECTIONS ON THE INTRODUCTION OF CLASSES AND RELATIONS

We now consider the theory obtained as follows: Start with a theory T having, for the sake of simplicity, only one type. Add to it a number of other types obtained as follows: to each type we shall assign a well-defined number, its height. (1) To every type of height h will correspond another type of height $h+1$, called the type of classes of elements of the preceding types. If x is in the first type and α in the second,[61] we shall have an atomic proposition $x \in \alpha$ (read 'x is in the class α'). (2) To every pair of types τ_1 and τ_2, taken in this order, the greater of the two heights being h, there will correspond another type of height $h+1$, called the type of relations between elements of the two preceding types. If x and y are in the types τ_1 and τ_2, respectively, and ρ is in the new type, we shall have the atomic proposition $x\rho y$ (read 'x bears the relation ρ to y').

The initial type will be of height 0 and every other type can be obtained from it by one of these two procedures.

We add the following new hypotheses:

$$(\exists\alpha)(\beta): \alpha = \beta . \equiv . (x) . x \in \beta \equiv \Phi(x)$$
$$(\exists\rho)(\sigma): \sigma = \rho . \equiv . (xy) . x\sigma y \equiv \Phi(xy)$$

for all possible propositions $\Phi(x)$ and $\Phi(xy)$ ($x=y$ is put here for (α). $x \in \alpha \equiv y \in \alpha$).

We thus obtain a theory that we shall denote by $T+R$ (by R if T has no hypotheses, in which case we may assume that we have at our disposal all the constants, functions, and atomic propositions we wish for arguments of the type of height 0). We recognize in R a theory equivalent to that developed by Russell and Whitehead in *Principia Mathematica* (to be more exact, it is a simple extension of that theory).[62]

[61] For the moment α, β, ρ, σ will denote variables.

[62] [[That is, R is the simple theory of types with the addition of arbitrary predicate letters with arguments of the type of height 0.]]

We can also add to the hypotheses the axiom of infinity (Inf Ax) or the multiplicative axioms for the various types (denoted all together by Mult Ax), as the authors of *Principia* have done; thereby obtaining the theories $R+$Inf Ax, $R+$Mult Ax, $R+$Inf Ax$+$Mult Ax.

In particular, in the theory $R+$Inf Ax$+$Mult Ax all of classical mathematics, up to Cantor, can be reconstructed.

Let us assume henceforth that this theory is consistent (which up to now has not been proved) and that the decision problem has been solved. Let P be a proposition, Π the elementary proposition associated with P (or, to exhibit all the variables, $\Pi(x_1x_2\dots x_n)$); Π contains certain atomic propositions $\varphi_i(x_1x_2\dots x_{n_i})$ and certain elementary functions $f_j(x_1x_2\dots x_{n_j})$.

P is or is not an identity; we shall assume henceforth that it is not.

(1) It follows from the theory of descriptions of Russell and Whitehead [63] (and, moreover, from the considerations of Chap. 2, § 2) that we can introduce into $R+$Inf Ax$+$Mult Ax functions $f(x_1x_2\dots x_n)$ with hypotheses of the form

$$f(x_1x_2\dots x_n)=y.\equiv.\Phi(x_1x_2\dots x_n y)$$

when

$$(\exists y)(z):\Phi(x_1x_2\dots x_n y)\equiv.z=y$$

is already a true proposition.

(Recall that in the theory of Russell and Whitehead $x=y$ is put for $(\alpha).x\in\alpha\equiv y\in\alpha$). If we do that, we have a simple extension of the theory. Hence we can consider the elements of a denumerable set C (for example, the set of finite ordinal numbers; see *Principia Mathematica* *120) as the elements of an infinite canonical domain, by introducing among these elements suitable functions (see, for example, Chap. 3, § 3) corresponding to the functions that have to be considered in the canonical domain corresponding to P; we shall give the same name to these new functions as to the former ones.

(2) Consider all the systems of logical values making Π false in a domain of order k. For one of these systems, consider the set of systems such as

---

[63] On this point see *Principia Mathematica* *13.

$\beta_1, \beta_2, \ldots, \beta_n$ for which $\Pi(\beta_1\beta_2 \ldots \beta_n)$ has the logical value 'true'[64] and let us conduct our reasoning about it in $R + \text{Inf Ax} + \text{Mult Ax}$. All the arguments carried out concerning these logical values and the canonical domain, in particular those necessary for solving the decision problem, can be translated into proofs carried out in this theory. They show us that the proposition that reads, when translated into ordinary language, 'for every number k there is at least one system of logical values making Π false in the domain of order k' is true in this theory. By using Mult Ax and observing that knowledge of such a system for a domain of order k permits us to deduce from it another system for every domain of lower order, we obtain the truth of the proposition that is translated as follows: 'In the infinite domain C there is a unique system of logical values making Π false.' We readily obtain the result that we can replace in Π the propositions $\varphi_i(x_1x_2 \ldots x_{n_i})$ by others in such a way that, if $\Pi(x_1x_2 \ldots x_n)$ becomes $\Pi'(x_1x_2 \ldots x_n)$, the proposition $x_1 \in C \,\&\, x_2 \in C \,\&\, \ldots \,\&\, x_n \in C .\supset. \sim\Pi'(x_1x_2 \ldots x_n)$ is false [[rather, true]] in $R + \text{Inf Ax} + \text{Mult Ax}$. We can now readily see that, if this theory is not inconsistent, P cannot be a true proposition in it[65] (because P can be made false by suitably specifying the atomic propositions that occur in it).

Thus, in the end, *P cannot be true in R + Inf Ax + Mult Ax unless it is an identity*. We draw several important consequences of this:

1. Suppose that we add to the rules of reasoning already considered other rules that are not consequences of the former; then there will be propositions P that were not identities but that now become so. However, since they can be 'made false' in $R + \text{Inf Ax} + \text{Mult Ax}$, we obtain a contradiction. Therefore,

If we assume that the decision problem has been solved and if we do not

---

[64] [[This should be 'false'; $\Pi(\beta_1 \ldots \beta_n)$ never has the logical value 'true' under one of these systems of logical values. Hence, the set of systems $\beta_1, \ldots, \beta_n$ for which $\Pi(\beta_1 \ldots \beta_n)$ has the value 'false' is just all n-tuples from the domain.]]

[65] The method we outline here essentially comes down to translating (and completing, thanks to Mult Ax) into a suitable theory the arguments carried out in metamathematics. In the last analysis, it comes to a strict use of the proposition known as the Skolem paradox, which we can state imprecisely by saying that "every proposition that is not an identity can be made false in a denumerable domain". [[See Note N, p. 265 below.]]

wish $R + Inf\ Ax + Mult\ Ax$ to be inconsistent, we must not add any rule of reasoning to those already considered.

This theorem corresponds to what in German is called the *Vollständigkeit* [completeness] of our system of rules.[66]

2. Let T be a theory with only one type.

With the same hypotheses, $T + R + Inf\ Ax + Mult\ Ax$ *is a simple extension of* T.

If indeed P, which is a proposition of T, were not true in T and became true in $T + R + Inf\ Ax + Mult\ Ax$, there would be a product $\mathscr{H}$ of hypotheses of T such that $\mathscr{H} \supset P$ would not be an identity and nevertheless would be true in $R + Inf\ Ax + Mult\ Ax$. But this would be impossible with the above-mentioned hypotheses.

The same result would be true, moreover, if we added to Inf Ax and Mult Ax other hypotheses, H, such that $R + H + Inf\ Ax + Mult\ Ax$ remained consistent (for example, hypotheses on the number of individuals of the type of order 0).

Let us now explain how to remove an objection that may present itself. In T we can have, for example, the atomic proposition $x = y$, with the hypotheses already made explicit in Chap. 2, § 1. Assume that $(\exists y)\,(x).x = y$ is true in T, and therefore that all the objects there are 'equal'. How can that be reconciled with Inf Ax? We know that in *Principia Mathematica* the relation of equality, which we shall now denote by $x \equiv y$, is defined by $(\alpha).x \in \alpha \equiv y \in \alpha$. Now we can easily prove that $x \equiv y\,.\supset.\,x = y$ is true in $T + R + Inf\ Ax + Mult\ Ax$; but $x = y\,.\supset.\,x \equiv y$ will not be true there. These two relations of equality are not equivalent; and, in ordinary verbal reasoning, it will be necessary to take into account the fact that there is an infinite number of objects x such that $x = y$, none of these objects being such that $x \equiv y$ is true. In other words, the introduction of classes allows us to define in T a new relation of equality, 'finer' than the first.

3. All the preceding results are valid only if the decision problem has been effectively solved. Perhaps this is impossible; perhaps it can even be proved metamathematically that it is impossible (by an axiomatization of metamathematics itself), and this chain of impossibilities can easily be continued. Nevertheless, it seems to us interesting to sketch the new aspect

---

[66] [[See Note N, p. 265 below.]]

that certain mathematical questions will take if the problem with which we are concerned is solved, whatever the difficulty this solution seems to present in the current state of mathematical knowledge.

APPENDIX

Since the time (September 1929) when the preceding lines were written, the way in which the question poses itself has been entirely changed by the results obtained by Gödel [*1931*]. The outcome is that, under some rather slight restrictions (which all the theories considered in § 2 of the preceding chapter satisfy), it is impossible to prove the consistency of a theory through arguments formalizable in the theory.[67] In particular, if we could solve the decision problem in the restricted sense, it would follow that every theory which has only a finite number of hypotheses and in which this solution is formalizable would be inconsistent (since the question of the consistency of a theory having only a finite number of hypotheses can be reduced to this problem).

All this has no effect on the results of our § 1. But those of § 2 have to be modified. We can indeed readily prove that there are theories with a finite number of hypotheses in which $R + \text{Inf Ax} + \text{Mult Ax}$ can be interpreted and which can be interpreted in this latter theory (at least if we admit in this theory only a definite bounded number of types, which suffices for the arguments of § 2). The question of the consistency of these two theories is then equivalent. Therefore, if the decision problem were solved and if, as we assume implicitly in § 2, its solution could be formalized in $R + \text{Inf Ax} + \text{Mult Ax}$, the latter theory would be inconsistent and our arguments would lose all interest. Moreover, there are mathematicians who believe, astonishing as it may seem, that there may be intuitionistic arguments that are not formalizable in $R + \text{Inf Ax} + \text{Mult Ax}$. Taking this fact into account and also the remark that most of the arguments of § 2 assume only that the decision problem has been solved for the proposition P considered there (or a class of propositions con-

---

[67] By this phrase we mean that the metamathematical signs can be interpreted by the constants and functions of the theory in such a way that every metamathematical argument considered can be translated by an argument carried out in the theory (as in § 2).

taining *P*), we see that to avoid any objection we should state our final results as follows:

If the decision problem is solved for a proposition P, if the solution is formalizable in R + Inf Ax + Mult Ax (which is the case for all the particular cases of the decision problem solved up to now), and if P is not an identity, then

(1) *New rules of reasoning that make P an identity cannot be added without entailing an inconsistency in R + Inf Ax + Mult Ax;*

(2) *P cannot be true in R + Inf Ax + Mult Ax.*[66]

Note finally that, although at present it seems unlikely that the decision problem can be solved, it has not yet been proved that it is impossible to do so.

NOTE K

(footnote 43, p. 246 above)

Although the domains over which expansions are taken are always finite, Herbrand is here restricting the expression 'finite-domain' to domains *D* with the property that all functions of arguments in *D* have values in *D*. (In this note we hyphenate 'finite-domain' to indicate this special use.) By definition, *P* is true in the finite-domain *D* if the common expansion *C*(*P*, *D*) of *P* over *D* is truth-functionally valid, and *P* is false in the finite-domain *D* if *C*(*P*, *D*) is not valid. (See *1930*, Chap. 2, § 8, p. 91 above, and Chap. 3, 1.42, p. 104 above. Occasionally in *1930* Herbrand shifts the meaning of 'true in a finite-domain' as indicated in footnote 2, p. 105 above, but in the present paper he returns to the original sense.) The truth of *P* in a finite-domain *D* depends only on the cardinality of *D* and the values in *D* of the descriptive functions appearing in *P*. Hence, *P* is true in a domain of *n* elements (in the sense of *1930*, Chap. 2, 8.3), or *P* is *n-valid*, if and only if *P* is true in all finite-domains *D* of cardinality *n*, that is, no matter what values are assigned in *D* to descriptive functions.

There is another notion of falsity in *D*, arising from the definition on p. 229 above. Let $\Pi(x_1 \ldots x_n)$ be the elementary proposition associated with *P* (that is, what we called the 'strict validity functional form of *P*' on p. 8 above), and let the *finitized expansion of P over D* be the disjunction *R*(*P*, *D*) of all instances $\Pi(\alpha_1 \ldots \alpha_n)$, where the α_i are elements of *D*. (We assume that the functional terms appearing in $\Pi(\alpha_1 \ldots \alpha_n)$ have been replaced by their values in *D*.) Thus, the finitized expansion is constructed like the standard expansion (p. 9 above and p. 194 above), except that the special domain *D*, rather than a canonical domain, is used. *P* is false in *D* if and only if *R*(*P*, *D*) is not truth-functionally valid. Hence we have two distinct notions: 'falsity in *D*' and 'falsity in the finite-domain D'. The former notion is based on the finitized expansion and depends on the values in D of the index functions; the latter is based on the common expansion, and does not depend on these values. To avoid confusion, we shall use the term 'false' as infrequently as possible. The following facts connect the two notions:

(I) If $C(P, D)$ is not valid, then there is a D' such that $R(P, D')$ is not valid, and D' differs from D only in the assignment of values to index functions.

(II) If $C(P, D)$ is valid, then so is $R(P, D)$.

A rigorous proof of (I) is rather long and tedious, so we shall merely outline how it proceeds. We must define the values of the index functions in D'; since in $C(P, D)$ the index functions play no role, this must be done in some way based only on the assignment of logical values that makes $C(P, D)$ false. The possibility of doing this so as to preserve falsity under the assignment of logical values depends on the syntactic similarity between $C(P, D)$ and the 'second expansion of P over D' (defined in *1930*, p. 154 above, and also p. 8 above); and the second expansion is equivalent to $R(P, D)$ (see Note G, p. 194 above). Note that we must permit D' to differ from D. For example, let P be $(\exists y)(x).Fyx \vee \sim Fxy$. Then $C(P, D)$ is not truth-functionally valid, yet $R(P, D)$ is, where D is the finite-domain $\alpha_0, \alpha_1, \alpha_2$, with $f_x(\alpha_0) = \alpha_1, f_x(\alpha_1) = \alpha_2$, and $f_x(\alpha_2) = \alpha_1$. However, $R(P, D')$ is not valid when D' is like D except $f_x(\alpha_2) = \alpha_0$.

However, since (II) plays an essential role in Herbrand's solutions of special cases of the decision problem (see below, p. 262), we shall present a complete proof of it. Assume $C(P, D)$ is valid, where D is the finite-domain $\alpha_1, \alpha_2, ..., \alpha_n$. Let $Q = (\pm x_1) ... (\pm x_m) M$ be any prenex form of P, where $(\pm x_i)$ means the quantifier may be universal or existential. By *1930*, Chap. 2, 8.2, if $C(P, D)$ is valid then so is $C(Q, D)$. Let $N_i(x_1 ... x_i)$ be $C((\pm x_{i+1}) ... (\pm x_m) M, D)$; hence, N_0 is $C(Q, D)$ and $N_m(x_1 ... x_m)$ is M. (Note that in N_0 all descriptive functions have been replaced by their values in D.) A proposition $N_i(\alpha_{j_1} ... \alpha_{j_i})$ is said to be *lexical* if the following holds for all k, $k \leqslant i$, such that x_k is a general variable of P (hence universal in Q): if in the elementary proposition associated with P the variable x_k is replaced by $f(x_{k_1} ... x_{k_p})$ for some function sign f (p possibly zero; note that all k_j are less than k), then in $N_i(\alpha_{j_1} ... \alpha_{j_i})$ the element α_{j_k} is the value in D of $f(\alpha_{j_{k_1}} ... \alpha_{j_{k_p}})$. Clearly, $N_m(\alpha_{j_1} ... \alpha_{j_m})$ is a disjunct of $R(P, D)$ if and only if it is lexical.

Finally, let $\mathscr{A}$ be any assignment of logical values to the atomic propositions in $R(P, D)$; we must show at least one disjunct of this expansion has the logical value 'true' under $\mathscr{A}$. Since $\mathscr{A}$ is arbitrary, it will then follow that $R(P, D)$ is truth-functionally valid.

If necessary, we can extend $\mathscr{A}$ to an assignment to all atomic propositions in N_0; we do this in any way we choose, and also call the resulting assignment $\mathscr{A}$. Since by hypothesis N_0 is valid, it has the logical value 'true' under $\mathscr{A}$. We now define a sequence of propositions $B_1, \ldots, B_m$, where each B_i is a lexical $N_i(\alpha_{j_1} \ldots \alpha_{j_i})$ for some elements α of D.

(1) If x_1 is restricted, then $N_0 = N_1(\alpha_1) \vee \ldots \vee N_1(\alpha_n)$. We pick B_1 to be any $N_1(\alpha_j)$ that has the logical value 'true'. If x_1 is general, then $N_0 = N_1(\alpha_1) \& \ldots \& N_1(\alpha_n)$. We then pick B_1 to be the lexical $N_1(\alpha_j)$, that is, such that α_j is the constant replacing x_1 in the elementary proposition associated with P.

(2) Suppose $B_i = N_i(\alpha_{j_1} \ldots \alpha_{j_i})$ has been defined, and has the logical value 'true' under $\mathscr{A}$.

If x_{i+1} is restricted, $B_i = N_{i+1}(\alpha_{j_1} \ldots \alpha_{j_i}\alpha_1) \vee \ldots \vee N_{i+1}(\alpha_{j_1} \ldots \alpha_{j_i}\alpha_n)$. We pick B_{i+1} to be any of these disjuncts having the logical value 'true' (from the induction hypothesis, there must be at least one such disjunct). Note that B_{i+1} is lexical, if B_i was.

If x_{i+1} is general, $B_i = N_{i+1}(\alpha_{j_1} \ldots \alpha_{j_i}\alpha_1) \& \ldots \& N_{i+1}(\alpha_{j_1} \ldots \alpha_{j_i}\alpha_n)$. We pick B_{i+1} to be the lexical proposition among these conjuncts (this choice is well-defined since the restricted variables superior to x_{i+1} are all among $x_1, \ldots, x_i$).

From this construction, it is clear that all the B_i are lexical and have the logical value 'true'. Hence B_m is a disjunct of $R(P, D)$, so that this expansion has the logical value 'true'. Q.E.D.

Although Herbrand never states (I) and (II), he does exploit them. For example, in *1930*, Chap. 5, 6.4 (p. 176 above), and in *1931*, p. 246 above, he asserts that by using the Fundamental Theorem we can show that P is derivable in Q_H only if P is n-valid for every n, or, equivalently, that if $C(P, D)$ is not valid for some finite-domain D then P is false in an infinite domain. The nonconstructive proof of this (for the model-theoretic notion of 'false in an infinite domain') is trivial; see for example *Hilbert and Ackermann 1938*, p. 92. However, a rigorous proof using Herbrand's notions is not. We must define an assignment of logical values to the atomic propositions appearing in an expansion of P over a domain of arbitrarily high order so that the expansion has the logical value 'false'. The elements of the domain are constructed in a particular manner, that is, the domain is generated by the index and descriptive functions of P. The assignment to propositions $\varphi(\alpha_1 \ldots \alpha_n)$ will depend on the relations of the α_i, that is, on whether one is the value of a function some of whose arguments are other α_i. This is not the case in the nonconstructive proof. Once (I) is proved, however, the rest is easy, for suppose we have a finite domain D' and an assignment $\mathscr{A}$ of logical values to atomic propositions under which $R(P, D')$ has the value 'false'. Now consider for any h the standard expansion $R(P, h)$ (see p. 9 and p. 194 above). Every element α_i of the canonical domain of P is the value of a unique function of the initial elements (p. 228 above); let $\mu(\alpha_i)$ be the value of the same function in D' (since D' is a finite domain, $\mu(\alpha_i)$ exists). Finally, assign logical values to $R(P, h)$ so that each atomic proposition $\varphi(\alpha_1 \ldots \alpha_n)$ is assigned the same value as $\mathscr{A}$ assigns to $\varphi(\mu(\alpha_1) \ldots \mu(\alpha_n))$. Under this assignment, $R(P, h)$ clearly has the logical value 'false'; hence, it is not truth-functionally valid. This can be done for any h, so P is false in an infinite domain. (This proof is a special case of the derivation of the second statement of the Fundamental Theorem (p. 230) from the first (p. 229); our function μ plays the same role as Herbrand's notion of equating elements of the domain.)

More importantly, Herbrand used (II) as follows in the course of solving the decision problem for a class of propositions. He proves that for any P in this class we can calculate a number k such that if $R(P, k)$ is not valid, then there is a finite-domain D of cardinality less than that of the canonical domain of order k such that $R(P, D)$ is not valid. By the proof immediately above, this implies that P is derivable in Q_H if and only if it cannot be made false in the canonical domain of order k. Furthermore, by (II), it shows that any proposition P of the class is either derivable or else not n-valid, where n is the cardinality of the domain. The dual considerations, for irrefutability rather than provability (or, assuming a completeness proof, for satisfiability rather than validity) yield the following sort of criterion: if P is irrefutable (satisfiable) then it has a finite model whose cardinality we can calculate. This property of a class of propositions is called *finite controllability* (for validity in the first case, and for satisfiability in the second). Obviously, finite controllability implies decidability. The converse is not true, although all of the cases Herbrand deals with in *1931* are finitely controllable. Dreben, Kahr, and Wang (*1962*) give a class of propositions that is not finitely controllable (for satisfiability), although for each P in the class we can calculate a k such that P is irrefutable if and only if P is true in the canonical domain of order k (that is, the satisfiability expansion of P of order k is truth-functionally satisfiable; see the Introduction, p. 11 above). The class is of prenex propositions of the form $(x) (\exists y) (z) M(xyz)$, where M contains only dyadic atomic propositions whose arguments are xx, xy, yx, yy, zz, xz, or yz.

NOTE L

(footnote 49, p. 247 above)

In this paragraph, Herbrand argues that the class of prenex propositions P whose matrix is a disjunction of atomic propositions and negations of atomic propositions is a decidable class. However, the argument he offers is rather difficult to carry out in detail; we can extract a simpler proof from *1930*, Chap. 5. Let P be a proposition of this class. In *1930*, Chap. 5, 2.34 (p. 146 above), Herbrand shows that if P has property A then P has property A with an associated scheme of two lines (this terminology is defined in §§ 1–2 of Chap. 5). From this, by using the other results of Chap. 5 (suitably corrected) we obtain: P is derivable in Q_H if and only if it has property A with an associated scheme of two lines. This furnishes a decision procedure for the class.

The proof Herbrand sketches in this paragraph is rather different; it takes the form of showing that P is not derivable if and only if certain inequalities of terms built up from variables and function signs are consistent. These inequalities arise from considering the atomic propositions φ that appear both negated and not negated in P; for if P is not an identity, then, for all h, for every positive occurrence and every negative occurrence of φ in $R(P, h)$ there must be an argument place of each filled by unequal elements, or else we would obtain a subdisjunction of the expansion of the form $\varphi(a_1 \ldots a_n) \vee \sim\varphi(a_1 \ldots a_n)$. It is then easily decidable whether such a set of inequalities is inconsistent (see *Hilbert and Bernays 1939*, p. 161). This approach can be seen to be based on Herbrand's general arithmetical form of the decision problem (p. 245 above); that there is only one system of logical values making the expansion false simplifies the problem enough to permit its effective solution.

Neither of these proofs shows that the class is finitely controllable (Note K, p. 262 above). Hilbert and Bernays, in *1934* (p. 146), assert as Herbrand does that the class does have this property. However, in *1939* (p. 161) they retract this, and remark that this fact has a 'misleading plausibility', but that "K. Schütte has indicated that the truth of this assertion is not at all settled." Gladstone (*1966*) proves that if a finite system of inequalities is consistent, it has a finite model; he remarks that this shows the class of propositions to be finitely controllable.

NOTE M

(footnote 51, p. 248 above)

We wish to show that if P is not derivable in Q_H, we can find a finite domain in which it is false (see Note K), where P is of the form $(x_1 \ldots x_m)\,(\exists y)\,(z_1 \ldots z_p)\,\Phi(x_1 \ldots x_m y z_1 \ldots z_p)$. We suppose that we have an assignment $\mathscr{A}$ of logical values to the atomic propositions appearing in $R(P, h')$, the standard expansion of P over the canonical domain of order h', such that $R(P, h')$ has the logical value 'false', where h' will be specified below.

We assume the canonical domain to be in the form shown on p. 248, and use the notion of line as defined there. For every x in the domain, consider the logical values assigned by $\mathscr{A}$ to atomic propositions whose arguments are among x and the α_i. If h' is large enough, in every line we can find two elements $\alpha_\mathbf{a}$ and $\alpha_{\mathbf{a}\ldots n}$ such that these logical values are the same (a denotes a sequence of integers, all less than p), and such that the order of $\alpha_{\mathbf{a}\ldots n}$ is at least three greater than the order of $\alpha_\mathbf{a}$ and $\alpha_\mathbf{a}$ is not one of the α_i. For every such $\alpha_{\mathbf{a}\ldots n}$, we take $f_k(\alpha_{\mathbf{a}\ldots n}) = \alpha_{\mathbf{a}k}$, for $k = 1, 2, \ldots, p$ (we call the element $\alpha_{\mathbf{a}\ldots n}$ *finitized*). The result is a finite domain D; we must show that the finitized expansion $R(P, D)$ can be made false (see Note K above).

First, we note that all atomic propositions appearing in $R(P, h')$ have the following property: if $\alpha_{\mathbf{a}\ldots n}$ is among the arguments, then any other arguments must be either among the α_i or else of order differing by at most 1 from that of $\alpha_{\mathbf{a}\ldots n}$. (We can see this by noting that $\alpha_{\mathbf{a}\ldots n}$ appears in only two disjuncts of $R(P, h')$: once when it replaces z_n and once when it replaces y.) Hence in $R(P, D)$, $\mathscr{A}$ does not assign a logical value to some atomic propositions appearing in disjuncts in which y has been replaced by a finitized element, but $\mathscr{A}$ assigns 'false' to all other disjuncts (since they are the same in $R(P, D)$ as in $R(P, h')$). Hence we need to extend $\mathscr{A}$ so that the former disjuncts will also have the logical value 'false'.

$\mathscr{A}$ does not assign a value to $\varphi(\beta_1 \ldots \beta_n)$ if and only if at least one of the β_i is a finitized element $\alpha_{\mathbf{a}\ldots n}$ and another is $\alpha_{\mathbf{a}k}$ (which is the value of $f_k(\alpha_{\mathbf{a}\ldots n})$ in D), since $\alpha_{\mathbf{a}k}$ differs in order from $\alpha_{\mathbf{a}\ldots n}$ by at least 2. Therefore, we can extend $\mathscr{A}$ as follows: we assign to each such atomic proposition the same logical value that $\mathscr{A}$ assigns to the atomic proposition obtained from it by replacing all occurrences of $\alpha_{\mathbf{a}\ldots n}$ by $\alpha_\mathbf{a}$.

It is clear that the disjunct $\Phi(\alpha_1, \ldots, \alpha_m, \alpha_{\mathbf{a}\ldots n}, \alpha_{\mathbf{a}1}, \ldots, \alpha_{\mathbf{a}p})$ now has the same logical value as $\Phi(\alpha_1, \ldots, \alpha_m, \alpha_\mathbf{a}, \alpha_{\mathbf{a}1}, \ldots, \alpha_{\mathbf{a}p})$ has under $\mathscr{A}$ (viz., 'false') since

1. An atomic proposition in the former disjunct whose arguments do not include $\alpha_{\mathbf{a}\ldots n}$ remains the same in the latter disjunct;

2. An atomic proposition in the former disjunct whose arguments do not include any $\alpha_{\mathbf{a}k}$ has the same logical value as the corresponding proposition in the latter disjunct, from the way in which we selected $\alpha_{\mathbf{a}\ldots n}$ and $\alpha_\mathbf{a}$;

3. All other atomic propositions in the former disjunct have the same logical value as the corresponding atomic propositions in the latter disjunct by the definition of the extension of $\mathscr{A}$.

Hence, $R(P, D)$ is made false by this extension of $\mathscr{A}$.

If μ_i is the number of atomic propositions of i arguments appearing in P, and C_n^m is the number of permutations of n things taken m at a time, then there are $\Sigma \mu_i C_{m+1}^i$ atomic propositions whose arguments are among the x_i and y, hence at most $2^{\Sigma \mu_i C_{m+1}^i}$ systems of logical values we must consider when finding finitized elements. Therefore, we have to consider at most $h' = 3 \cdot 2^{\Sigma \mu_i C^i_m + 1} + 1$ elements in a line before finding two with the required property. The above proof thus shows that if $R(P, h')$ is not truth-functionally valid, there is a finite domain of cardinality at most equal to that of the canonical domain of order h' such that P is false in it. (Note that this bound is smaller than the one Herbrand claims to have found.)

The finite controllability of more difficult cases containing more than one restricted quantifier, such as of propositions $(x_1 \ldots x_m) (\exists y_1 y_2) (z_1 \ldots z_p) \Phi$, can also be proved by considering the standard expansion (although it was first proved by different methods by Gödel (*1933*) and Schütte (*1933, 1934*) – indeed, in the latter case by using the Fundamental Theorem), but since the above property no longer holds, the proof is much more difficult (see *Dreben, Denton, and Scanlon 1972*).

NOTE N

(footnote 66, p. 257 above)

§ 1. At the time Herbrand was writing, the term "Vollständigkeit" was used for several distinct but related notions. The root notion was that a complete theory is adequate for the subject matter it is intended to formalize; that is, in such a theory "all correct formulas of a contentually [[inhaltlich]] characterized sphere can be obtained" (*Hilbert and Ackermann 1928*, p. 33). Both Hilbert and Herbrand claim that we have experimental evidence for the completeness, in this vague sense, of the rules of quantification theory, for, they claim, these rules suffice in practice to capture all general logical reasoning. (See *Hilbert 1928*, p. 140, and *Herbrand 1930* and *1931*, p. 48 and 231 above. See also *Hilbert and Ackermann 1928*, p. 68.)

A familiar way to make this notion precise is to say that a theory is *syntactically complete* when every closed sentence in the language of the theory either is provable or has a provable negation. Herbrand said such a theory was *à complète détermination* in *1930* (p. 105 above) and simply *complète* in *1930a* (p. 209 above). However, most theories whose languages include sentence or predicate letters do not have this property, nor should they. A second precise notion of completeness is given thus: a theory is complete if and only if the addition of any unprovable formula to its axioms yields a contradiction. Hilbert and Ackermann call this notion "completeness in the sharper sense" (p. 33). When this definition is used with respect to theories containing predicate or sentence letters, the added unprovable formula is, of course, subject to the same rules of substitution as the other axioms. (For a theory without sentence or predicate letters, completeness in the sharper sense is equivalent to syntactic completeness, provided the underlying logic is classical.)

Hilbert and Ackermann prove that the propositional calculus is complete in the sharper sense – apparently unaware that Post proved the same result in *1921* – and that quantification theory is not (*Hilbert and Ackermann 1928*, p. 33 and p. 66). Hence they specify yet another notion to make precise the sort of completeness quantification theory might be expected to have, namely, that "all logical formulas which are true in every domain of individuals can be derived in it [[the axiom system]]" (p. 68), and ask whether their formulation of quantification theory has this property. Today, their notion is often called "semantic completeness" and for our purposes can best be put thus:

(I) If a formula P of quantification theory is not provable in Herbrand's system Q_H, then it can be given a falsifying interpretation over a denumerable universe.

The explicit answer to Hilbert and Ackermann's question was first given in *Gödel 1930*, although we argue in § 2 that a semantic completeness proof for Q_H is implicitly contained in Chap. 5 of *Herbrand 1930* (this is also noted in *Hilbert and Ackermann 1959*, p. 104). Moreover, various forms of semantic completeness proofs can be extracted from *Skolem 1928* and *1929* when taken in conjunction with *Skolem 1922*; see the introduction by Dreben and van Heijenoort to *Skolem 1928* in *van Heijenoort 1967*. (In a letter to van Heijenoort dated 14 August 1964, Gödel writes, "As for Skolem, what he could justly claim, but apparently does not claim, is that, in his 1922 paper, he implicitly proved: 'Either A is provable or $\sim A$ is satisfiable' ('provable' taken in an informal sense). However, since he did not clearly formulate this result (nor apparently had made it clear to himself), it seems to have remained completely unknown, as follows from the fact that Hilbert and Ackermann in 1928 do not mention it in connection with their completeness problem." (See *van Heijenoort 1967*, p. 510.)

However, the notion of semantic completeness is not proof-theoretically meaningful – at least in Hilbert's and Herbrand's sense of proof theory – since it turns on the model-theoretic notion of denumerable interpretation. Nevertheless, in his Bologna lecture (*1928*) Hilbert includes completeness questions for quantification theory among the tasks of his proof theory. After posing the problem of the completeness in the sharper sense of elementary number theory, he says that this completeness assertion "includes the assertion that the formal rules of logical inference are sufficient at least in the sphere of number theory" (p. 140). He then says:

The question of the completeness of the system of logical rules, put in general form, constitutes a problem of theoretical logic. Up till now we have come to the view that these rules suffice only through experiment.

We are in possession of an actual proof of this in the case of the pure propositional calculus. In the case of monadic quantification theory, we can obtain a proof from the methods for the solution of the decision problem [[for this case]] ...

(It is worth noting that in both of the instances for which Hilbert asserts an 'actual proof' of completeness, we can give a finitistic explication of semantic completeness; in the propositional calculus by the method of truth-tables, and in monadic quantification theory from the fact that every unprovable formula can be given a falsifying interpretation over a finite universe; see *Hilbert and Bernays 1934*, p. 199.)

In the revised version of *1928* (*1929*, *1930a*), Hilbert shows in more detail how the question of the completeness of quantification theory arises from the question of the completeness in the sharper sense of number theory. He tells us to consider all formulas containing predicate letters and the predicate sign '=', but no occurrences of the successor function sign (and presumably no occurrences of other arithmetical function signs). Hilbert says "this means essentially that we abstract from the ordered nature of the system of numbers, and consider it as an arbitrary system of things" (*1930a*, p. 322). Among these formulas, we are now to consider those that "do not become refutable [[widerlegbar]] when the predicates are defined in any way", for "these represent the generally valid logical propositions". Hilbert then states that the completeness problem for the usual logical rules amounts to whether all such formulas are derivable using these rules.

This formulation is subject to two interpretations. First, Hilbert might mean 'false' by 'widerlegbar'; that is, he is using a semantical notion. Then the formulas we consider are precisely those true in every denumerable model, so that problem here is exactly that of semantic completeness. Or Hilbert might mean 'refutable in number theory' by 'widerlegbar'; that is, the formulas under consideration are those whose negations are not provable in number theory for any definition of the predicates as arithmetical relations. Hence, under this interpretation completeness is equivalent to the following: For each formula P of quantification theory, if P is not provable then $\sim P'$ is provable in number theory, where P' is a formula of pure number theory obtained from P by replacing the n-adic predicate letters by formulas of number theory with n free variables. This implies that if any unprovable formula of quantification theory is added to a system of number theory whose language also includes predicate letters, then the resulting system is inconsistent. The analogy with completeness in the sharper sense is clear.

Remarkably, although Herbrand cites only *Hilbert 1928*, on p. 256 above he arrives at a formulation of completeness very similar to the second interpretation of Hilbert's formulation:

Let R + Inf Ax + Mult Ax be the simple theory of types with the axioms of infinity and choice, let the language of this theory include predicate letters with arguments of lowest type, and let the rules of inference include a substitution rule for these predicate letters; if to R + Inf Ax + Mult Ax is added any unprovable formula of quantification theory, then the resulting system is inconsistent.

To prove this Herbrand has to assume that the decision problem for quantification theory is solved; in § 3 we explain why and distill a theorem from Herbrand's work that does not depend on this hypothesis.

§ 2. Herbrand's Fundamental Theorem states that if P is not provable in Q_H, then it is false in an infinite domain. By *1930*, Chap. 5, 4.1 (p. 164 above), if P is false in an infinite domain, then by a 'principle of choice' the formula P can be given a falsifying interpretation over a denumerable universe. Hence statement (I) in § 1 above follows immediately. (Note that this proof holds for both the *1930* and *1931* definitions of 'false in an infinite domain'; see the Introduction, p. 12 above, and footnote 24, p. 230 above. Note further that by a 'principle of choice' Herbrand intends some form of the axiom of choice; see § 3 below. He was apparently not aware that the falsifying interpretation for P can be obtained without the axiom of choice: the method of *Skolem 1922* can be used instead; see the Introduction, p. 12 above, and also *van Heijenoort 1967*, p. 510. *Skolem 1922*, however, is not mentioned in the Bibliography of *Hilbert and Ackermann 1928*, a bibliography which Herbrand calls 'complete' on p. 214 above.)

However, this argument rests, in its use of the Fundamental Theorem, on Lemma 1 of *1930*, Chap. 5, 5.1 (p. 169 above), the proof of which is incorrect. So we cannot say that Herbrand *proved* (I) unless we include in the argument footnotes 37 and 43 to *1930*, Chap. 5, and especially Note G. Nevertheless, we can say that Herbrand implicitly proved:

(II) If a prenex formula P is not provable in Q_H then it can be given a falsifying denumerable interpretation.

For we have: If P is not provable, it does not have property A (1930, Chap. 5, 2.3, p. 144 above); if P does not have property A it does not have property C (*1930*, Chap. 5, 5.1, the proof of which is correct for prenex formulas P); and if P does not have property C it is false in an infinite domain, in the sense of *1931* (p. 230 above; see footnotes 21 and 24, pp. 229 and 230 above). Finally, by a 'principle of choice', if P is false in an infinite domain, it can be given a falsifying denumerable interpretation. Hence (II) follows.

Now, by the rules of passage every formula can be turned into a prenex one. But this, by itself, permits us to say only that Herbrand has shown that if a formula is not provable, then it is provably equivalent to a prenex formula that has a falsifying denumerable interpretation. To establish (I), Herbrand must show that if a prenex formula P has a falsifying interpretation, then so does any formula obtained from P solely by the rules of passage. Of course, it is not hard to give simple arguments showing this. And one such argument is easily extracted from *Hilbert and Ackermann 1928*, a book to which Herbrand refers in *1930* (p. 53 above).

On a quick reading, the first sentence of Remark 3 of *1930*, Chap. 5, 6.4 (p. 177 above) might be taken as an assertion of something similar to the completeness in the sharper sense of Q_H. But in fact Herbrand's assertion is strictly equivalent to "If P is not provable in Q_H, then it is false in an infinite domain", which is merely one half of the Fundamental Theorem. Hence, when we remember that Herbrand thought of his definition of 'false in an infinite domain' as providing a proof-theoretically acceptable explication of 'having a falsifying denumerable interpretation', we see that for Herbrand the Fundamental Theorem itself furnishes a proof-theoretic version of semantic completeness. (See also *Dreben 1952*, especially p. 1051, and the Introduction, p. 13 above.) However, the parenthetical sentence in Remark 3 *is* intimately connected with the argument for semantic completeness. For, as we shall see in § 3, although Herbrand here has directly in mind the proof-theoretic notion of completeness stated at the end of § 1, his attempt in *1931* to establish this (pp. 254–257 above) rests on a formalization within the simple theory of types of the use of the axiom of choice in the first argument above for (I).

§ 3. A formula P' lacking predicate letters is said to be a (number-theoretic) *interpretation* in R + Inf Ax + Mult Ax of a formula P of Q_H if P' results from P by relativizing the quantifiers of P to the natural numbers and replacing each n-adic predicate letter of P by a formula of R with n free variables. (The notion of interpretation is present, although never explicitly defined, in *1931*.) Herbrand intends to show, on the assumption that the decision problem for Q_H is solved, that if a formula P of quantification theory is not provable in Q_H then there is an interpretation P' of P such that $\vdash \sim P'$ (where '$\vdash$' is to be read 'derivable in R + Inf Ax + Mult Ax'), or as he opaquely puts it, if P is not provable in Q_H then 'P can be made false by suitably specifying the atomic propositions that appear in it' (p. 256 above).

Assume a formula P of Q_H is given; let $\Pi(x_1 \ldots x_n)$ be the formula Herbrand calls the "elementary proposition associated with P" (that is, what we call on p. 8 above the 'strict validity functional form of P'). By suitably selecting the index functions of $\Pi(x_1 \ldots x_n)$, Herbrand can stipulate that the canonical domain of each order q is to be a bounded set D_q of natural numbers (see *1931*, p. 250 above). Assume that there are k truth-assignments falsifying $\Pi(x_1 \ldots x_n)$, and number them $1, \ldots, k$. Then the formula P is false in the canonical domain of order q if and only if

(A) There is a function h from n-tuples of D_q to the set $\{1, ..., k\}$ such that h satisfies certain conditions that depend on the syntactic structure of P.

(These conditions are of the form Herbrand specifies on p. 245 above, where he gives what he calls the "purely arithmetical problem equivalent to the decision problem".) The statement (A) can easily be formalized, once the 'certain conditions' are specified, in the language of R; let $(\exists h)\ \Psi_P(q, h)$ be this formalization.

Obviously, if r is less than q then $\vdash \Psi_P(q, h) \supset \Psi_P(r, h \upharpoonright r)$, where $h \upharpoonright r$ is the restriction of the function h to n-tuples of elements of D_r. Hence using Mult Ax

$$\vdash (q)\ (\exists h)\ \Psi_P(q, h) \supset (\exists h')\ (q)\ \Psi_P(q, h' \upharpoonright q), \tag{1}$$

where h' is a function from *all* n-tuples of natural numbers to $\{1, ..., k\}$. Note that h' can be construed to be a truth-assignment that falsifies all instances of $\Pi(x_1 ... x_n)$ over the natural numbers. Hence in R a falsifying interpretation $\Pi'(x_1 ... x_n)$ of $\Pi(x_1 ... x_n)$ can be specified in terms of h', and so

$$\vdash (\exists h')\ (q)\ \Psi_P(q, h' \upharpoonright q) \supset : x_1 \in C \ \& \ ... \ \& \ x_n \in C \ . \supset . \sim \Pi'(x_1 ... x_n), \tag{2}$$

where C is the set of natural numbers. From (2),

$$\vdash (\exists h')\ (q)\ \Psi_P(q, h' \upharpoonright q) \supset\ \sim P',$$

where P' is that interpretation of P with the same substitutions for predicate letters as $\Pi'(x_1 ... x_n)$. Hence from (1)

$$\vdash (q)\ (\exists h)\ \Psi_P(q, h) \supset\ \sim P'. \tag{3}$$

Now by the Fundamental Theorem, if P is not derivable in Q_H then in the intended model of R + Inf Ax + Mult Ax the formula $(q)\ (\exists h)\ \Psi_P(q, h)$ is true. But, of course, to obtain $\vdash \sim P'$ from (3), Herbrand must show that if P is not derivable in Q_H then $\vdash (q)\ (\exists h)\ \Psi_P(q, h)$. Hence at this point he assumes that a positive solution to the decision problem for Q_H is formalizable in R + Inf Ax + Mult Ax; this assumption immediately implies that $(q)\ (\exists h)\ \Psi_P(q, h)$ is provable in R + Inf Ax + Mult Ax if it is true.

However, by Theorem IX of *Gödel 1931* there are unprovable formulas P of Q_H that do not have interpretations P' such that $\vdash \sim P'$. Hence there are unprovable formulas P of Q_H such that the formulas $(q)\ (\exists h)\ \Psi_P(q, h)$ are not provable in R + Inf Ax + Mult Ax. Nevertheless, the argument of the previous paragraph does establish the following:

(III) Let P be an unprovable formula of Q_H such that $\vdash (q)\, (\exists h)\, \Psi_P(q, h)$. If P is added to the axioms of R + Inf Ax + Mult Ax, then the resulting system is inconsistent.

Assertion (III) is essentially the theorem formulated in the Appendix to *1931* (p. 259 above) written by Herbrand after he became acquainted with Gödel's incompleteness results. (In Herbrand's formulation, his hypothesis "the decision problem is solved for a proposition P and the solution is formalizable in R + Inf Ax + Mult Ax" is to be taken to mean that $(q)\, (\exists h)\, \Psi_P(q, h)$ is either provable or refutable in R + Inf Ax + Mult Ax. Note that this hypothesis is always satisfied whenever P belongs to a class of formulas of Q_H for which the decision problem is solved; for example, the classes with which Herbrand deals in pp. 246ff. above.)

The cryptic sentence in parentheses at the end of Remark 3 of *1930*, Chap. 5, 6.4, p. 178 above, refers to the argument just given for (III). More precisely, it refers to the brief argument in (1) on p. 256 as well as to the argument just given; see also the first conclusion of the theorem of the Appendix to *1931*, p. 259 above. This is easily seen when we remember that Herbrand says "all of classical mathematics can be reconstructed in ... R + Inf Ax + Mult Ax", p. 255 above, and when we take Herbrand's requirement that we *prove* that a formula P is underivable in Q_H to mean that (q) $(\exists h)\, \Psi_P(q, h)$ is provable in R + Inf Ax + Mult Ax.

Herbrand's argument can be made to yield another theorem, in which an assumed solution to the decision problem plays no role.

(IV) If an unprovable formula P of Q_H is added to the axioms of R + Inf Ax + Mult Ax, then the resulting system is ω-inconsistent.

We argue thus: If P is not provable in Q_H, then, for each number q, $\vdash (\exists h)\, \Psi_P(q, h)$. For, every quantifier in $\Psi_P(q, h)$ can be taken to be a number quantifier ranging over the finite set D_q, and h is a function from a finite set to a finite set; hence the formula $(\exists h)\, \Psi_P(x, h)$ can be taken to be effectively decidable, and each of its true instances is provable. Moreover, if $\vdash P$, then $\vdash P'$ by the rule of substitution, so by contrapositing (3), $\vdash \sim (q)\, (\exists h)\, \Psi_P(q, h)$.

We noted in § 2 that the use of the axiom of choice to obtain the falsifying interpretation can be replaced by Skolem's argument of *1922* or some similar argument. If in addition we have a first-order formula with one free variable x expressing 'P is false in the domain of order x', then such an argument can be formalized in elementary (first-order) number theory. This is carried out in *Hilbert and Bernays 1939*, pp. 234–253. On the basis of this formalization, Kleene (*1952*, p. 395) proves a theorem strictly analogous to (IV) with elementary number theory taking the place of R + Inf Ax + Mult Ax.

VIII

UNSIGNED NOTE ON HERBRAND'S THESIS WRITTEN BY HERBRAND HIMSELF

(1931a)

The work under consideration is devoted to mathematical investigations of questions raised by a theory of logic. The essence of this theory, which Hilbert, its creator, called "metamathematics", is the attempt to resolve problems in the philosophy of mathematics not by verbal discussions but by the solution of precise questions. This is not the place to discuss how far this theory gets to the basis of the issues; however, from the analysis that we give of it, one will see that it is in accordance with the strictest positivism and the most perfect rigor, but also that it refuses to consider certain questions pertaining to the theory of knowledge – perhaps here lies its insufficiency from the philosophical point of view. In any case, the theory is of great interest, if only in the problems it raises. Heretofore, all sciences – physics, chemistry, sociology, and even biology (we should remember the fine investigations recently made by Volterra) – have raised new problems for mathematicians, and have caused them to forge new instruments. For the first time, because of metamathematics, philosophy itself has appeared in this role.

The point of departure of this theory comprises the investigations of Russell, themselves an outgrowth of those of the nineteenth century logicists. Russell had shown in the *Principia Mathematica* that instead of ordinary language a sort of stenography, or symbolic language, utilizing only a very limited number of signs, could be used to do mathematics. Three signs suffice in this language; combinations of them form sentences. But he went further, and this is the interesting thing for us: he showed that all the proofs that can be carried out in mathematics can be reduced to several simple rules of reasoning, which he stated. Every mathematical theory begins with certain propositions admitted as true, the axioms of the theory, which, once translated, are combinations of signs. And all proofs that can be carried out in this theory reduce to the repeated use of certain determinate rules allowing the formation of new true propositions starting from propositions already known to be true. If the whole proof is translated into the symbolic language, these rules can be stated as rules concerning determinate combinations of signs of this language. Consequently, we see that the problem 'Is such-and-such a proposition provable in a theory having such-and-such axioms?' is a problem concerning the signs of this language and their combinations, and can be subjected to a mathematical treatment. This is the most general form of the problem called the *Entscheidungsproblem* by the Germans. In a sense it is the most general problem of mathematics.

To Hilbert belongs the honor of first having shown that this problem is a well-defined mathematical problem, solvable in at least some particular cases. But Hilbert's theory contains more. For several years, the Dutch mathematician Brouwer had undertaken a systematic critique, which he called "intuitionism", of the foundations of mathematics. In its extreme form, this theory allows only arguments dealing with the integers (or with objects that can actually be numbered by means of integers), and satisfying the following conditions: all the functions introduced must be actually calculable for all values of their arguments by means of operations described wholly beforehand. Whenever we come to say 'A proposition is true for every integer', this means 'We can actually verify it for every integer'; whenever we come to say 'There exists an integer x having such-and-such a property', this means implicitly 'In what precedes we have given a means of constructing such an x'. We see that it is difficult to imagine rules more Draconian; but the Brouwerians consider any argument not of this type to have used, at least implicitly, the notion of an infinity of elements, which they do not consider to be well-founded. According to them, it would not be surprising if such arguments (that is, arguments that mathematicians use every day) were to lead to contradictions and we 'would not have the right' to use them at all. In any case, it is quite certain that an intuitionistic argument, which reduces in the end to an argument dealing with a finite and determinate number of objects and determinate functions, is free from all objections, and that we can even actually establish the truth of all intermediate propositions occurring in it and of its conclusion. The most intransigent critic of mathematical methods could not object to anything in it unless he professed that the consideration of a determinate finite number of objects is itself illegitimate; but no one has yet gone that far...

Hilbert then raised the problem of resolving the questions indicated above by the use of exclusively intuitionistic arguments. But, as a result of this, from the start he was led to pose problems such as the following: Consider the axioms of arithmetic. Starting from these axioms and using Russell's rules of inference, we can formulate arguments which Brouwer rejects; however, if we could prove with complete rigor, using intuitionistic procedures, that there is no risk of arriving at a contradiction (that is, of being able to prove both a theorem and its negation), then Brouwer's critique would lose its point. Thus, we are led to study the consistency of the axioms of arithmetic, of analysis, and then of set theory (in the latter, we could study the consistency of the axiom of choice), etc. These are now well-determined mathematical problems. Furthermore, the most general case of the *Entscheidungsproblem* mentioned above always reduces to the problem of the consistency of an axiom system: for, if P can be proved in an axiom system, then the system obtained by adding the negation of P to the original one is inconsistent; and, conversely, if the new system formed by making this addition is inconsistent, this obviously means that in the original system P is provable.

Hence, we are now faced with the problem of studying, with the method described above, the consistency of all axiom systems imaginable, using only intuitionistic modes of reasoning.

Before indicating the results obtained, we shall mention that Hilbert creates a philosophy of mathematics on the basis of this. One of its fundamental theses, for example, is that once the consistency of an axiom system has been proved (for example, that of analysis), then its use is 'legitimate'; and that mathematical existence amounts to nothing else than consistency. For example, to say of an object that it exists and to prove that it exists are the same thing. But it is not the aim of this work to discuss these ideas and their insufficiency, if any. It attempts only to resolve the mathematical problem mentioned above in the most general case possible.

At the time when these investigations were begun, the status of these questions was as follows: Hilbert had limited himself to giving schemata for proofs, nearly all of which were subsequently seen to be false. Only his proof of the consistency of the simplest axioms of arithmetic could be sketched in a somewhat complete manner by his pupil Bernays. The only important contribution to the theory had been furnished by von Neumann, who proved in a complete manner the consistency of a fragment of the axioms of arithmetic. In addition, several other particular cases of the *Entscheidungsproblem* had been solved, and furthermore the first steps of the theory had been presented by Hilbert and Ackermann in a book [[1928]].

It seemed necessary to consider the entire theory again, starting from the very first lemmas. The first part of the thesis that we are analyzing is devoted to this work. It is concerned with proving in a completely rigorous manner the elementary theorems of the theory, and with pointing out a large number of details, for example, showing that the rules of reasoning employed, which are not the same as Russell's, are nonetheless equivalent to his, etc.

The result of von Neumann is proved again there, but using much simpler and more complete methods than his; moreover, these can be generalized in various ways.

But all this work is merely preparatory to a result of much greater importance. This result concerns the finding of a general method allowing us to avoid in all cases the problem posed above. The theorem obtained is, in its complete form, extremely complex; we shall try to give an idea of it in a few words by means of a comparison that must not be allowed to mislead, for it is only a translation into ordinary language of facts which deal exclusively with certain systems of signs. Consider an axiom system dealing with certain objects, and assume that a model [[réalisation]] of these axioms can be constructed. That is, a set of objects can be constructed in which, by means of suitable definitions of the different relations and functions which appear in the axioms, the axioms are true. Then the theorem in question amounts to the assertion that the axiom system cannot be inconsistent. But all this must be translated into a statement satisfying the intuitionistic rules of reasoning, and using only the properties of the signs of our symbolic language.

The applications of this theorem are quite numerous. First, it permits the proof of the consistency of all the axioms of arithmetic, with, however, still several small restrictions. However, it has not yielded a consistency proof for the axioms of analysis; there are difficulties here of an extremely curious nature, of a nature which contradicts many ideas currently accepted; these difficulties were not recognized until quite recently. On the other hand, the theorem in question permits us to show that the system of rules of reasoning can be changed profoundly while still remaining equivalent to the original ones, so that the rule of the syllogism, the basis of Aristotelian logic, is of no use in any mathematical argument.

The theorem also permitted the reduction of the most general case of the *Entscheidungsproblem* to the remarkable form of a problem about number-theoretic functions that is but a generalization of the problem of the effective solution of diophantine equations. By means of this, all questions which can be raised in metamathematics are 'arithmetized'.

Such is the collection of results obtained. We allow ourselves to insist yet on a point which seems particularly worthy of attention. We have just seen that the general problem 'Is a theorem true in a given theory?' is equivalent to a problem of pure arithmetic. Thus, we have the following alternatives: Either the first problem, one of immense generality, is solvable; or else there are unsolvable problems of arithmetic. For example, there would then be diophantine equations such that it could never be proved that they do not have solutions, and yet such that each time we attempt to verify that a determinate system of integers is a solution of the equation, we find a negative answer. There are mathematicians who would be as shocked by one as by the other alternative. Recent results lead us to think that it is the second alternative that holds; this would involve the falsity of an extremely widespread idea.

We thus see the principles on which this new branch of mathematics has arisen. We would like to insist again, in conclusion, on the fact that it is independent of any philosophical opinion; the results obtained are positive; and no more than the mathematician who studies Einstein's equations necessarily partakes of Einstein's ideas must the mathematician who studies the present theories adhere to Hilbert's philosophical principles. There is in these questions a scarcely explored domain of arithmetical investigations of the greatest interest, which may well contain surprises.

IX

NOTE FOR JACQUES HADAMARD

(1931b)

⟦This note describes Herbrand's works, and was submitted by him at the beginning of 1931 to Jacques Hadamard, who was responsible for presenting the notes written by Herbrand to the Academy of Sciences. This note was published in *Herbrand 1968* for the first time, from a copy preserved in the papers of Albert Lautman, and reproduced here due to the permission of Mme. Suzanne Lautman, who is thanked very deeply.⟧

I

All of my first works concerned the mathematical questions raised by the new ideas brought to mathematical logic by Hilbert. The problem was the following: Peano and then Russell had shown that there exists a symbolic mathematical language into which all sentences which can be stated in mathematics are translatable. Russell moreover showed how all mathematical reasoning reduces to rules of combinations of signs, which he specified. Certain propositions (that is, certain collections of signs) are called axioms, and Russell's rules allow us to obtain propositions said to be true by combining these axioms. Consequently, every collection of signs called a true proposition is the translation of a proven theorem, and conversely every argument made by a mathematician, translated into the symbolic language, yields combinations of axioms leading to a proposition said to be true which is nothing but the translation of the conclusion. Of course, the axioms depend on the particular theory envisaged (they are not the same for arithmetic as for set theory, etc., which is quite natural since the objects these theories are concerned with are different).

Hilbert had the idea of considering the combinations of signs of this symbolic language as mathematical objects, capable of being studied mathematically. Metamathematics thus appeared as the mathematical theory which has as its object the study of the mathematical language. Its problems are of the following type: Can such-and-such a proposition be proved starting from such-and-such axioms? This is an arithmetical problem regarding the signs of the symbolic language. Furthermore, to escape the destructive critique of Brouwer, Hilbert required that all reasoning done in metamathematics should be of the type called 'intuitionistic', that is, when we say 'there exists an object such that' this means 'we have constructed an object such that', and when we say 'such-and-such a property is true for all x' this means 'we can verify the property for any determinate x.'

The first problems which arise are obviously the problems of consistency, of the following type: can the axioms ordinarily admitted as the basis of arithmetic (or of analysis, and so on) lead to a contradiction; that is, do they permit us to prove both a theorem and its negation?

When I first attacked these questions, the status of them was as follows: the principal ideas of proofs, and some proof-schemata, had been explained by Hilbert in a series of articles; but the schemata were almost all false, as Hilbert himself subsequently recognized. The only one which was undoubtedly correct has not yet been completely developed. All the first principles of the theory had been explained in a book by Hilbert and his student Ackermann [[1928]]. Finally, the only important step had been taken by von Neumann, who had proved the consistency of a part of the axioms of arithmetic [[1927]]. It was necessary to consider the whole theory again from top to bottom in order to attain the desired rigor in its beginnings and to arrive at precise results.

My investigations in this subject have been summarized in four notes in *Comptes Rendus* (*1928, 1929, 1929a, 1929b*). These were developed in my thesis (*1930*), and certain complementary results in an article as yet unpublished (although long since written) [[1931]]. Finally, the philosophical principles of the theory were sketched in an article in the *Revue de métaphysique et de morale* (*1930a*).

I was obliged to start by establishing all the lemmas, in general easily proved, which lie at the base of these theories and which had not previously been stated in a satisfactory manner. I was very often led to complete them.

Then I considered the question of consistency again. By a method whose principle is very simple, I found results much more complete than those of von Neumann (*Herbrand 1929*).

After this, I looked for a general method which would enable us to attack all metamathematical problems. I found this by reconsidering an idea of Löwenheim; but the developments due to him were entirely insufficient for the goal I had. I thus arrived at a theorem which is stated something like the following: When some axioms can be interpreted using the objects of a set, if it is infinite, then these axioms are not inconsistent. The exact statement of the theorem is of course more precise, but much more complicated.

This theorem has as an immediate consequence the consistency of all the axioms of classical arithmetic (with one very slight restriction concerning the axiom of mathematical induction). But there are numerous other consequences. I shall limit myself to indicating to you that it allows us to approach the study of the *Entscheidungsproblem*, that is, the problem of finding a method permitting us to decide at once if a theorem is true or false in a determinate theory. My theorem permits us to solve this in particular cases more extensive than those known until now, and to reduce the general case to an arithmetical problem, which I stated, and which can be seen to be a diophantine problem. I find it simpler to send you separately an offprint of the note in which I state this result completely [apparently *1929b*].

Such are the principal results which I have obtained in this domain. Recent results (not mine) show that we can hardly go any further: it has been shown that the problem of the consistency of a theory containing all of arithmetic (for example, classical analysis) is a problem whose solution is impossible. [Herbrand is here alluding to *Gödel 1931*.] In fact, I am at the present time preparing an article in which I will explain the relationships between these results and mine [this article is *1931c*].

II

In a note in *Comptes rendus*, October 28, 1929 [['Recherche des solutions bornées de certaines équations fonctionnelles', *Comptes rendus hebdomadaires des séances de l'Académie des sciences* (Paris) *189*, 669–671, 811]], I resolved the following question: to solve the functional equation

$$\frac{1}{b-a}\int_a^b f(x)\,dx = \alpha_1 f(a) + \alpha_2 f\left(\frac{a+b}{2}\right) + \alpha_3 f(b),$$

where α_1, α_2, and α_3 are constants. This is an easy problem, suitable for the *spéciales* examination, when we assume the existence of the first four derivatives. By assuming only that there are bounded solutions, the application of a theorem of M. Denjoy about derived numbers [nombres dérivés] permits us to show stepwise the existence and continuity of all derivatives, and even analyticity; the problem is consequently elementary.

As I indicate in this note, the method can be generalized; perhaps I shall return to this.

III

In a note in *Comptes rendus*, November 24, 1930 [['Détermination des groupes de ramifications d'un corps à partir de ceux d'un sous-corps', *Comptes rendus hebdomadaires des séances de l'Académie des sciences* (Paris) *191*, 980–982, 1272]], I indicate the solution of the following problem: given a base-field k, and knowing the ramification groups of a prime ideal **P** of a field K Galois over k, to find the ramification groups in a subfield K' of K, also Galois over k, of the prime ideal of K' divisible by **P**.

I note several applications. These and the proof of the theorem are developed in an article which I am now finishing [[apparently, 'Sur la théorie des groupes de décomposition, d'inertie et de ramification', *Journal de mathématiques pures et appliquées 10* (1931), 481–498]].

IV

In the two notes in *Comptes rendus* which you have just presented [['Nouvelle démonstration et généralisation d'un théorème de Minkowski', *Comptes rendus hebdomadaires des séances de l'Académie des sciences* (Paris) *191* (1930), 1282–1285, *192* (1931), 188; 'Sur les unités d'un corps algébrique', *ibid. 192* (1931), 24–27, 188]], I prove by group-theoretic methods a generalization of Minkowski's theorem which asserts the existence of a system of independent conjugate units in every Galois field.

V

I will merely mention here the results of two notes which I shall soon ask you to present.

One, written in collaboration with Chevalley [['Groupes topologiques, groupes fuchsiens, groupes libres', *Comptes rendus hebdomadaires des séances de l'Académie des sciences* (Paris) *192* (1931), 724–726]] shows how the theory of topological groups, or of Fuchsian groups (which reduces to the same thing) easily permits the proof of certain theorem of the theory of infinite groups, in particular the fundamental theorems of the theory of free groups (groups generated by independent non-permutable elements) which asserts that every subgroup of a free group is a free group.

The other [['Nouvelle démonstration du théorème d'existence en théorie du corps de classes', *Comptes rendus hebdomadaires des séances de l'Academie des sciences* (Paris) *193* (1931) 814–815, published after Herbrand's death and signed by Herbrand and Chevalley]] will summarize an article on cyclotomic fields and Fermat's theorem, in which in particular I show how present-day class-field theory permits the considerable simplification of the proofs of Kummer and their extension to new cases for which Fermat's theorem had not yet been proved.

X

ON THE CONSISTENCY OF ARITHMETIC

(1931c)

⟦Dated "Göttingen, 14 July 1931", this paper was sent by Herbrand for publication (to the *Journal für die reine und angewandte Mathematik*) just before he left for a vacation trip in the Alps. The paper was received on 27 July and on that day Herbrand was killed in a fall.

The paper presents a consistency proof for a segment of arithmetic and was intended, no doubt, to be a contribution to the realization of the Hilbert school's program. Consistency is proved for an arithmetic in which the well-formed formula that can be substituted in the induction schema does not contain any bound variable (or, if it does, does not contain any function but the successor function). Consistency proofs likewise requiring some restriction on the induction axiom schema had been presented by Ackermann (*1924*) and von Neumann (*1927*). Herbrand's proof remains relatively simple and straightforward because he has at his disposal his powerful fundamental theorem (*1930*). Section 1 consists of a very clear presentation of this theorem.

Throughout his work Herbrand applies the word 'intuitionistic' to the methods that he considers admissible in metamathematics, and, although there may be some variations in the meaning that he gives to the term, this meaning is on the whole much closer to that of Hilbert's word 'finitary' ('finit') than to 'intuitionistic' as applied to Brouwer's doctrine. Herbrand writes, for instance, that Hilbert had undertaken to solve metamathematical problems "exclusively through intuitionistic arguments" ("uniquement par des raisonnements intuitionnistes", *1931a*, p. 274 above), and in the paper below (p. 288) he writes that the statement and the proof of his fundamental theorem are "intuitionistic". The identification of 'intuitionistic' with 'finitary' was then current among members of the Hilbert school (see, for example, *von Neumann 1927*, p. 2); the distinction between the two notions was to be made explicit a few years later (*Hilbert and Bernays 1934*, pp. 34 and 43, *Bernays 1934a, 1935*, and *1938*).

A key part of Herbrand's proof is the elimination of the induction axiom schema (with no apparent variables) through the introduction of functions; the definition conditions for each of these functions are such that, for every set of arguments, a well-determined number can be proved in a finitary way to be the value of the function (Group C of hypotheses). The functions are, in fact, (general) recursive functions, and here is the first appearance of the notion of recursive (as opposed to primitive recursive) function. It is interesting to see how, a few months earlier, Herbrand had been led to this notion by his conception of 'intuitionism'. (Let us note in passing that, it seems, Herbrand's knowledge of Brouwer's ideas is not first-hand, but derived from Hilbert.) He writes (*1931a*, p. 273 above):

In its extreme form this theory [[intuitionism]] allows only arguments dealing with the integers (or with objects that can actually be numbered by means of integers) and satisfying the following conditions: all the functions that are introduced must be actually computable for all values of their arguments, by means of operations that are completely described in advance; every time that we come to say 'A proposition is true for every integer', this means 'We can actually verify it for every integer'; every time that we come to say 'There exists an integer x that has such and such a property', this means implicitly 'In what precedes we gave a means of constructing such an x'.

Gödel (*1934*, p. 26) gives, as 'suggested by Herbrand', the following definition of a recursive function:

If φ denotes an unknown function and $\psi_1, \ldots, \psi_k$ are known functions, and if the ψ's and the φ are substituted in one another in the most general fashions and certain pairs of the resulting expressions are equated, then, if the resulting set of functional equations has one and only one solution for φ, φ is a recursive function.

Answering a query of mine about the history of Herbrand's suggestion, Professor Gödel wrote in a letter dated 23 April 1963:

I have never met Herbrand. His suggestion was made in a letter in 1931, and it was formulated *exactly* as on page 26 of my lecture notes, that is, without any reference to computability. However, since Herbrand was an intuitionist, this definition for him evidently meant that there exists a *constructive* proof for the existence and unicity of φ. He probably believed that such a proof can be given only by exhibiting a computational procedure. (Note that, if Church's thesis is correct, it is *true* that, if $(\exists !\varphi)\, A(\varphi)$ holds intuitionistically, then $(\imath\varphi)\, A(\varphi)$ is general recursive, although, in order to obtain the computational procedure for φ, it may be necessary to add some equations to those contained in $A(\varphi)$.) So I don't think there is any discrepancy between his two definitions as he meant them. What he failed to see (or to make clear) is that the computation, for *all* computable functions, proceeds by *exactly the same rules*. It is this fact that makes a precise definition of general recursiveness possible. Unfortunately I do not find Herbrand's letter among my papers. It probably was lost in Vienna during World War II, as many other things were. But my recollection is very distinct and was still very fresh in 1934.

Herbrand's consistency proof for a fragment of arithmetic still belongs to the period that preceded Gödel's famous result (*1931*). He probably started to write his paper before Gödel's paper reached him. But he had ample opportunity to examine Gödel's result and he wrote a last section dealing with it. Herbrand explains very clearly why this result does not hold for the fragment of arithmetic that he considers: whatever functions may be introduced by definition conditions of Group C, these functions never include a function that enumerates them (this is shown by a diagonal argument), hence the metamathematical description of the system cannot be projected into the system.

When published, Herbrand's text was preceded by a bibliographical note written by Helmut Hasse in German. Here is its translation:

Jacques Herbrand, born on 12 February 1908 in Paris, had a fatal accident on 27 July 1931 while mountain climbing in the Alps. The same day the editors received the manuscript published below.

He spent the last six months of his life at German universities, in close contact with a number of German mathematicians and engaged in a lively exchange of ideas with them. They were all profoundly impressed by his noble personality, which was endowed with rich scientific gifts. With him an extraordinarily gifted mind has perished in the bloom of youth. The beautiful and important results that he found in the field of number theory and of mathematical logic and the fruitful ideas that he expressed in mathematical conversations justified the greatest hopes. The science of mathematics has suffered a severe and irreparable loss by his untimely death.

JEAN VAN HEIJENOORT]]

In two previous papers[1] we stated and proved a general theorem that

---

[1] *1930, 1931*. In what follows these papers are denoted by D I and D II. We take advantage of the present opportunity to make the following two remarks about them.

(a) The theorem in Chap. 3, 3.3, of D I is correct only if $A(x)$ contains no restricted variables (only under this condition is the relativization of $(x) A(x)$ true).

(b) In D II, at the bottom of p. 229, we point out that the elements of a domain can be 'equated'. This calls for a clarification, since the values of the index functions are not well-determined in the new domain. Among all elements α_i equal to a given one, we choose one, β. These β form the new domain. In this domain the value of a function $f(\beta_1, \beta_2, ..., \beta_n)$ (which may be either an elementary descriptive function or makes it possible to solve many problems in metamathematics, and we gave some applications of it. In the present paper we wish to apply it to the problem of the consistency of arithmetic more completely than we did in D I. The fundamental result is stated at the beginning of Section 3.

1. Statement of a general theorem

Let us first recall the statement of the theorem in question.

(a) We use Russell's signs, with slight changes: $\vee$, $\sim$, & (and), $\supset$ (for implication), $\equiv$, $(\exists x)$, and (x),[2] as well as Russell's rules of inference, which we have slightly modified. In particular, we shall not use Hilbert's logical ε function in propositions, and instead of his transfinite axiom we shall use the axioms and rules of Russell that are equivalent to it. We complete Russell's formal system by allowing the use of functions (in the ordinary sense of the word); the functions of 0 variable are the constants. For more details see D I, Chaps. 1 and 3.

In a given theory we have certain elementary [[that is, atomic]] propositions and functions, and all propositions considered within the theory are combinations of logical signs with elementary propositions and functions. We have, moreover, certain propositions called *hypotheses*, and the propositions true in the theory are those that we can obtain from the hypotheses by applying the rules of inference.

If a proposition can be proved by application of these rules without the use of any hypothesis, we call it an *identity*. If a proposition P is true in a given theory, there exist certain hypotheses $H_1, H_2, ..., H_n$ such that H_1 & H_2 & $\cdots$ & $H_n . \supset P$ is an identity; and conversely (see D I, Chap. 3, 2.4), if this is the case, P is true in the theory in question.

an index function) will be the β equal to the value of $f(\beta_1, \beta_2, ..., \beta_n)$ in the former domain. We thus see that every proposition true in the former domain remains true in the new one.

[2] We recall that the signs &, $\supset$, and $\equiv$ can be defined by means of the signs $\sim$ and $\vee$, these alone being taken as primitive. Let us recall their meaning. $\vee$, $\sim$, &, $\supset$, $\equiv$, $(\exists x)$, (x) mean: or, not, and, implies, is equivalent to, there exists an x such that, for all x, respectively. [[In the French text, Herbrand uses $\times$ rather than &, $\rightarrow$ rather than $\supset$, and (Ex) rather than $(\exists x)$, and adds that the latter is used "instead of Russell's inverted E". We have altered the notation in the interest of uniformity.]]

The part of a proposition on which a logical sign operates is called the *scope* of the sign. Thus in $(x) \sim A(x, y) . \vee . (\exists y) \sim B(y)$ the scope of (x) is $\sim A(x, y)$, that of $(\exists y)$ is $\sim B(y)$, that of the first $\sim$ is $A(x, y)$, that of the second $\sim$ is $B(y)$. Instead of the scope of (x) or $(\exists y)$ we shall also speak of the scope of x or y.

The variables that occur in signs of the form (x) or $(\exists x)$ are said to be *apparent*; the others are said to be *real*.

An apparent variable x occurring either in a sign $(\exists x)$ that is within the scope of an even number of signs $\sim$ or in a sign (x) within the scope of an odd number of signs $\sim$ is said to be *restricted*. Otherwise, it is said to be *general*. Thus in $\sim (x) A(x, x) . \vee . (\exists y) \sim \sim (z) A(y, z)$, x and y are restricted, z is general.

(b) When a proposition contains neither apparent variables nor functions, there is a simple criterion that enables us to decide whether or not it is an identity.

Let us consider the elementary propositions occurring in this proposition (they may or may not contain variables; of course, we consider those that contain the same variables in the same order to be identical); let us assign to each of them a *logical value*, that is, let us associate with each of them one of the signs T or F, and let us agree that to all propositions without apparent variables formed from these propositions we assign a logical value according to the following rules (see footnote 2):

(α) If F (or T) is associated with P, then T (or F) is associated with $\sim P$;

(β) F is associated with $P \vee Q$ only if F is associated with P and with Q.

It can then be proved (D I, Chap. 1, 5.21) that P is an identity if and only if P has the logical value T whatever may be the logical values assigned to the elementary propositions. Hence, if P contains n distinct elementary propositions, we need 2^n trials to decide the truth of P.

(c) Let us consider an arbitrary proposition P (we assume that all the variables are represented by different letters). We shall apply the remarks that follow to the proposition $(x)(\exists y).A(x, y)$, which we shall take as an example (A is a proposition with no variable other than x and y, formed from elementary propositions and functions).

We shall consider functions that include, first, the elementary functions occurring in P and, then, new functions obtained as follows (it should be clear that by a function we understand a mere logical sign and that we are not concerned, at least for the time being, with its 'values'): with every restricted variable $[\![x]\!]$ of P we associate a function whose arguments are the real variables of P and the general variables having a scope containing a quantifier in x, (x) or $(\exists x)$; if there are no such real or general[3] variables, the function has 0 argument (and is a constant). For example, for $(x)(\exists y).A(x, y)$ we have the function $\varphi(x)$ associated with y.

Let us now consider all the distinct elementary propositions occurring in P (here two elementary propositions differing only in their variables are considered identical), denoting them by $A_i(x_1, x_2, ..., x_{n_i})$; let us also consider all distinct functions (elementary functions as well as those just introduced, with the same convention), denoting them by $f_i(x_1, x_2, ..., x_{m_i})$. For example, if $A(x, y)$ is $B(x, x) \,\&\, B(y, y)\,.\vee.\sim B(x, y)$, we have $B(x, y)$ as the only elementary proposition and $\varphi(x)$ as the only function.

Let us now consider finite sets of the letters $a_0, a_1, ..., a_n$; these sets we shall call *domains*; let us assume that we assign a 'value' to each $f_i(a_{\alpha_1}, a_{\alpha_2}, ..., a_{\alpha_{n_i}})$, that is, we associate one of the a_i with this collection of signs. Let us assume that this has been done for some of the $f_i(a_{\alpha_1}, a_{\alpha_2}, ..., a_{\alpha_{n_i}})$ (not necessarily for all).

From our elementary functions we can construct other functions by 'substitution'; for example, from the functions $f_1(x)$, $f_2(x)$, and $f_3(x, y)$ we can construct $f_3(f_2(x), f_1(y))$, and so on. What we should understand by the value of such a function is clear. Let us denote by $F_i(x_1, x_2, ..., x_{p_i})$ any one of these functions (old or new).

To every function we assign a *height* in the following way: elementary functions have height 1; if the maximum of the heights of $F_{u_1}, F_{u_2}, ...,$ $F_{u_{m_i}}$ (the variables are omitted) is h, then the height of $f_i(F_{u_1}, F_{u_2}, ..., F_{u_{m_i}})$ is $h+1$.

If in the domain there exist values of a sufficient number of the $f_i(a_{\alpha_1}, a_{\alpha_2}, ..., a_{\alpha_{m_i}})$ for us to compute the values of all $F_i(a_0, a_0, ..., a_0)$ of at most height h and if h is the greatest number having this property, the domain is said to be of order h, and a_0 is the *initial element* (this element is not always uniquely determined).

In our example let us set $\varphi_1(x) = \varphi(x)$, $\varphi_2(x) = \varphi(\varphi(x)), ..., \varphi_{n+1}(x) = \varphi(\varphi_n(x)), ...$; then the functions of at most height h are $\varphi_1(x), \varphi_2(x), ..., \varphi_h(x)$. A domain of order h will be formed by the letters $a_0, a_1, a_2, ..., a_h$

---

[3] [[Instead of "générales" the original text has "restreintes", which is an oversight.]]

if to $\varphi(a_i)$ we assign the value a_{i+1} (to express this we shall often write $\varphi(a_i) = a_{i+1}$. We see that $\varphi(a_h)$ has no value in the domain.

Let us now associate a logical value with every $A_i(a_{\alpha_1}, a_{\alpha_2}, ..., a_{\alpha_{n_i}})$.

Let us consider P, delete in it all signs of the form (x) and $(\exists x)$, and then replace each restricted variable by the associated function. We thus obtain a certain proposition without apparent variables (for example, $A(x, \varphi(x))$.[4]

Let us replace the variables by some of the a_i in any way whatsoever and, in the expression thus obtained, let us replace the functions of the form $F_i(a_{\alpha_1}, a_{\alpha_2}, ..., a_{\alpha_{n_i}})$ by their values. (This is not possible for every choice of the a_i; in our example we obtain $A(a_i, a_{i+1})$, and the operation is impossible if we replace x by a_h.)

Since the $A_i(a_{\alpha_1}, a_{\alpha_2}, ..., a_{\alpha_{n_i}})$ have a logical value, the same holds of the proposition obtained. If this logical value is always T, in whatever way the variables are replaced by the a_i, then P is said to be true in the domain of order h considered. (We see that this domain is characterized by the values of the functions and the logical values of the $A_i(a_{\alpha_1}, a_{\alpha_2}, ..., a_{\alpha_{n_i}}.$)

We then have the following fundamental theorem:

(α) *If P is an identity, we can find, given the proof of P, a number h such that $\sim P$ is not true in any domain of order h;*

(β) *If P is not an identity, for every h we can construct a domain of order h in which $\sim P$ is true.*

The statement and the proof of this theorem are intuitionistic.[5]

(d) If for every h we can construct a domain of order h in which P is true, we say that there is an *infinite domain* in which P is *true*. We say that P is *false* in an infinite domain if $\sim P$ is true in it. (This expression 'infinite domain' is merely an abbreviation; in order to have the intui-

---

[4] [[For a proposition P without real variables, the proposition Herbrand defines here is what we called the strict satisfiability functional form of P in the Introduction, p. 11 above and Note J, p. 201 above. The conjunction of instances of this proposition which Herbrand considers here is the satisfiability expansion of P over the domain (see the Introduction, p. 11 above).]]

[5] By an intuitionistic argument we understand an argument satisfying the following conditions: in it we never consider anything but a given finite number of objects and of functions; these functions are well-defined, their definition allowing the computation

tionistic meaning of the statements we have to return to the precise statements (α) and (β).) We can then state:

*P is not an identity if and only if there exists an infinite domain in which
P is false.*

In this form the theorem is a more precise statement of the well-known
Löwenheim-Skolem theorem;[6] in fact, if there exists, in our sense, an
infinite domain in which P is true, we can easily obtain from it by non-
intuitionistic procedures a denumerable set in which P is true for certain
values of the functions, that is, a model [[*réalisation*]] of P, and conversely.[7]
But

(α) Our statement is completely intuitionistic; we even have the means,
once P has been proved, of finding a number h such that in the 'partial'
domain of order h, that is, at the hth step in the construction of the infinite domain, it is impossible to make P false;

(β) We do not restrict ourselves to propositions in canonical form,
as Löwenheim and, even more, Skolem do;

(γ) Löwenheim and Skolem implicitly assume that, once we have a
model of $\sim P$, P cannot be proved; but this means that the consistency
of mathematics (or at least of arithmetic) is implicitly assumed; our
theorem, on the contrary, will allow us to investigate the consistency of
arithmetic.

(e) Let us now consider a theory with given hypotheses.

*If we can determine an infinite domain such that all the hypotheses of
the theory are true in it, the theory is not contradictory.*

For, if the theory were contradictory, there would be n hypotheses
$H_1, H_2, ..., H_n$ such that $\sim .H_1 \& H_2 \& \cdots \& H_n$ would be an identity (see
D I, Chap. 5, 6.5 [[above, p. 178]]). But, since $H_1, H_2, ..., H_n$ are true in the
infinite domain, $H_1 \& H_2 \& \cdots \& H_n$ would also be true in it (this is easy

of their value in a univocal way; we never state that an object exists without giving
the means of constructing it; we never consider the totality of all the objects x of an
infinite collection; and when we say that an argument (or a theorem) is true for all
these x, we mean that, for each x taken by itself, it is possible to repeat the general
argument in question, which should be considered to be merely the prototype of these
particular arguments.

[6] See *Löwenheim 1915* and *Skolem 1920*.

[7] [[See the Introduction, p. 12 above and Note N, p. 268 above.]]

to see); hence $\sim.H_1$ & H_2 & $\cdots$ & H_n would be false in it, which is impossible if it is an identity.

The foregoing theorems have a large number of applications (see D I and especially D II). In particular they allow us

(1) To solve many special cases of the decision problem;

(2) To prove rigorously (intuitionistically, which Löwenheim did not do) that the decision problem can always be reduced to the case in which there are only *three elementary propositions of two variables* or *one of three variables*.[8]

By means of them we shall deal with the consistency of arithmetic (see already D I, Chap. 5, 6.8 [above, pp. 182–187]).

2. THE AXIOMS OF ARITHMETIC

The theory that we shall study, which is the formal translation of classical arithmetic, has only one elementary proposition (of two variables), $x=y$; it has one constant, 0, one function of one variable, $x+1$, and other functions that we shall indicate later.

The hypotheses are the following:

$$\left.\begin{array}{l} x = x, \\ x = y . \supset . y = x, \\ x = y \ \& \ y = z . \supset . x = z, \\ x = y . \equiv . x + 1 = y + 1, \\ \sim . x + 1 = 0. \end{array}\right\} \quad \textbf{(Group A)}$$

Then come all the hypotheses obtained when in

$$\Phi(0) \ \&: (x) . \Phi(x) \supset \Phi(x + 1) :\supset . (x) \Phi(x)$$

$\Phi(x)$ is replaced by any proposition containing the variable x (**Group B**, mathematical induction).

We can also introduce any number of functions $f_i(x_1, x_2, ..., x_{n_i})$ together with hypotheses such that

(a) *The hypotheses contain no apparent variables*;

---

[8] [[See above, p. 242.]]

(b) *Considered intuitionistically,[9] they make the actual computation of the $f_i(x_1, x_2, ..., x_{n_i})$ possible for every given set of numbers, and it is possible to prove intuitionistically that we obtain a well-determined result* (**Group C**).

As a specific example, let us assume that we have already introduced a certain number of such functions; then a new one, $f(x)$, can be introduced, together with the new hypotheses

$$f(0) = \alpha,$$
$$f(x + 1) = \beta(f(x)),$$

α and $\beta(y)$ being functions formed from previously introduced functions. This is the ordinary schema of definition by recursion.

But we can introduce much more complicated definition schemata, for example, multiple recursions on several variables. Thus we can introduce Hilbert's function[10] together with the hypotheses

$$\varphi(n + 1, a, b) = \varphi(n, a, \varphi(n + 1, a, b - 1)),$$
$$\varphi(n, a, 1) = a,$$
$$\varphi(0, a, b) = a + b.$$

Let us finally introduce, following Hilbert,[11] a fourth group of hypotheses, which does not belong to classical arithmetic:

Let $A(x)$ be a proposition without apparent variables; if it can be proved by intuitionistic procedures that this proposition, intuitionistically considered,[9] is true for every x, then we add $(x) A(x)$ to the hypotheses. (**Group D**)

3. THE PROBLEM OF CONSISTENCY

The fundamental result is the following:

The hypotheses A, B, C, and D yield a consistent theory if we assume that, in the hypotheses B, $\Phi(x)$ contains no apparent variables.

---

[9] This expression means: when they are translated into ordinary language, considered as a property of integers and not as a mere symbol.

[10] See *Hilbert 1925*.

[11] See *Hilbert 1930*, p. 491.

The proof is very simple.

For every $\Phi(x)$ without apparent variables we introduce a new function $\varepsilon(x, y_1, y_2, ..., y_n)$, the y_i being the variables of $\Phi(x)$ that are distinct from x. We write $\varepsilon(x)$ for short, omitting the y_i. We introduce the following hypotheses:

$$\varepsilon(0) = 0, \tag{1}$$
$$\Phi(0) \& \sim \Phi(x+1) \& \varepsilon(x) = 0 . \supset . \varepsilon(x+1) = x+1 \tag{2}$$
$$\sim [\Phi(0) \& \sim \Phi(x+1) \& \varepsilon(x) = 0] : \supset . \varepsilon(x+1) = \varepsilon(x), \tag{3}$$
$$\varepsilon(x) = y+1 . \supset : \varepsilon(y+1) = y+1 \& \varepsilon(y) = 0. \tag{4}$$
$$\textbf{(Group E)}$$

Translated into ordinary language, they mean that, if a is the least number for which $\Phi(a)$ is false, $\varepsilon(x)=0$ for $x < a$ and $\varepsilon(x)=a$ for $x \geqq a$. If the number a does not exist, $\varepsilon(x)=0$ for every x.

We can then prove that

(a) *The hypotheses B follow from these new hypotheses.*

To see that, we have merely to formalize the following argument.

Let us assume that $\Phi(0)$ and $(x).\Phi(x) \to \Phi(x+1)$ are true and also that there exists an x such that $\sim \Phi(x+1)$ is true, then it follows from E(2) and E(3) that

$$\varepsilon(x+1) = x+1 \quad \text{if } \varepsilon(x) = 0,$$
$$\varepsilon(x+1) = \varepsilon(x) \quad \text{if } \varepsilon(x) \neq 0.$$

Let us then take $\varepsilon(x+1)=y+1$. By E(4) we have

$$\varepsilon(y+1) = y+1,$$
$$\varepsilon(y) = 0.$$

Because of E(2) and E(3), this entails that $\sim \Phi(y+1)$ is true (since $\Phi(0)$ is assumed to be true). We have $y \neq 0$, since otherwise $\Phi(0)$ and $\sim \Phi(0+1)$ would be true, which is contrary to the assumption made. Hence we can take $y = z+1$. By this assumption, $\sim \Phi(z+1)$ and $\Phi(0)$ are true. E(2), together with the fact that $\varepsilon(z+1) \neq z+1$, entails that $\varepsilon(z) \neq 0$; then E(3) entails that $\varepsilon(z) = \varepsilon(z+1)$, which leads to a contradiction.

(b) *The new hypotheses are of the form C if $\Phi(x)$ contains no apparent variables.*

For in this case we can actually determine whether $\Phi(x)$ is true or not, and the hypotheses E allow us to actually compute the $\varepsilon(x)$ in a univocal and consistent way.[12]

It is therefore sufficient to prove the consistency of the hypotheses A, C, and D. But this follows immediately from the general theorem. We can indeed construct, by intuitionistic procedures, a domain of order h that consists of ordinary integers and in which the hypotheses are true; this domain consists of the values (in the intuitive sense of the word) of the functions of at most height h that are constructed from the elementary functions, here the latter being merely the function $x+1$ and the functions introduced in the hypotheses C; 0 is the initial element. According to what has been said above, it can then be proved by intuitionistic procedures that all the hypotheses are true in that domain.

The foregoing provides a procedure that enables us to construct, for every h, a domain of order h in which all the hypotheses are true. These hypotheses are therefore true in an infinite domain, and the theory cannot be inconsistent (compare D I, Chap. 5, 6.8 [above, pp. 182–188]; the present argument is simpler because we reduce the hypotheses B to the hypotheses C).

We see how simple the proof is, once we have the general theorem. However, the question is not entirely solved. Still to be considered is the case in which, in Group B, $\Phi(x)$ contains apparent variables. We can only say:

In case $\Phi(x)$ contains apparent variables we can add the hypotheses B without introducing a contradiction if the only function occurring in $\Phi(x)$ (besides the constant 0) is the function $u+1$.

---

[12] [[We must prove, intuitionistically, that $\varepsilon(x)$ is well-defined for every x. This requires a use of metamathematical induction on x; but since all the operations involved are effective, it falls within the limits of clause (b) of the specification of Group C. (Indeed, the values of ε are already determined by clauses (1)–(3) of Group E.) Thus, Herbrand is in effect eliminating the use of mathematical induction in the theory by using induction in the metamathematics. See also Note O, p. 297 below, for a different proof of consistency.]]

For we can introduce the function $\delta(x)$ together with the hypotheses

$$\delta(0) = 0,$$
$$\delta(x + 1) = x.$$

From this it follows that the proposition

$$x = 0 \,.\lor.\, (\exists y)(x = y + 1)$$

is true.[13] However, we have shown in D I (Chap. 4, 8.1) that the propositions of the form $x \neq x+1+1+\cdots+1$ follow from some hypotheses of Group B in which the $\Phi(x)$ have no apparent variables. Finally, we have proved in D I (Chap. 4, 8.1) that in the case under consideration the propositions above, together with the hypotheses A, entail the hypotheses B. Q.E.D.[14]

We would have a still more general problem by admitting other schemata of definition by recursion. For example, we could introduce a function $f(x)$ together with the hypotheses

$$A(f(0)),$$
$$B(f(x), f(x + 1)),$$

$(\exists x)\, A(x)$ and $(x)\,(\exists y).B(x, y)$ being true propositions, proved without the use of the new function.[15]

---

[13] [[That is, when the index function of one argument arising from the restricted quantifier $(\exists y)$ is given the same value in the domain as is $\delta(x)$.]]

[14] [[Herbrand has just shown that in the theory with $x+1$ as the only descriptive function and Group A as the only hypotheses, all induction axioms are derivable from quantifier-free induction axioms and $x = 0 \,.\lor.\, (\exists y)(x = y + 1)$. We know that the former are derivable from certain axioms of Group B, and that the latter is true in any infinite domain in which the function $\delta(x)$ has a value. Hence, all induction axioms are true in any infinite domain in which certain axioms of Group B are true (as well as those of Group A); therefore, the theory is consistent.]]

[15] Bernays drew our attention to the fact that, if an arithmetic containing hypotheses A, B, and, as functions, those occurring in $A(x)$ and $B(x, y)$, as well as addition and multiplication, were proved consistent, it would follow that we could add the new hypotheses without contradiction, for any argument carried out with the new function $f(x)$ could be carried out in the arithmetic just described.

4. COMPARISON WITH A THEOREM OF GÖDEL'S

Following Gödel's argument, we can prove that[16]

The consistency of a theory cannot be proved by arguments formalizable in the theory, whenever the theory contains arithmetic.

The exact meaning of this proposition is easy to understand. For the details one can consult Gödel's paper, where the theorem is proved for the system of Russell and Whitehead. Let us recall briefly the essence of his argument.

We can intuitionistically number all the propositions containing just one real variable and all the proofs of the theory considered. Let $P(x, y, z)$ be a proposition, intuitionistically defined, whose meaning is: proof number x is a proof of proposition number y for the value z of its variable. (In his paper Gödel effectively constructs this function for the theory he considers.) Let us observe that the computation that we have to do in order to check whether $P(x, y, z)$ is true or false for given x, y, and z – a computation that is intuitionistically carried out – can also be formally carried out in the theory; hence, if $P(x, y, z)$ is true, it is provable in the theory. Let us assume that the theory is consistent. Then, if β is the number of the proposition $(x). \sim P(x, y, y)$, the proposition $P(x, \beta, \beta)$ cannot be true, for it would mean that proof number x is a proof of $(x). \sim P(x, \beta, \beta)$; hence $\sim P(x, \beta, \beta)$ could be proved in the theory, and we would have a contradiction. Moreover, $(x). \sim P(x, \beta, \beta)$ is not provable in the theory, for, if proof number y were a proof of it, $P(y, \beta, \beta)$ would be true (by definition); hence, because of what we have said, it would be provable in theory, and we would again have a contradiction. If we formalize the foregoing considerations in the theory (and they are intuitionistic), we obtain the following result: w being the trans-

---

[16] See *Gödel 1931*. To understand this proposition, one has to imagine that all signs occurring in metamathematics are represented by objects of the theory being considered, for example, by integers in arithmetic; the properties of these signs and the relations among them will then be represented by certain propositions of the theory; every argument in the theory in question carried out with these objects and these propositions will correspond to a metamathematical argument, of which it will be, in a way, the translation.

lation[17] of the proposition 'The theory is consistent', $w \supset \sim P(x, \beta, \beta)$ is a true proposition of the theory (x being a variable). If w were provable in the theory so would be $\sim P(x, \beta, \beta)$, hence also $(x). \sim P(x, \beta, \beta)$, and we have just seen that this would make the theory inconsistent. Hence *w is unprovable.*

Let us apply this method to the arithmetic that contains the hypotheses A, B, and C (leaving out the hypotheses D for the sake of simplicity). Our arguments, as well as those necessary to establish the fundamental theorem, are formalizable in this theory. But, if we want to carry out Gödel's argument, we have to consider a definite theory. In Group C we merely have a description of the hypotheses that may be introduced. We must consider a definite group of schemata of hypotheses of type C, say, Group C'. We shall see that, if we wish to carry out Gödel's argument, we must introduce other schemata for the definition of functions; it is therefore impossible to apply his considerations to our arithmetic.

One could object that it is perhaps possible to describe at once all the schemata that are included in C for the construction of functions. This would mean that it is possible to describe outright all intuitionistic procedures for the construction of number-theoretic functions. But this is impossible. For, if this were the case, we could, by an intuitionistic procedure, number all the functions of just one variable, $f_1(x), f_2(x), ...,$ $f_n(x), ...$; then $f_x(x) + 1$ would be an intuitionistically defined function that would not be among the functions previously listed, hence a contradiction.

Let us apply this result to all functions definable by C' and those obtained by compounding these functions with one another and with $x + 1$. The function $f_x(x) + 1$ cannot be among these functions. But, to carry out Gödel's argument, we have to number all objects occurring in proofs; we are thus led to construct the function of two variables $f_y(x)$; this justifies what we were saying above, namely, that it is impossible, in an arithmetic containing the hypotheses C', to formalize Gödel's argument about this arithmetic.

Let us make two more remarks.

(a) Every intuitionistic argument can always be carried out with ordinary integers, because we can always replace the objects considered in the argument by ordinary integers, for example, if we number them.

---

[17] See footnote 16.

It seems to us almost certain that every intuitionistic argument can then be carried out in an arithmetic containing the hypotheses A, B, and C [only]. But the justification of this point (a *proof*, in the mathematical sense of the word, is obviously impossible, just as it is for any statement involving the totality of *all* intuitionistic arguments) would lead us to a detailed discussion, which we shall perhaps undertake some other time. It would show that the hypotheses of Group D follow from those that precede them.

(b) It seems to us impossible, contrary to Gödel's opinion,[18] that there could be intuitionistic arguments not formalizable in ordinary analysis. Thus we believe that the arithmetic containing the hypotheses A, B, C, and D is a part of ordinary analysis. It seems to us probable that the question stands as follows: it will never be possible to give an example of an intuitionistic argument not formalizable in ordinary analysis, and also it will always be impossible to prove that there exists no such argument; for we have shown that it is impossible to describe all intuitionistic procedures of reasoning (since it is impossible to describe all procedures for the construction of functions). *There might be some sort of logical postulate here.* It would follow that it is impossible to prove the consistency of ordinary analysis.

It is not even impossible that every intuitionistic argument could be carried out in an arithmetic containing the hypotheses A and B and allowing in C only ordinary addition and multiplication.[19] If this were so, the consistency of ordinary arithmetic would already be unprovable.

NOTE O

(footnote 12, p. 293 above)

Yet another consistency proof for the fragment of arithmetic in which induction axioms can be used only when $\Phi(x)$ is quantifier-free can be formulated by means of Herbrand's Fundamental Theorem (the idea is from *Kleene 1952*, p. 472).

For any quantifier-free formula $\Phi(x)$ containing the real variables $x_1, ..., x_n$ and x, let

$$\varphi(x_1, ..., x_n, x) = \begin{cases} \text{the least } y \text{ such that: } y \leqslant x \,\&\, \Phi(y) \,\&\, \sim \Phi(y+1), \text{ if such a } y \text{ exists} \\ 0, \text{ if no such } y \text{ exists.} \end{cases}$$

[18] See *Gödel 1931*, p. 197.

[19] See *Gödel 1931*, Theorem VII, and also footnote 15 above.

Since the least number operator is bounded and $\Phi(x)$ is quantifier-free, the function φ is primitive recursive in the functions appearing in Φ. Hence the above equation can be put into the form required by Group C.

Then if the axioms of Groups A, C, and D are true in an infinite domain, so is the formula $\Phi(0) \&. (y).\Phi(y) \supset (y+1) :\supset. \Phi(x)$ when the index function $f(x_1, ..., x_n, x)$ arising from the restricted variable y is given the same value in the domain as is $\varphi(x_1, ..., x_n, x)$.

This proof seems weaker than Herbrand's in that it does not show immediately that the fragment of arithmetic under consideration can be reduced to one without induction axioms. However, we do prove that any quantifier-free induction axiom is true in any infinite domain in which axioms A, C, and D are true. Hence, by Herbrand's remarks in *1931*, p. 233 (Method 3), we have that the theory with quantifier-free induction is a conservative extension of the theory without it. This amounts to the same result as Herbrand derives in his proof.

We note in addition that Kleene (*1952*, p. 474) proved that the fragment of arithmetic dealt with here is equivalent to the one in which induction axioms can be used if in $\Phi(x)$ the variable x never appears within the scope of a quantifier.

REFERENCES

Throughout this volume, an author's name followed by a year number, both in italics, denotes an entry in this list of references. When the context leaves no doubt as to the author, the year number alone is used. For papers that originally were addresses or lectures, the year indicated is that in which they were delivered; for communications to learned societies, it is that in which they were made; for other papers, it is that of the complete volume of the periodical in which they appear (there are a few exceptions, with irregular publications). For one author, additional titles in the same year are distinguished by *a*, *b*, and so on; an attempt has been made to follow the actual chronological order.

Aanderaa, Stål
    See Dreben, Burton, and Stål Aanderaa; also Dreben, Burton, Peter Andrews, and Stål Aanderaa.
Ackermann, Wilhelm
    1924 Begründung des 'tertium non datur' mittels der Hilbertschen Theorie der Widerspruchsfreiheit, *Mathematische Annalen 93*, 1–36.
    1928 Über die Erfüllbarkeit gewisser Zählausdrücke, *ibid. 100*, 638–649.
    1940 Zur Widerspruchsfreiheit der Zahlentheorie, *ibid. 117*, 162–194.
    See Hilbert, David, and Wilhelm Ackermann.
Andrews, Peter
    See Dreben, Burton, Peter Andrews, and Stål Aanderaa.
Artin, Emil, and Otto Schreier
    1926 Algebraische Konstruktion reeller Körper, *Abhandlungen aus dem mathematischen Seminar der Hamburgischen Universität 5* (1927), 85–99.

Behmann, Heinrich
    1922 Beiträge zur Algebra der Logik, insbesondere zum Entscheidungsproblem, *Mathematische Annalen 86*, 163–229.

Bernays, Paul

1927 Zusatz zu Hilberts Vortrag über 'Die Grundlagen der Mathematik', *Abhandlungen aus dem mathematischen Seminar der Hamburgischen Universität 6*, 89–92. English translation by Stefan Bauer-Mengelberg and Dagfinn Føllesdal in *van Heijenoort 1967*, 485–489.

1932 Methoden des Nachweises von Widerspruchsfreiheit und ihre Grenzen, *Verhandlungen des Internationalen Mathematiker-Kongresses Zürich 1932* (Orell Füssli, Zürich and Leipzig), vol. 2, 342–343.

1934 Sur le platonisme dans les mathématiques. *L'enseignement mathématique 34*, (1935–1936), 52–69.

1934a Quelques points essentiels de la métamathématique, *ibid.*, 70–95.

1935 Hilberts Untersuchungen über die Grundlagen der Arithmetik, in *Hilbert 1935*, 196–216.

1936 *Logical calculus*, lecture notes 1935–36 (The Institute for Advanced Study, Princeton, N.J.).

1938 Sur les questions méthodologiques actuelles de la théorie hilbertienne de la démonstration, in *Gonseth 1938*, 144–152; Discussion, 153–161.

1954 Über den Zusammenhang des Herbrand'schen Satzes mit den neueren Ergebnissen von Schütte und Stenius, *Proceedings of the International Congress of mathematicians, Amsterdam, September 2–September 9*, vol. 2, 397.

See Hilbert, David, and Paul Bernays.

Bernays, Paul and Moses Schönfinkel

1928 Zum Entscheidungsproblem der mathematischen Logik, *Mathematische Annalen 99*, 342–372.

Beth, Evert Willem

1955 *Semantic entailment and formal derivability* (Mededelingen der Koninklijke Nederlandsche Akademie van wetenschappen, afd. letterkunde, new series, vol. 18, no. 13, N.V. Noord-Hollandsche Uitgevers Maatschappij, Amsterdam).

1956 *La crise de la raison et la logique* (Gauthier-Villars, Paris; Nauwelaerts, Louvain; 1957).

1959 *The foundations of mathematics* (North-Holland, Amsterdam).

Chevalley, Claude

 1934 Sur la pensée de J. Herbrand, *L'enseignement mathématique 34* (1935–36), 97–102. (25–28 of the present volume.)

Chevalley, Claude and Albert Lautman

 1931 Notice biographique sur Jacques Herbrand, *Annuaire de l'Association amicale de secours des anciens élèves de l'École normale supérieure*, 66–68. (21–23 of the present volume.)

Craig, William

 1957 Three uses of the Herbrand-Gentzen theorem in relating model theory and proof theory, *The journal of symbolic logic 22*, 269–285.

 1960 Bases for first-order theories and subtheories, *The journal of symbolic logic 25*, 97–142.

Denton, John

 See Dreben, Burton, and John Denton; also Dreben, Burton, John Denton, and Thomas M. Scanlon.

Dreben, Burton

 1952 On the completeness of quantification theory, *Proceedings of the National Academy of Sciences of the U.S.A. 38*, 1047–1052.

 1961 Solvable Surányi subclasses: An introduction to the Herbrand theory, *Proceedings of a Harvard symposium on digital computers and their applications, 3–6, April 1961* (The annals of the Computation Laboratory of Harvard University *31*; Harvard University Press, Cambridge, Mass.), 32–47 (1962).

 1963 Corrections to Herbrand, *American Mathematical Society, Notices 10*, 285; abstract presented by title at the 29 April–3 May 1963 meeting of the American Mathematical Society.

Dreben, Burton and Stål Aanderaa

 1964 Herbrand analyzing functions, *Bulletin of the American Mathematical Society 70*, 697–698.

Dreben, Burton, Peter Andrews, and Stål Aanderaa

 1963 Errors in Herbrand, *American Mathematical Society, Notices 10*, 285; abstract presented by title at the 29 April–3 May 1963 meeting of the American Mathematical Society.

 1963a False lemmas in Herbrand, *Bulletin of the American Mathematical Society 69*, 699–706.

Dreben, Burton and John Denton
  1966 A supplement to Herbrand, *The journal of symbolic logic 31*, 393–398.
  1968 Herbrand-style consistency proofs, in *Myhill, Kino, and Vesley 1970*.
Dreben, Burton, John Denton, and Thomas M. Scanlon
  1972 The Herbrand theorem and the consistency of number theory, in preparation.
Dreben, Burton, A. S. Kahr, and Hao Wang
  1962 Classification of *AEA* formulas by letter atoms, *Bulletin of the American Mathematical Society 68*, 528–532.

Feferman, Solomon
  1967 Lectures on proof theory, in *Löb 1968*, 1–109.
Fraenkel, Abraham A.
  1934 Sur la notion d'existence dans les mathématiques, *L'enseignement mathématique 34* (1935–36), 18–32.

Gentzen, Gerhard
  1934 Untersuchungen über das logische Schliessen, *Mathematische Zeitschrift 39*, 176–210, 405–431.
  1936 Die Widerspruchsfreiheit der reinen Zahlentheorie, *Mathematische Annalen 112*, 493–565.
  1938 Neue Fassung des Widerspruchsfreiheitsbeweises für die reine Zahlentheorie, *Forschungen zur Logik und zur Grundlegung der exakten Wissenschaften*, new series, no. 4, 19–44.
  1969 Collected papers, edited and translated by M. E. Szabo (North-Holland, Amsterdam). (Includes translations of the above three papers.)
Gladstone, M. D.
  1966 Finite models for inequalities, *The journal of symbolic logic 31*, 581–592.
Gödel, Kurt
  1930 Die Vollständigkeit der Axiome des logischen Funktionenkalküls, *Monatshefte für Mathematik und Physik 37*, 349–360. English translation by Stefan Bauer-Mengelberg in *van Heijenoort 1967*, 582–591.

1931 Über formal unentscheidbare Sätze der Principia mathematica und verwandter Systeme I, *ibid. 38*, 173–198. English translation by Jean van Heijenoort in *van Heijenoort 1967*, 592–616.

1933 Zum Entscheidungsproblem des logischen Funktionenkalküls, *ibid. 40*, 433–443.

1934 *On undecidable propositions of formal mathematical systems*, lecture notes by Stephen Cole Kleene and John Barkley Rosser (The Institute for Advanced Study, Princeton, N.J.).

1940 *The consistency of the continuum hypothesis* (Princeton University Press, Princeton, N.J.); 2nd printing 1951; 3rd printing 1953.

1958 Über eine bisher noch nicht benützte Erweiterung des finiten Standpunktes, *Dialectica 12*, 280–287.

Gonseth, Ferdinand (ed.)

1938 *Les entretiens de Zürich sur les fondements et la méthode des sciences mathématiques, 6–9 décembre 1938* (Leemann, Zürich, 1941).

Herbrand, Jacques

1928 Sur la théorie de la démonstration, *Comptes rendus hebdomadaires des séances de l'Academie des sciences* (Paris) *186* (7 May 1928), 1274–1276. (29–34 of the present volume.)

1929 Non-contradiction des axiomes arithmétiques, *ibid. 188* (21 January 1929), 303–304. (35–37 of the present volume.)

1929a Sur quelques propriétés des propositions vraies et leurs applications, *ibid.* (22 April 1929), 1076–1078. (38–40 of the present volume.)

1929b Sur le problème fondamental des mathématiques, *ibid. 189* (14 October 1929), 554–556, 720. (41–43 of the present volume.)

1930 *Recherches sur la théorie de la démonstration*, Thesis at the University of Paris; also Prace Towarzystwa Naukowego Warszawskiego, Wydział III, no. 33. (44–202 of the present volume.)

1930a Les bases de la logique hilbertienne, *Revue de métaphysique et de morale 37*, 243–255. (203–214 of the present volume.)

1931 Sur le problème fondamental de la logique mathématique, *Sprawozdania z posiedzeń Towarzystwa Naukowego Warszawskiego, Wydział III, 24*, 12–56. (215–271 of the present volume.)

1931a Unsigned note on *Herbrand 1930, Annales de l'Université de Paris 6*, 186–189. (272–276 of the present volume.)

1931b Notice pour Jacques Hadamard, in *Herbrand 1968*, 215–219. (277–281 of the present volume.)

1931c Sur la non-contradiction de l'arithmétique, *Journal für die reine und angewandte Mathematik 166*, 1–8. (282–298 of the present volume.)

1968 *Écrits logiques*, ed. by Jean van Heijenoort (Presses Universitaires de France, Paris).

Hilbert, David

1922 Neubegründung der Mathematik (Erste Mitteilung), *Abhandlungen aus dem mathematischen Seminar der Hamburgischen Universität 1*, 157–177; reprinted in *Hilbert 1935*, 146–156.

1922a Die logischen Grundlagen der Mathematik, *Mathematische Annalen 88* (1923), 151–165; reprinted in *Hilbert 1935*, 178–191.

1925 Über das Unendliche, *Mathematische Annalen 95* (1926), 161–190. English translation by Stefan Bauer-Mengelberg in *van Heijenoort 1967*, 367–392.

1927 Die Grundlagen der Mathematik, *Abhandlungen aus dem mathematischen Seminar der Hamburgischen Universität 6* (1928), 91–122. English translation by Stefan Bauer-Mengelberg and Dagfinn Føllesdal in *van Heijenoort 1967*, 464–479.

1928 Probleme der Grundlegung der Mathematik, *Atti del Congresso internazionale dei matematici, Bologna 3–10 settembre 1928* (Bologna, 1929), vol. 1, 135–141. Reprinted, with emendations and additions, as *Hilbert 1929* and in *Hilbert 1930a*, 313–323.

1929 Emended version of *Hilbert 1928, Mathematische Annalen 102*, 1–9.

1930 Die Grundlegung der elementaren Zahlenlehre, *Mathematische Annalen 104* (1931), 485–494. Reprinted in part in *Hilbert 1935*, 192–195.

1930a *Grundlagen der Geometrie* (Teubner, Leipzig and Berlin), 7th ed.

1935 *Gesammelte Abhandlungen* (Springer, Berlin), vol. 3.

Hilbert, David and Wilhelm Ackermann

1928 *Grundzüge der theoretischen Logik* (Springer, Berlin).

1938 – 2nd ed.

1959 – 4th ed.

Hilbert, David and Paul Bernays
  1934 Grundlagen der Mathematik (Springer, Berlin), vol. 1.
  1939 – vol. 2.
Hintikka, K. Jaakko J.
  1955 Form and content in quantification theory, *Acta philosophica fennica 8*, 7–55.

Kahr, Andrew Seth
  See Dreben, Burton, A.S. Kahr and Hao Wang.
Kino, Akiko
  See Myhill, John, Akiko Kino, and Richard Vesley.
Kleene, Stephen Cole
  1952 Introduction to metamathematics (Van Nostrand, New York and Toronto; North-Holland, Amsterdam; Noordhoff, Groningen).
Kolmogorov, Andrei Nikolaevich (Андрей Николаевич Колмогоров)
  1925 О принципе tertium non datur, *Математический сборник 32*, 646–667. English translation by Jean van Heijenoort in *van Heijenoort 1967*, 414–437.
Kreisel, Georg
  1951 On the interpretation of nonfinitist proofs, Part I, *The journal of symbolic logic 16*, 241–267; Part II, *ibid. 17* (1952), 43–58.
  1952 On the concepts of completeness and interpretation of formal systems, *Fundamenta Mathematicae 39*, 103–127.
  1958 Review of *Beth 1956, The journal of symbolic logic 23*, 35–37.

Lautman, Albert
  See Chevalley, Claude and Albert Lautman.
Löb, M. H. (ed.)
  1968 Proceedings of the summer school in logic, Leeds, 1967 (Springer Verlag, Berlin, Heidelberg and New York).
Löwenheim, Leopold
  1915 Über Möglichkeiten im Relativkalkül, *Mathematische Annalen 76*, 447–470. English translation by Stefan Bauer-Mengelberg in *van Heijenoort 1967*, 228–251.

Myhill, John, Akiko Kino, and Richard Vesley
  1970 Intuitionism and Proof Theory: Proceedings of the Conference on

Intuitionism and Proof Theory, Buffalo, New York, August 1968 (North-Holland, Amsterdam).

Nicod, Jean
1916 A reduction in the number of primitive propositions of logic, *Proceedings of the Cambridge Philosophical Society 19* (1917–20), 32–41.

Post, Emil Leon
1921 Introduction to a general theory of elementary propositions, *American journal of mathematics 43*, 163–185; reprinted in *van Heijenoort 1967*, 264–283.

Presburger, Mojzesz
1929 Über die Vollständigkeit eines gewissen Systems der Arithmetik ganzer Zahlen, in welchem die Addition als einzige Operation hervortritt, *Sprawozdanie z I Kongresu matematyków krajów słowiańskich, Warszawa 1929* (Warsaw, 1930), 92–101, 395.

Quine, Willard Van Orman
1950 *Methods of logic* (Holt, New York); see *Quine 1955*.
1955 *Appendix. Completeness of quantification theory. Löwenheim's theorem,* enclosed as a pamphlet with part of the third printing (1955) of *Quine 1950* and incorporated in the revised ed. (1959), 253–260.

Russell, Bertrand
See Whitehead, Alfred North, and Bertrand Russell.

Scanlon, Thomas M.
See Dreben, Burton, John Denton, and Thomas M. Scanlon.

Schmidt, Arnold
1938 Über deduktive Theorien mit mehreren Sorten von Grunddingen, *Mathematische Annalen 115*, 485–506.

Schönfinkel, Moses
See Bernays, Paul, and Moses Schönfinkel.

Schreier, Otto
See Artin, Emil, and Otto Schreier.

Schütte, Kurt

1933 Untersuchungen zum Entscheidungsproblem der mathematischen Logik, *Mathematische Annalen 109*, 572–603.

1934 Über die Erfüllbarkeit einer Klasse von logischen Formeln, *ibid.* 110, 161–194.

1951 Beweistheoretische Erfassung der unendlichen Induktion in der Zahlentheorie, *Mathematische Annalen 122*, 369–389.

1960 *Beweistheorie* (Springer Verlag, Berlin, Göttingen, and Heidelberg).

Skolem, Thoralf

1920 Logisch-kombinatorische Untersuchungen über die Erfüllbarkeit oder Beweisbarkeit mathematische Sätze nebst einem Theoreme über dichte Mengen, *Videnskapsselskapets skrifter, I. Matematisk-naturvidenskabelig klasse*, no. 4. English translation of § 1 by Stefan Bauer-Mengelberg in *van Heijenoort 1967*, 252–263.

1922 Einige Bemerkungen zur axiomatischen Begründung der Mengenlehre, *Matematikerkongressen i Helsingfors den 4–7 July 1922, Den femte skandinaviska matematikerkongressen, Redogörelse* (Akademiska Bokhandeln, Helsinki, 1923), 217–232. English translation by Stefan Bauer-Mengelberg in *van Heijenoort 1967*, 290–301.

1928 Über die mathematische Logik, *Norsk matematisk tidsskrift 10*, 125–142. English translation by Stefan Bauer-Mengelberg and Dagfinn Føllesdal in *van Heijenoort 1967*, 508–524.

1929 Über einige Grundlagenfragen der Mathematik, *Skrifter utgitt av Det Norske Videnskaps-Akademi i Oslo, I. Matematisk-naturvidenskapelig klasse*, no. 4.

Spector, Clifford

1961 Provably recursive functionals of analysis: A consistency proof of analysis by an extension of principles formulated in current intuitionistic mathematics, *Recursive function theory, Proceedings of symposia in pure mathematics* (American Mathematical Society, Providence, Rhode Island, 1962), vol. 5, 1–27.

Szabo, M. E.

See *Gentzen 1969*.

Tait, William W.

1965 Functionals defined by transfinite recursion, *The journal of symbolic logic 30*, 155–174.

1965a The substitution method, *ibid.*, 175–192.

Tarski, Alfred

1948 *A decision method for elementary algebra and geometry* (Rand Corporation, Santa Monica, Calif.).

1951 2nd ed., revised, of *Tarski 1948* (University of California Press, Berkeley and Los Angeles).

van Heijenoort, Jean

1967 *From Frege to Gödel, A source book in mathematical logic, 1879–1931* (Harvard University Press, Cambridge, Mass.).

See *Herbrand 1968.*

Vesley, Richard

See Myhill, John, Akiko Kino, and Richard Vesley.

von Neumann, John

1925 Eine Axiomatisierung der Mengenlehre, *Journal für die reine und angewandte Mathematik 154*, 219–240; Berichtigung, *ibid. 155*, 128; reprinted in *von Neumann 1961*, 34–56. English translation by Stefan Bauer-Mengelberg and Dagfinn Føllesdal in *van Heijenoort 1967*, 393–413.

1927 Zur Hilbertschen Beweistheorie, *Mathematische Zeitschrift 26*, 1–46; reprinted in *von Neumann 1961*, 256–300.

1928 Die Axiomatisierung der Mengenlehre, *Mathematische Zeitschrift 27*, 669–752. Reprinted in *von Neumann 1961*, 339–422.

1929 Über eine Widerspruchsfreiheitsfrage in der axiomatischen Mengenlehre, *Journal für die reine und angewandte Mathematik 160*, 227–241; reprinted in *von Neumann 1961*, 494–508.

1961 *Collected works* (Pergamon Press, New York), vol. 1.

Wang, Hao

1952 Logic of many-sorted theories, *The journal of symbolic logic 17*, 105–116.

See Dreben, Burton, A. S. Kahr, and Hao Wang.

Whitehead, Alfred North, and Bertrand Russell

1910 *Principia Mathematica* (Cambridge University Press, Cambridge, U.K.), vol. 1.

1912 *Ibid.*, vol. 2.

1913 *Ibid.*, vol. 3.

1925 Ibid., 2nd ed., vol. 1.
1927 Ibid., vol. 2.
1927a Ibid., vol. 3.

Zaremba, Stanislas
1926 La logique des mathématiques (Mémorial des sciences mathématiques, fasc. 15; Gauthier-Villars, Paris).

INDEX